A DECADE OF
HEALTH
SERVICES

THE GRADUATE SCHOOL OF BUSINESS

UNIVERSITY OF CHICAGO

FIRST SERIES (1916–1938)

Materials for the Study of Business
Edited by DEAN LEON CARROLL MARSHALL and
DEAN WILLIAM HOMER SPENCER

SECOND SERIES (1938–1956)

Business and Economic Publications
Edited by DEAN WILLIAM HOMER SPENCER

THIRD SERIES (1959–)

Studies in Business and Society
Edited by DEAN W. ALLEN WALLIS
and DEAN GEORGE P. SHULTZ

A DECADE OF HEALTH SERVICES

SOCIAL SURVEY TRENDS
IN USE AND EXPENDITURE

RONALD ANDERSEN
AND ODIN W. ANDERSON

THE UNIVERSITY OF CHICAGO PRESS
CHICAGO & LONDON

Library of Congress Catalog Card Number: 67-30125

THE UNIVERSITY OF CHICAGO PRESS, CHICAGO & LONDON
THE UNIVERSITY OF TORONTO PRESS, TORONTO 5, CANADA

FOREWORD

The paramount concerns of a university—the discovery and promulgation of knowledge—are sovereign concerns also of the Graduate School of Business. Here scholars drawn from many disciplines bring their varied approaches and methods to bear in performing research on special problems of business and society.

The truth is sought assiduously wherever the search may lead, and the findings are articulated both in the teaching programs of the School and in published works that make knowledge available to all who have the need and capacity to use it.

Equally, discovery and communication are major purposes of the Center for Health Administration Studies, an interdisciplinary research and teaching unit of the Graduate School of Business and The University of Chicago. Research at the Center is producing substantial new knowledge concerning the economic, social, and managerial problems of health care.

This volume, based upon work done at the Center, is the most recent expression of a significant publishing program inaugurated by the School more than half a century ago. A series of publications, *Materials for the Study of Business,* was initiated in 1916, under the editorship of Dean Leon Carroll Marshall, and was continued by Dean William Homer Spencer. Fifty titles were published, and many became classics in their fields. In 1938 a second series, *Business and Economic Publications,* was launched; under the editorship of Dean Spencer, thirteen titles were published. In addition, in the two decades prior to 1948 the School published some seventy monographs under the general title, *Studies in Business Administration.*

The third (current) series, *Studies in Business and Society* (formerly

v

Studies in Business), was initiated in 1959 under Dean W. Allen Wallis, who edited the first six volumes.

The present volume is based upon three comparable national surveys, made at five-year intervals, covering consumers' use of and expenditures for health care, and methods of meeting health costs. The decade under study, 1953–63, bridges a period of sharp growth in all aspects of health care—use, expenditures, personnel and facilities, insurance programs, benefit payments, and other measurable factors.

Two of the surveys, in 1953 and 1958, were financed by the pharmaceutical industry through the Health Information Foundation, as part of that industry's contribution to a better understanding of social and economic problems in the health field. The 1963 survey was financed in part by funds of the Health Information Foundation, but to a large extent was supported by a grant from the Public Health Service.

The Health Information Foundation is now a unit of the Center for Health Administration Studies. The studies reported in this volume were conducted by the Associate Director and staff of the Center for Health Administration Studies, in cooperation with the National Opinion Research Center of the University.

This work, addressing itself to trends in health services over a critical span of years, has important implications for both the public and private sectors, and undoubtedly will prove useful as public policy issues in health care are joined, discussed, and moved toward resolution.

GEORGE P. SHULTZ, Dean
Graduate School of Business
University of Chicago

PREFATORY NOTE

Three national surveys separated by five-year intervals give us a fair description of the consumer's use of medical care, the degree of his health insurance protection, and expenditures for care. Data so describing consumer behavior have been analyzed in detail in this report. The results contribute to better understanding of the health system in the United States. Trends in the use of health services generally have been upward. Most people would agree that this increased use has contributed to better health. Enrollment in hospital and medical insurance has grown at a consequential rate during this decade as has the extent of benefits provided. The decade under study bridges a period of sharp rise in medical care costs and health insurance benefits.

Important national policy decisions are at issue. The enactment of health insurance for older people has immediately raised questions as to the desirability of extending enrollment and increasing benefits. Inevitably, too, increased costs have proliferated suggestions for containment. With well over half the income of hospitals being paid by a cost reimbursement formula, a major policy issue is the wisdom with which payment rates are set to provide adequate funds for a good health system in the face of competition for funds in government budgets. These three studies of consumer use and expenditures are useful as these public policy issues move toward resolution.

Surveys of personal health services in 1953 and 1958 were financed by the pharmaceutical industry through the Health Information Foundation as part of that industry's contribution to a better understanding of social and economic problems in the health field. The survey in 1963 was in some part financed from the funds of the Health Information Foundation but to a large extent by Grant No. HM 00298-01 from the Public Health Service.

The Health Information Foundation is now a unit of the Center for Health Administration Studies of the University of Chicago. This series of national studies has been conducted by the Associate Director and staff of the Center for Health Administration Studies in cooperation with the National Opinion Research Center of the University of Chicago.

GEORGE BUGBEE
Director, Center for Health Administration Studies

ACKNOWLEDGMENTS

In the course of developing and carrying out this series of studies, many people have been involved. Persons connected with the earlier studies have been mentioned in previous reports. The authors wish to take this opportunity to mention some of those who have contributed to various stages of the last study.

First, we wish to acknowledge the National Institutes of Health, which provided the grant through which the study was financed. George Bugbee, Director of the Center for Health Administration Studies, gave necessary support for the inauguration of the study and helpful suggestions during the writing phase of the study.

Jacob Feldman and Patricia Collette, co-authors for earlier studies, were important sources of advice during the initial phases of the study. Seymour Sudman supervised the sampling procedure and provided invaluable technical assistance during the preparation of the methodological appendix. Harold Levy contributed substantially to the preparation of the questionnaire. Darlene Sampley, who was advised and supported by Eve Weinberg, provided conscientious "field" supervision during the data collection phases of the study.

Carol Bowman and Abbie Littleton were in charge during the various phases of the coding. Much of the coding was under the supervision of John Naples who, in addition, ably assisted in the coordination and preparation of the data.

Thomas Taylor served the study well as its primary processor of data through almost the entire study. Patrick Page and James Jasper provided important advice and programming assistance during the data processing.

Elaine Meetze typed two drafts of the manuscript in creditable fashion. Joanna Kravits provided valuable assistance in the editing and proofreading of the manuscript as well as preparing the index. Diane Andersen provided moral as well as material help at various seemingly "crucial" points during the study.

To all the people mentioned above, as well as to the many others who worked on this study, we express our appreciation.

RONALD ANDERSEN
ODIN W. ANDERSON

CONTENTS

xi

LIST OF CHARTS AND TABLES

CHARTS

TABLES

A DECADE OF HEALTH SERVICES

I

INTRODUCTION

This is a study of people's use of, and expenditures for, health services in the United States. It is based on three parallel studies of representative samples of the nation's families done at five-year intervals from 1953 through 1963. Trends through this ten-year period as well as the situation in 1963 are emphasized.

A. THE HEALTH SERVICES SYSTEM

People in the United States use a large, complex health care system. The health services industry employs close to 3 million persons in hospitals, clinics, health organizations, private offices, laboratories and other places where health services are provided.[1] An additional million persons work in occupations or industries related in some way to health services. These workers involved in all the many aspects of health services represent 6 percent of the labor force. Over 7,000 hospitals in the country provide 1.7 million beds for inpatient care.[2] Some 8,000 other institutions providing nursing care maintain over 300,000 beds.[3]

The health care system is not only large in absolute terms but it is experiencing rapid growth. In 1900 there were fewer than 0.2 million college-educated or professionally trained health personnel. By 1930 there were 0.6 million and by 1960 they exceeded 1.1 million. The professional health personnel population ratio increased during this sixty-year period from 2.6 per 1000 persons to 6.4 per 1000. In the recent decade 1950–60

[1] U.S. Public Health Service, Division of Public Health Methods, "Health Manpower Source Book, Section 18, Manpower in the 1960's" (Washington, D.C., 1964), p. 1.

[2] *Guide Issue, Journal of the American Hospital Association*, 39, pt. 2 (August 1, 1965): p. 431.

[3] National Center for Health Statistics, "Institutions for the Aged and Chronically Ill: United States—April–June 1963," ser. 12, no. 1 (July, 1965), derived from pp. 4 and 18.

the number of persons employed in the health services increased by 54 percent.[4] Among the nine largest industries only government educational services had a larger gain. We are rapidly becoming the first major society in history to employ more people to provide health care than to provide food.

The growth of the health care system reflects the increased demand for its services by the public. This demand is based on past experience and future expectation. The services have been highly effective in combating acute, infectious diseases. The future looks more and more promising regarding the management and control of chronic diseases. In addition, use of health services for preventive health practices is becoming more common.

There can be little question of the growing impact of the health care system on the population and the increasing demands for service by the population. For instance, in 1940, 56 out of every 100 births were delivered in hospitals or allied institutions compared to 88 per 100 in 1950 and 97 in 1960.[5] The proportion of births attended by a physician between 1940 and 1963 rose from 81 percent to 98 percent.[6] More people are dying as well as being born in the hospital today. Between 1935 and 1958 the percentage of all deaths occurring in the hospital increased from 34 percent to 53 percent.[7] At present the proportion is probably near three-fifths. We also find the health care system playing a more important part in the span between the critical points of birth and death. This book describes this increasing interplay between the system and the population.

Chart 1 provides an overview of the use of health services during 1963 by the non-institutionalized population. One person in 12 was admitted to a hospital at least once and 40 per cent of those admitted had some surgery performed. Two-thirds of the people saw a physician at least once during the year. This figure becomes more significant if we consider that 250,000 physicians providing patient care have direct contact with some 125 million people each year. No other single professional group has so much intimate contact with such a large proportion of the population. To complete this profile of health services use, Chart 1 shows that roughly two-fifths of the population received dental care and purchased prescribed drugs and one-fifth received eye care from an ophthalmologist, optometrist, or optician during 1963. The following report will attempt to

4 "Manpower in the 1960's," p. 3.

5 National Center for Health Statistics, "Natality Statistics Analysis, United States 1962," ser. 21, no. 1 (October, 1964), p. 26.

6 *Ibid.*, no. 8 (March, 1966), pp. 18–21.

7 Monroe Lerner and Odin W. Anderson, *Health Progress in the United States: 1900–1960* (Chicago: University of Chicago Press, 1963), pp. 248–49.

describe in detail people's use of the health care system as it has been sketched out in Chart 1.

Use of the health care system will be explored according to the services received by various segments of the population, how much they spend for the services they receive, and the methods they use to pay for such services. Distributions of use, expenditure, and methods of payment are examined for families and individuals, the insured and the uninsured, and for people in different age, sex, income, and education categories. In addition changes in these relationships between 1953 and 1963 are noted.

Chart 1 Percent of the population using selected health services: 1963

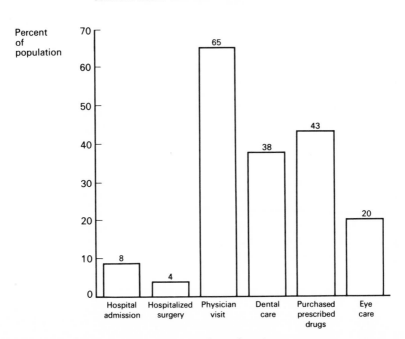

B. HEALTH SURVEY DEVELOPMENT

The first nationwide survey of the costs of medical care and morbidity among a representative sample of families in the United States was begun in 1928 and published in 1933.[8] In 1936 the U.S. Public Health Service

8 Isadore S. Falk, Margaret C. Klem, and Nathan Sinai, *The Incidence of Illness and the Receipt and Costs of Medical Care among Representative Families: Experiences in Twelve Consecutive Months during 1928–31* (Chicago: University of Chicago Press, 1933). (Publication of the Committee on the Costs of Medical Care, Report 26.)

published the results of a morbidity survey of a large urban population.[9] These studies, known as "Report 26 of the Committee on the Costs of Medical Care" (hereafter, C.C.M.C. Survey) and "The National Health Survey," provided the two chief sources of information on the costs of medical care and the extent of morbidity in the United States until 1953.

In 1953 Health Information Foundation and National Opinion Research Center conducted their first survey of an area-probability sample of the country's civilian non-institutionalized population.[10] People were interviewed in their homes in the summer of 1953 concerning their utilization of personal health services, the charges they incurred for these services, methods of meeting costs, coverage under voluntary health insurance, and other matters pertaining to health in the twelve months prior to the interview. This survey together with the C.C.M.C. Survey permitted gross comparisons of the expenditures for, and the utilization of, personal health services for twelve-month periods approximately 25 years apart. In addition, the 1953 study evaluated the impact of voluntary health insurance, which had been virtually nonexistent at the time of the earlier study.

Beginning about 1953, the entire field of medical care and voluntary health insurance entered a period of dynamic development. Reports of annual private expenditures for personal health services prepared by the Department of Commerce and the Social Security Administration and the annual enrollment reports in voluntary health insurance released by the Health Insurance Council showed steady growth.[11] Such reports are most valuable for showing gross averages. Social surveys, however, can in addition reveal distributions of expenditures and use according to characteristics of individuals and families such as age, sex, and family income. Accordingly, Health Information Foundation and National Opinion Research Center undertook another survey in 1958 designed to make possible detailed comparisons with the survey of 1953.[12]

The National Health Survey was established in 1956 and began to pro-

---

[9] U.S. Public Health Service, Division of Public Health Methods, *The National Health Survey, 1935–1936: Significance, Scope and Method of a Nation-wide Family Canvas of Sickness in Relation to Its Social and Economic Setting*, 1938.

[10] Odin W. Anderson and Jacob J. Feldman, *Family Medical Costs and Voluntary Health Insurance: A Nationwide Survey* (New York: McGraw-Hill Book Co., Inc., 1956).

[11] These reports are published annually in: *Social Security Bulletin*, in the December issue through 1964, and in the January issue, beginning with 1966; Department of Commerce, *Survey of Current Business, National Income Number*, July issue; and Health Insurance Institute, *Source Book of Health Insurance Data*, published yearly.

[12] Odin W. Anderson, Patricia Collette, and Jacob J. Feldman, *Changes in Family Medical Care Expenditures and Voluntary Health Insurance* (Cambridge: Harvard University Press, 1963).

vide nationwide morbidity and use data on a continuing basis.[13] This was the first such morbidity data since the National Health Survey report of 1936. During this period the HIF-NORC surveys and the National Health Survey complemented each other. The former concentrated on expenditures and health insurance while the latter was initially concerned with patterns of morbidity.

The most recent HIF-NORC study was conducted in early 1964 and covered the experience of the population for the year 1963.[14] It was initiated in response to the continued rapid changes taking place in health care. The three parallel studies provide a unique opportunity to study trends occurring during a critical ten-year period in the development of the health care system.[15] Building on the previous studies, some additional analyses of use patterns are provided and further implications regarding the relationships of use, expenditure, and methods of payment are presented.[16] In addition, data from this survey are also being used in an

13 U.S. National Health Survey, "Origin and Program of the National Health Survey," ser. A-1, May, 1958.

14 Data from this survey have previously been released. See the following issues of the bulletin, *Progress in Health Services*, published by Health Information Foundation: "Trends in Personal Health Spending," vol. 14, no. 5 (November–December, 1965); "Trends in Voluntary Health Insurance," vol. 15, no. 1 (January–February, 1966); "Maternity Care and Costs: A Ten-Year Trend," vol. 15, no. 2 (March–April, 1966); and "Patterns in Use of Health Services," vol. 15, no. 3 (May–June, 1966). Preliminary data used in the bulletins have undergone minor adjustments in a few instances for this final report. In no instance have the adjustments altered the trends or general conclusions reported in the bulletins.

15 In studying these trends considerable effort has been made to keep the data comparable from one time period to another. However, the reader should remember that even if the methodology remained exactly the same, secular changes might affect this comparability. For instance, change in institutional arrangements may have modified the extent to which charges to consumers represented care received. Over the ten-year period the amount of free care provided increased. Thus the total amount of care not represented by consumer expenditures increased. Also, the additional free medical care was not equally distributed over the total population but was concentrated in certain segments, including those eligible for care provided through publicly financed vendor payments and those eligible for free services such as are provided by plans of some labor unions. These particular segments of the population would consequently have a smaller proportion of the services they received represented by direct consumer expenditures.

16 The data presented in the final report on three surveys as comprehensive as these must necessarily be selective. In general this report includes trend data on the most basic measures of use, expenditures, and health insurance coverage used in the earlier studies. In some instances data from the 1958 study have been omitted for the sake of brevity. Such 1958 omissions usually occurred when, in the authors' judgment, trends for the entire period could be adequately described by reference to the 1953 and 1963 data alone. Referral to the 1958 report will generally provide comparable data. In other instances comparisons are limited to the last two studies. This usually means that comparable data from the 1953 report are not available or were not relevant (as in the case of major medical insurance coverage). Finally, a considerable part of the analysis includes 1963 data

international comparative study of health care systems in Sweden, Great Britain, and the United States.[17]

Since its conception the National Health Survey has greatly expanded its program and is now also providing survey data on personal expenditures for health care and health insurance coverage.[18] Some of the data reported here are paralleled by NHS reports.

While some effort has been duplicated by these parallels, there is value in having independent sources to provide comparisons. Also, much of the analysis in this report is not duplicated by NHS publications. Finally, the HIF-NORC data are unique in two respects: 1) all information on use, expenditures and health insurance was collected for the same sample, allowing examination of interrelations not possible when the samples are not the same; and 2) direct comparisons with data from ten years earlier are possible.

In addition to the national studies discussed above, other health surveys with important implications have been made of more limited populations. The first HIF-NORC report cites those published between the C.C.M.C. study and 1956.[19] The second includes studies published in the next interval.[20] This report footnotes some of the most recent of these studies.[21]

---

only. Some of this analysis was not done in the earlier reports and consequently no comparable measures were available. Another part of the analysis based on 1963 data alone does have some parallels in the earlier reports. Direct trend comparisons were not made when the authors felt that the most pertinent points involved the relationships of variables in 1963 rather than a view over time. The reader who disagrees with this judgment is again invited to consult the earlier reports for comparative purposes.

[17] This comparative study, now in its initial stages, will be based on parallel social survey data from Sweden supplied by Dr. Björn Smedby, Department of Social Medicine, Uppsala University, and national aggregate data on expenditures and use from all three countries. In addition, social and political literature from the three countries is being reviewed to give some insight into how the health services developed within the social and political context of each country and why they assumed the characteristics they did. A final source of data is interviews with leaders in government, business, health services administration and academia concerning welfare state policy in general and health services in particular. For a general orientation to this approach see Odin W. Anderson, "Health Services Systems in the United States and Other Countries—Critical Comparisons," in *Medical Care: Social and Organizational Aspects*, ed. Leslie J. DeGroot (Springfield, Ill.: Charles C Thomas, 1966), pp. 216–33. See also, Odin W. Anderson, *The Uneasy Equilibrium: Private and Public Financing of Health Services in the United States 1875–1965* (New Haven: College & University Press, 1967).

[18] National Center for Health Statistics, "Origin, Program and Operation of the U.S. National Health Survey," ser. 1, no. 1 (August, 1963).

[19] Anderson and Feldman, *Family Medical Costs*, pp. 1–2.

[20] Anderson, Collette, and Feldman, *Changes in Medical Care Expenditures*, p. 3.

[21] Odin W. Anderson and Paul B. Sheatsley, *Hospital Use: A Survey of Patient and Physician Decisions*, Center for Health Administration Studies Research Series No. 24 (Chicago: University of Chicago, 1967); Margaret C. Klem, "Physician Services Received in

C. THE CURRENT SURVEY

In the latest survey 2,367 families were interviewed in their homes in early 1964. One or more members of each family provided information regarding family use of health services, expenditure for these services, and methods of payment for the year 1963. In this manner information was collected for 7,803 individuals. These individuals constituted an area probability sample of the civilian non-institutionalized population. Since the data in the report are based on a sample, they are subject to sampling variability. Particular care should be exercised where small differences or small numbers of observations are involved.

In addition to data provided by the families, information was collected from hospitals, employers, and insuring organizations about hospitalizations and health insurance coverage reported in the family interview. This additional information served to verify and provide additional detail to the family report. A complete account of the methodology is found in Appendix I.

The findings are divided into five chapters. The first three treat consecutively people's use of health services, how much they are charged for these services, and how they go about paying for them. The next chapter considers some of the relationships among use, expenditure, and method of payment. For example it deals with such problems as the extent to which increased expenditure results from increased "price" as opposed to increased "use," and differences in use and expenditure between insured and uninsured people. The final section summarizes the findings and points out some implications of these results.

an Urban Community in Relation to Health Insurance Coverage," *American Journal of Public Health,* vol. 55 (November, 1965); Columbia University, School of Public Health and Administrative Medicine, *Family Medical Care Under Three Types of Health Insurance* (New York, 1962); Thomas Ford, *Health and Demography in Kentucky* (Lexington: The University of Kentucky Press, 1964); Charles H. Goodrich, "The New York Hospital—Cornell Medical Center Project: An Experiment in Welfare Medical Care," *American Journal of Public Health,* 53 (August, 1963): 1252–59; Elizabeth A. Langford, "Medical Care Costs for the Aged: First Findings of the 1963 Survey of the Aged," *Social Security Bulletin,* vol. 27 (July, 1964); Dorothy P. Rice, "Health Insurance Coverage of the Aged and Their Hospital Utilization in 1962: Findings of the 1963 Survey of the Aged," *Social Security Bulletin,* vol. 27 (July, 1964); Cecil G. Sheps, "Medical Care in Aluminum City: Families and Their Regular Doctors," *Journal of Chronic Diseases,* 17 (1964): 815–26; H. Ashley Weeks, *Family Spending Patterns and Health Care* (Cambridge: Harvard University Press, 1961); Grover Wirich, James M. Morgan, and Robin Barlow, "Population Survey: Health Care and Its Financing," in Walter McNerney *et al., Hospital and Medical Economics,* vol. 1 (Chicago: Hospital Research and Educational Trust, 1962).

II

USE OF HEALTH SERVICES

Use of health services varies considerably among subgroups of the population. This chapter on use begins by characterizing those people who have serious episodes of illness and consequently make the greatest demands for health services. How people use health services is in large part determined by the characteristics of the practitioner they first see for advice or treatment. Thus, the second topic is people's usual source of medical care. Provision of medical services often begins with a general physical examination or in response to some symptom the patient experiences. These two subjects are covered under the third topic regarding reasons for seeing the physician. The final topic treats patterns of use in respect to particular types of services including physician visits, hospitalized surgery, hospital use, obstetrical care, and other services.

A. PEOPLE WITH EPISODES OF ILLNESS

Much of the total use of health services is accounted for by the relatively small portion of the population with serious illness episodes. Certainly, a considerable amount of preventive care, obstetrical care, and treatment for minor conditions is given. The burden on the system, however, comes from people with conditions requiring extensive care. For example, people with illnesses requiring hospitalizations account for about one-half of all private expenditures for health but amount to only 8 percent of the population.

Since people with illness episodes use such a large portion of all health services, their characteristics are of special interest. Table 1 provides some idea of the nature of people with hospitalized[1] and non-hospitalized[2] ill-

[1] See definition 16 (refers to Appendix II: Definition of Terms).

[2] A non-hospitalized illness episode describes an illness or condition for which a patient received "substantial" medical care during 1963 but for which he was not hospitalized. See definition 28.

ness episodes and allows comparisons with the population as a whole. It should be remembered that these illnesses are defined in terms of care provided and not "need for care" or illness. No direct inferences can be made about the actual health of the groups considered. Only their response to illness in terms of care received is documented.

People with hospitalized illness do not differ from the population as a whole with regard to sex distribution. However, those with non-hospitalized illness include proportionately more females and fewer males than the total population.

Table 1 also shows that people with illness episodes are considerably

TABLE 1
Selected characteristics of people with one or more hospitalized or non-hospitalized illness episodes: 1963

CHARACTERISTIC	PERCENT OF PERSONS WITH ILLNESS EPISODES		PERCENT OF ALL PERSONS
	Hospitalized illness[1]	Non-hospitalized illness[2]	
Sex			
Male	49	46	49
Female	51	54	51
Age			
0-17	26	18	38
18-54	46	47	45
55 and over	28	35	17
Family income[3]			
$0-3,999	25	25	24
4,000-6,999	30	30	31
7,000 and over	45	45	45
Race[4]			
White	91[a]	88[b]	85[c]
Non-white	9	12	15
Residence[5]			
Urban	64	68	67
Rural non-farm	27	22	23
Rural farm	9	10	10
Total	100[d]	100	100
Number of observations (N)	(643)	(1181)	(7803)

[a] Excludes 5 NA

[b] Excludes 11 NA

[c] Excludes 192 NA

[d] In this and subsequent tables and charts, percent distributions for inclusive and mutually exclusive categories have been adjusted to sum to 100 percent.

"NA" in this and subsequent tables and charts refers to sample persons for whom information was not provided in the interview and was not determined through verification procedures.

more likely to be 55 or over than would be expected by chance. Thus, 28 percent of those with hospitalized illness and 35 percent of those with non-hospitalized illness are 55 or over compared to 17 percent of all persons. In contrast, children 0–17 make up a much smaller proportion of individuals with illness episodes than they do of the total population.

Family income[3] does not differentiate people with illness episodes from the population as a whole. However, if the income distributions are examined separately by age groups, we find some differences for children 0–17, as shown in Table A.

The illness episode groups include slightly smaller proportions of children from low income families than does the total child population. In contrast, the proportion of children from families with incomes above

TABLE A

FAMILY INCOME	AGE 0-17		
	Hospitalized illness	Non-hospitalized illness	Total population
$0-3,999	16	17	22
4,000-6,999	37	30	34
7,000 and over	47	53	44
Total	100	100	100
N	(169)	(208)	(2938)

$7,000 among those with illness episodes is higher than in the total population. The income distributions of those with illness episodes and the population as a whole were similar for persons 18 years of age and older.

Race[4] also differentiates those with illness episodes from the total sample (Table 1). While 15 percent of the total sample were non-white, only 9 percent of those with hospitalized illnesses and 12 percent of those with non-hospitalized illnesses were non-white. No large differences are found in the residence[5] patterns of those with illness episodes and all people.

In sum, differences have been shown between people with major illness episodes and the rest of the population. These differences reflect differential exposure to illness, differential response to illness, or a combination

[3] See definition 8.

[4] See definition 33. In this and subsequent considerations of race, the low incomes of non-white persons should be remembered. Thus 29 percent of all people with family incomes below $4,000 were non-white compared to only 9 percent of those with family incomes of $7,000 or more.

[5] See definition 35.

of both. Differential response may be the more important in understanding race and income differences. Low income and non-white people may generally receive less care for illness conditions than do other segments of the population. Differential exposure is certainly an important aspect of the age differences. Older people have more conditions generally considered to require extensive treatment than the rest of the population. The greater proportion of women among those with non-hospitalized illnesses might indicate that while men are as likely to be hospitalized for serious conditions, they receive less care for conditions which are not defined as requiring hospitalization.

B. SOURCES OF REGULAR MEDICAL CARE

In our health care system it is the patient's personal physician who is largely responsible for the type and amount of health services he receives. This is especially true once the decision is made by the patient or his family to see a physician with regard to an episode of illness or for preventive care. Consequently, the characteristics of regular physicians as well as the characteristics of patients themselves are important considerations regarding health service use.

TABLE B

REGULAR SOURCE OF MEDICAL CARE: 1963	PERCENT
General practitioner	41
Specialist	31
Clinic	10
Osteopath	3
"Other" care	2
No regular source of care	12
NA	1
Total	100
N	(7803)

This survey attempted to determine the regular source of medical care for each sample member.[6] The respondent information was verified and additional details were obtained from the American Medical Association and American Osteopathic Association Directories.

The distribution of regular sources of medical care[7] according to the best information available is given in Table B.

[6] For information regarding types of medical specialists consulted by the population and the annual number of visits per patient to each type, see: "Characteristics of Patients of Selected Types of Medical Specialists and Practitioners," National Center for Health Statistics, ser. 10, no. 28 (May, 1966).

[7] See definition 34.

Eighty-seven percent of the sample indicated some regular source and 12 percent reported no regular source. Four out of ten named a general practitioner as their regular source of care while three out of ten mentioned a specialist. One-tenth named a clinic rather than a particular individual. Three percent considered an osteopath to be their regular source of care and two percent named some "other" source such as a chiropractor or a visiting nurse.

TABLE 2
Source of regular medical care by selected characteristics: 1963

CHARACTERISTIC	SOURCE OF REGULAR CARE[7]					TOTAL	
	Percent specialist	Percent general practitioner	Percent clinic	Percent osteopath, other	Percent no regular care	Percent	N
Sex							
Male	29	42	11	5	14	100	3680
Female	33	41	11	4	11	100	3874
Age							
1-5	36	42	11	3	8	100	801
6-17	32	40	13	5	10	100	1941
18-34	27	42	10	4	17	100	1778
35-54	32	40	9	5	14	100	1720
55-64	31	44	9	4	12	100	603
65 and over	30	45	9	3	13	100	711
Family income							
$0-3,999	20	43	17	4	16	100	1830
4,000-6,999	29	46	10	4	11	100	2318
7,000 and over	38	37	7	6	12	100	3406
Race							
White	32	42	9	5	12	100	6326[a]
Non-white	24	38	20	3	15	100	1132
Total	31	41	11	4	13	100	7554

[a]Excludes 96 NA

Table N	7554
Infants	158
NA	99
Sample N	7803

Table 2 shows source of regular medical care of the population, excluding infants under one year of age, according to some basic population characteristics. Differences between males and females are not large. It appears, however, that females are slightly more likely to have specialists as their regular practitioner than are males. Males in turn reported that they had no regular practitioner more often than did females.

Of all age goups, young children are most likely to have specialists as regular physicians and least likely not to have any regular source. Children 6–17 use a clinic as the regular source of care more than any other age group. Young adults 18–34 have the largest percentage of all age groups reporting no regular source of care. People 35–54 are similar in their use to those 18–34. They are, however, somewhat more likely to use specialists and less likely to report no regular source of care than the younger adult group. The older age groups 55–64 and 65 and over are very similar to each other and in comparison to the other age groups are more likely to have a general practitioner as their regular source of medical care.

Considerable differences in regular source of care according to family income are found in Table 2. People with low family income are most likely to have no regular source of care or make use of clinics. Persons with family incomes in the middle range ($4,000–6,999) report the greatest use of general practitioners. Thirty-eight percent of those with high family incomes use specialists as their regular source of care. This proportion is nine percentage points greater than that for middle income people and almost twice as large as the proportion of low income people using specialists as their regular practitioners.

The biggest differences by race are found in the "specialist" and "clinic" categories. Almost one-third of the whites report a specialist as their regular practitioner compared to about one-fourth of the non-white group. In contrast, the proportion of non-whites reporting a clinic as their regular source of care (20 percent) is over twice the percentage of whites using a clinic (9 percent).

Up to this point we have considered all regular sources of medical care (M.D.'s, non-M.D.'s, and clinics) and have used respondent information when no verification was possible. The following distribution includes only M.D.'s verified in the AMA Directory. These regular practitioners are classified according to their primary specialty as listed in the directory (see Table C).

Fifty-six percent of these M.D.'s report themselves as general practitioners. Of the 44 percent reporting a primary specialty, general surgery was the most prevalent, followed by internal medicine, pediatrics, and obstetrics and gynecology in that order. An additional 7 percent reported some specialty other than those listed above.

Fourteen percent of the directory-verified physicians named as regular physicians were certified by one of the nineteen American Specialty Boards. The portion of board-certified specialists among regular doctors varies according to age and family income. This relationship for all persons one year of age and over is shown in Table 3.

Children 1–17 are more likely to have a board-certified specialist as a regular physician than are adults. Seventeen percent of the regular physicians of children are board-certified compared to 11 and 12 percent for the two adult groups. However, this relationship does not hold for children from low income families. Only 5 percent of the regular physicians of children from families with incomes below $4,000 are board-certified compared to 7 and 10 percent of the physicians of adults who are members of low income families.

Persons from families with incomes of $7,000 or more are much more likely to have board-certified specialists as regular physicians than those with lower incomes, according to Table 3. Almost one-fifth of these per-

TABLE C

PRIMARY SPECIALTY OF M.D.'S USED AS REGULAR SOURCES OF CARE: 1963	PERCENT	
Specialty reported	44	
General surgery		12
Internal medicine		10
Pediatrics		8
Obstetrics and gynecology		7
Other specialty[8]		7
General practitioner[9]	56	
Total	100	

Table N		5376
No verified M.D.		2427
M.D. reported but not verified	215	
Clinic or non-M.D.	1162	
No regular source	951	
NA	99	
Sample N		7803

[8] These "other" specialties reported included 108 people using medical specialties (allergy, cardiovascular disease, dermatology, gastroenterology, pulmonary diseases); 81 using surgical specialties (anesthesiology, colon and rectal surgery, neurological surgery, orthopedic surgery, plastic surgery, thoracic surgery, urology); 55 ophthalmology and otolaryngology; 23 psychiatry and neurology; and 37 using other specialties listed in the *AMA Directory* 1963.

[9] Includes 24 M.D.'s whose specialties are not specified or are unrecognized.

TABLE 3
Percent of verified physicians reported as regular sources of care who have American Board certification by age and family income of patient: 1963

AGE	FAMILY INCOME			
	$0-3,999	$4,000-6,999	$7,000 and over	All incomes
1-17	5 (330)[a]	11 (661)	24 (953)	17 (1944)
18-54	7 (362)	7 (753)	15 (1243)	11 (2358)
55 and over	10 (422)	7 (239)	20 (278)	12 (939)
All ages	8 (1114)	8 (1653)	19 (2474)	13 (5241)

[a]Numbers in parentheses in this and subsequent tables represent total cases upon which percentages are based.

Table N	5241
Verified M.D. for infant	135
No verified M.D.	2427
Sample N	7803

sons have board-certified specialists as regular physicians compared to 8 percent for middle and lower income people. This relationship holds for every age group and is especially pronounced for children, where almost one-fourth of those with family incomes of $7000 or more have a board-certified specialist as their regular physician compared to only 5 percent and 11 percent for children in lower income families.

TABLE D

AGE OF REGULAR PHYSICIAN: 1963	PERCENT
34 or less	5
35-44	32
45-54	33
55-64	23
65 and over	7
Total	100

Table N 5376
No verified M.D. 2427
Sample N 7803

TABLE 4
Percent of regular physicians 55 or over by age and family income of patient: 1963

	FAMILY INCOME						
AGE	$0-3,999		$4,000-6,999		$7,000 and over		All incomes
1-17	31	(330)	26	(661)	22	(917)	25 (1908)
18-54	36	(362)	29	(753)	29	(867)	30 (1982)
55 and over	40	(422)	41	(239)	42	(690)	41 (1351)
All ages	36	(1114)	30	(1653)	28	(2474)	30 (5241)

Table N 5241
Verified M.D. for infant 135
No verified M.D. 2427
Sample N 7803

Age of regular physician is another characteristic which might influence care prescribed for patients. The training of medical students is, of course, changing with the passage of time, and methods of treatment may also change as the physician grows older. The distribution of directory-verified M.D.'s shows that the modal age group for regular physicians was 45-54, followed closely by the 35-44 age group. Together these two groups included almost two-thirds of the regular physicians reported in the sample (see Table D).

Table 4 shows the percentage of physicians 55 and over according to age and family income of patients, excluding infants. Older patients are more likely to have physicians 55 and over than are younger patients. Thus, the percentage of patients with physicians 55 and over increases from 25 percent for persons 1–17 to 30 percent for those 18–54 and 41 percent for patients 55 and over. The direct relationship of age of patient and age of physician is found at every income level. This correlation leads to the question to what extent, if any, similarities in patterns of care within patient age groups and differences between age groups may be a function of the modal age of physicians treating each group. No answer is proposed here, but if methods of treatment do vary with age of physician, such a function might help to explain observed variations in care according to age of patient.

Patients with family incomes of $3,999 or less are more likely to have a physician 55 or over than are patients with higher family incomes (Table 4). Thirty-six percent of the patients with family incomes of less than $4,000 had a physician 55 or over compared to 30 percent for those with incomes of $4,000–6,999 and 28 percent for the highest income class. This inverse relationship of age and family income is strongest for children and holds for those 18–54. There is, however, no difference for persons 55 and over in age of physician according to income group.

This section has shown the varied sources of regular medical care used by the population. In addition, the characteristics of physicians used as regular sources of care are related to characteristics of the patient including age and family income. Physician characteristics such as primary specialty, board certification, and age need to be systematically examined as sources of variance in patterns of patient care in conjunction with patient attributes. These two sets of variables may have important joint and interaction effects as well as independent influences on use of health services.

C. REASONS FOR SEEING THE PHYSICIAN

While the physician channels much of the patient's care once the patient decides to see him, the patient must initiate the contact in most instances. This section considers two common reasons for physician-patient contact. One is a general physical examination and the second is presence of symptoms of illness. As we shall see, illness symptoms often result in physical examinations, but preventive health examinations and examinations required by work, school, etc., are also common among certain segments of the population.

1. Physical examinations

Over one-half of the population was reported to have had a "physical examination or checkup"[10] within one year of the time of the interview in

10 See definition 31.

1964 and one-third reported the time as six months or less. At the other extreme, 10 percent had never had a physical examination.

Table 5 shows how length of time since the last examination varies according to age, sex, family income, and race. Differences according to sex are minor. Females appeared slightly more likely than males to have

TABLE 5
Length of time since the last physical examination[10] by selected characteristics: 1963

CHARACTERISTIC	TIME SINCE LAST EXAMINATION				TOTAL	
	Percent 1 year or less	Percent between 1 and 5 years	Percent over 5 years	Percent never	Percent	N
Sex						
Male	52	30	8	10	100	3605
Female	54	29	7	10	100	3837
Age						
1-5	65	20	–	15	100	788
6-17	49	27	6	18	100	1910
18-34	56	32	6	6	100	1747
35-54	50	33	11	6	100	1708
55-64	50	32	11	7	100	587
65 and over	53	28	11	8	100	702
Family income						
$0-3,999	45	26	10	19	100	1807
4,000-6,999	51	32	7	10	100	2263
7,000 and over	59	29	6	6	100	3372
Race						
White	53	30	8	9	100	6254[a]
Non-white	55	25	4	16	100	1094
Total	53	29	8	10	100	7442

[a]Excludes 94 NA

Table N	7442
Infants	158
NA	203
Total N	7803

had an examination within a year. The difference is explained by two age groups. Sixty percent of all women in the age group 18–34 had a physical examination within the year compared to 51 percent of the men. The difference here includes the influence of physical examinations for prenatal care. A greater proportion of females also had recent examinations in the age category 65 and over. Fifty-nine percent of the females in this group had examinations within the year compared to 49 percent of the males. For all other age groups the distributions for each sex are similar.

Young children 1–5 years of age are more likely to have had a recent examination than people in any other age group (Table 5). However, this group, along with older children 6–17, is also most likely *never* to have had a physical examination. In part this reflects the fact that children simply have not lived as long and thus have not been exposed to as many possibilities for having examinations. Still, it should be noted that 17 percent of the children 17 and under have never had a general checkup, according to our interview data.

Young adults 18–34 are, with the exception of young children, most likely to have had examinations within the year. Examinations in connection with obstetrical care for women of childbearing age are, again, a factor here. As people reach middle age, they are more likely to have had their last examination over 5 years ago than are younger people. However,

TABLE 6
Length of time since the last physical examination by person's regular source of medical care: 1963

REGULAR SOURCE OF MEDICAL CARE	TIME SINCE LAST EXAMINATION				TOTAL	
	Percent 1 year or less	Percent 13 months to 5 years	Percent over 5 years	Percent never	Percent	N
Specialist	61	28	4	7	100	2306
General practitioner	52	29	8	11	100	3047
Clinic	52	27	7	14	100	785
Osteopath, other	53	27	10	10	100	344
No regular care	39	36	18	12	100	893

Table N	7375
Infants	158
NA source and/or time	270
Sample N	7803

more of the elderly, 65 and over, have had examinations within the year than have the age groups 35–64. The latter groups more often report an examination between 1 and 5 years in the past. Similar proportions of these older age groups have never had an examination.

Table 5 shows that the higher the family income of the individual, the more likely he is to have had a recent examination. Thus, 59 percent of those with incomes of $7,000 or more had an examination within one year compared to 45 percent of those with incomes under $4,000. As great a proportion of non-whites as of whites have had an examination within the year. However, the percentage of non-whites who report never having had an examination is almost twice as high as the percentage of whites.

The previous section stressed the importance of the characteristics of the person's regular practitioner as related to health care patterns. Thus, we might expect length of time since the person's last physical examination to vary by type of regular source of care he reports. Table 6 shows that people using specialists as their regular source of care are most likely, and persons without a regular source least likely, to have had an examination within a year. Sixty-one percent of those with specialists compared to slightly more than half of those using G.P.'s, clinics, and other sources and 39 percent of those with no regular source had an examination within one year.

Some of these differences are explained by illness level and by social characteristics of the patient. In addition, however, the attributes of the practitioner should not be overlooked.

The reason for the last physical examination for every person reporting an examination was elicited. The reason was selected from a card including the following alternatives: (1) Symptom: "wasn't feeling good, was bothered by some symptom or condition"; (2) Required: "examination was required for a job, school, insurance, armed forces, or something like that"; and (3) Preventive exam: "there was nothing particularly wrong and the examination wasn't required—it was just time for a checkup or physical examination."

The responses were fairly equally distributed over these three alternatives. Thirty-nine percent reported "symptoms" as the factor initiating their last physical examination. Thirty-two percent were "required" to get an examination, and 29 percent had "preventive" examinations. Those having preventive examinations included the largest percentage of individuals having an examination within the year. The percentage of each group having an examination within the year is given below:

TABLE E

REASON FOR EXAM	PERCENT HAVING EXAM WITHIN THE YEAR	
Preventive	65	(1239)
Symptom	59	(1505)
Required	54	(1125)

Table N	3869
Exam over 1 year ago	2682
NA time and/or reason	330
No exam ever	764
Infant	158
Sample N	7803

The reasons given for the most recent examination varied a great deal according to characteristics of the individual. Table 7 shows that the most prevalent reason for males having a physical examination was that it was required. Forty percent of the examinations for males were of this type compared to less than one-fourth for women. Many examinations for men are apparently given for purposes of work and insurance. Women are more likely to have examinations in response to symptoms or as preventive measures.

The age distributions in Table 7 show that preventive examinations are far more important for young children 1–5 than for any other age group. Over one-half of all examinations reported for young children were of this nature. Required examinations, many in connection with school, are the most frequent type for children in the 6–17 age group.

The biggest difference in reasons for examination between the sexes is found in the 18–34 age group. Sixty-one percent of all examinations for males in this age category are required compared to 33 percent for females. Apparently examinations under the auspices of our educational, employment, and military institutions are a dominant factor in the physician contact of American young men. Young women 18–34, to the contrary, are much more likely to have examinations in response to symptoms and as a measure of prevention on their own volition.

TABLE 7
Reason for last physical examination by selected characteristics: 1963

CHARACTERISTIC	REASON			TOTAL	
	Percent symptom	Percent required	Percent preventive	Percent	N
Age and Sex					
Male	35	40	25	100	3169
1-5	34	14	52	100	328
6-17	26	43	31	100	756
18-34	23	61	16	100	798
35-54	42	39	19	100	748
55-64	51	27	22	100	258
65 and over	60	14	26	100	281
Female	43	24	33	100	3382
1-5	32	14	54	100	312
6-17	31	38	31	100	765
18-34	37	33	30	100	827
35-54	49	17	34	100	840
55-64	57	15	28	100	287
65 and over	63	7	30	100	351
Family income					
$0-3,999	51	24	25	100	1416
4,000-6,999	38	35	27	100	1998
7,000 and over	34	34	32	100	3137
Race					
White	38	32	30	100	5601[a]
Non-white	44	31	25	100	885
Total	39	32	29	100	6651

[a]Excludes 165 NA

Table N	6651
NA	330
No exam ever	764
Infants	158
Sample N	7803

For older age groups the proportion of examinations reported for males as required decreases considerably compared to males 18–34 but is still higher than the corresponding percentage for females in each age group. From 35 on, examination in response to symptoms becomes increasingly important for both sexes. These examinations reach 60 percent of the total for males 65 and over and 63 percent for females in this age group.

Over one-half of all low income persons report that their latest examination was in response to some symptom or condition (Table 7). The corresponding percentages for people from families with higher incomes dropped to 38 for the middle category and 34 for the highest category. In contrast, people with higher family incomes were more likely to have preventive examinations and required examinations.

Whites appear more likely to have preventive examinations than non-whites, while the most recent examinations for non-whites are more likely to have resulted from illness. The proportion of required examinations was similar for each group.

This section has provided information on the length of time since the last physical examination. In addition, we have considered why people have such examinations. One of the reasons given (symptoms of illness) is treated in more detail in the following section.

2. Reaction to symptoms of illness

Symptoms of illness are the most frequent reasons given by people in the sample for seeing a physician for a physical examination. In this section some data are provided on the type of symptoms that bring people to doctors. In addition, a few of the symptoms are examined in more detail to see how different types of people react to them. The data presented here are based on a check list of twenty symptoms.[11] The respondents or their proxies were asked if they had had the symptom during 1963 or up to the time of the interview in 1964. If a symptom was reported, information was collected regarding if, and when, a physician had been seen about the symptom.

Table 8 shows that the symptoms reported most often were getting up tired; sore throat, fever; and waking up with stiff joints. Of most interest here, however, is how people respond to a given symptom. The two conditions for which people were most likely to see a physician during 1963 were acute conditions involving infections and irritation. Sixty-four percent of those with infections in eyes or ears, and 61 percent with sore throat, fever saw a physician during 1963.

11 See Appendix III (questionnaire) for the symptoms as they appeared on the check list given to respondents.

The symptoms for which people were most likely to have seen a doctor previously but not during the survey year were skin rash and frequent backaches. Combining the "physician seen" columns, we find that infections in eyes or ears, skin rashes, and pains in the heart most often result in physician visits. In contrast, getting up tired and waking up with stiff and aching joints are symptoms for which the majority of people have never

TABLE 8
Seeing a physician for symptoms occurring during survey year: 1963

	SEEING PHYSICIAN			TOTAL		
SYMPTOM[11]	Percent seeing physician in 1963[a]	Percent seeing physician earlier	Percent never seeing physician[b]	Percent	N having symptom	NA
Cough for weeks	53	12	35	100	646	22
Sudden weakness or faintness	53	16	31	100	787	23
Getting up tired	31	10	59	100	1254	31
Feeling tired for weeks	42	16	42	100	439	20
Frequent headaches	40	17	43	100	911	20
Skin rash	53	25	22	100	718	21
Diarrhea 4 or 5 days	50	12	38	100	235	28
Shortness of breath	46	19	35	100	610	23
Waking up with stiff joints	31	15	54	100	1078	26
Pains in any joint	49	19	32	100	525	28
Frequent backaches	44	23	33	100	776	25
Unexplained loss of 10 pounds	56	14	30	100	110	20
Pains in the heart	55	20	25	100	400	28
Repeated indigestion	44	20	36	100	677	28
Repeated vomiting	54	6	40	100	267	15
Sore throat, fever	61	6	33	100	1232	30
Nose stopped up	47	14	39	100	553	20
Unexpected bleeding	49	17	34	100	246	20
Abdominal pains	55	14	31	100	348	22
Infections in eyes or ears	64	16	20	100	639	27

[a]Includes people who saw physician in 1964 up to time of interview.

[b]Includes cases where it was not known if doctor was seen.

Table N	7645
Infants	158
Total N	7803

seen a physician. These conditions may seem more like a way of life than conditions necessitating treatment to some people, especially older people.

In Table 9 we have taken the six most commonly reported symptoms to see how different types of people react. More specifically, characteristics such as age and sex are related to the proportion of people who have ever seen a doctor about these symptoms.

For five of the six most frequently reported symptoms, females were more likely than males to see a doctor if they experienced the symptoms.

The single exception was sore throat, fever, for which 63 percent of the males and 60 percent of the females saw a doctor.

Differences in response to symptoms according to age are not so distinct as they are according to sex (Table 9). Responses vary considerably according to the symptom. For sore throat, fever we find an inverse relationship between age and the proportion of people seeing a doctor. Sixty-five percent of those 1–17 saw a doctor. The corresponding percentage decreased

TABLE 9
Percent of people with selected symptoms seeing a doctor within the year[a]
by sex, age, and income: 1963

CHARACTERISTIC	SYMPTOM					
	Percent getting up tired[b]	Percent sore throat, fever[c]	Percent waking up with stiff joints[d]	Percent frequent head-aches[e]	Percent sudden weakness or faintness[f]	Percent frequent back-aches[g]
Sex						
Male	24 (433)	63 (592)	27 (448)	31 (308)	46 (234)	39 (273)
Female	35 (821)	60 (640)	35 (630)	44 (603)	57 (553)	47 (503)
Age						
1-17	29 (69)	65 (716)	33 (18)	44 (79)	54 (54)	47 (15)
18-54	33 (799)	59 (396)	28 (559)	38 (611)	54 (425)	45 (499)
55 and over	29 (386)	46 (120)	35 (501)	43 (221)	52 (308)	43 (262)
Family income						
$0-3,999	31 (397)	46 (215)	30 (412)	33 (269)	50 (313)	42 (285)
4,000-6,999	32 (395)	61 (408)	30 (287)	42 (307)	54 (221)	45 (205)
7,000 and over	31 (462)	67 (609)	34 (379)	43 (335)	57 (253)	45 (286)

[a] Includes persons who saw physician in 1964 up to time of interview.
[b] Excludes 31 NA
[c] Excludes 30 NA
[d] Excludes 26 NA
[e] Excludes 20 NA
[f] Excludes 23 NA
[g] Excludes 25 NA

Table N   7645
Infants   158
Sample N   7803

to 59 for those 18–54 and to 46 for those 65 and over. For some symptoms there appears to be a curvilinear relationship with young and old people more likely to see a physician than those of middle age (headaches, stiff joints). For others there is little difference among age groups (getting up tired, sudden weakness or faintness).

People with higher family incomes generally seem more likely to respond to symptoms by going to a doctor than do those with lower incomes. For none of the six symptoms is the proportion of those with family incomes of $7,000 or more seeing a doctor less than the proportion of those with incomes of under $4,000. The largest differences are found for sore throat, fever, for which 67 percent of high income people see a doctor compared to 46 percent of those with low incomes, and frequent headaches, for which 43 percent of the high income group and 33 percent of the low income group see a doctor.

The differential response of the population to various symptoms of illness and of different classes of people to a particular symptom is helpful in attempting to understand health service use. Varying amounts and types of health services are used according to the response to illness symptoms. For example, in an earlier section we found that females were more likely to report non-hospitalized episodes of illness requiring considerable medical care than were males. Support is found here for the tentative conclusion that some of this difference is explained by the greater tendency of women to use health services in response to given symptoms. For five of the six most commonly reported symptoms, women were more likely to see a doctor than were men.

D. USE PATTERNS ACCORDING TO TYPE OF SERVICE

The previous parts of this chapter have dealt with use in a general fashion. Using data from the 1963 survey, we have characterized people who use large quantities of health services. In addition we have considered the population's regular sources of medical care, how often they receive physical examinations, and how they respond to symptoms of illness. This section deals with more direct and traditional measures of use of physicians, hospitals, and other types of services. Data from the earlier surveys are also incorporated to show trends from 1953 to 1963.

1. Physician visits

Almost two-thirds of the population saw a physician at least once during 1963.[12] Practically no change occurred in the proportion seeing a physician between 1958 and 1963.[13] In 1953 it was estimated that 60 percent of the population saw a physician as an outpatient during the survey year.[14] The mean number of outpatient visits[15] per person in a year was 4.4 in 1958 and 4.6 in 1963.

[12] See definition 32.

[13] The survey year was not the calendar year in the case of the first two studies. The survey year was roughly equally divided in the first study between 1952 and 1953 and in the second study between 1957 and 1958. However, for convenience in the text, tables and charts, the first study survey year is referred to as "1953" and the second study survey year is referred to as "1958."

[14] This estimate is not directly comparable to the data from the later studies. The estimates for 1958 and 1963 are based on reports for a twelve-month period and include

Among all age groups, children under 6 are *most* likely to see a physician at least once (Table 10). Children 6–17 are *least* likely to see a physician. Between 1958 and 1963 there was a 6 percentage point drop in the proportion of these older children seeing a doctor. One possible explanation for this change is the influenza epidemic of 1957–58. It may be that an

TABLE 10
Physician visits by age and sex: 1958 and 1963

AGE AND SEX	PERCENT OF PERSONS SEEING PHYSICIAN[12] DURING SURVEY YEAR[a]			MEAN NUMBER OF PHYSICIAN VISITS[14] PER PERSON-YEAR		
	1958[13]	1963	1963[b] N	1958	1963	1963 person-years[c]
Age						
1-5	73	75	812	4.6	4.0	896[d]
6-17	64	58	1955	2.7	2.5	1965
18-34	68	67	1769	4.1	5.0	1784
35-54	64	65	1728	4.7	4.9	1732
55-64	66	68	602	5.1	5.7	603
65 and over	68	68	694	7.4	8.2	706
Sex						
Male	62	62	3671	3.5	4.1	3741
Female	70	68	3889	5.3	5.0	3945
Total	66	65	7560	4.4	4.6	7686

[a]Includes only persons in sample for entire survey year.

[b]In this and subsequent tables only N's for the current survey are usually included. The reader is referred to the reports of the earlier surveys for the N's of the 1953 and 1958 estimates. Generally, the N's from the earlier surveys are slightly larger due to larger overall sample size. It should be noted that the sampling procedure used in the 1958 survey required the weighting of certain cases to compensate for the differential sampling rates used in the two strata. All 1958 estimates are based on the weighted distribution. But since the reliability of a given statistic is a function of the number of actual cases upon which it is based, the N's given in the 1958 report are unweighted. Consequently, the reader checking N's in that report cannot combine subgroups by weighting the relevant distributions by the given N's nor should he take the distribution of N's among the subgroups as being equivalent to the weighted distribution for the particular variable involved.

1963	
Table N	7560
Infants	158
Not in sample	
12 months	85
Sample N	7803

[c]Aggregate sum of months lived by all sample members in the sample population during the survey year divided by 12.

[d]Includes infants under 1 year of age.

inpatient visits. Those for 1953 are based in part on six-month reports and include only outpatient visits.

15 Includes office, clinic, and home visits but excludes hospital inpatient visits. Telephone calls to physicians were not considered in this report. National Health Survey data indicate the mean for phone calls per patient is about 0.5 visits. National Center for Health Statistics, "Volume of Physician Visits by Place of Visit and Type of Service," ser. 10, no. 18 (June, 1965).

unusually high number of children saw a physician in that year because of it.

While young children are most likely to see a doctor at least once, persons 65 and over have a considerably higher mean number of visits per year than any other age group (Table 10). The percentage of the oldest age group that sees a doctor at least once is not unusually high. However, those older people who do see a doctor are more likely to have several visits. The mean number of visits increased for all adult age groups between 1958 and 1963. The averages for children 17 or less actually showed a decline during this period.

Women are more likely to see a physician than are men. In 1963, 68 percent of the females compared to 62 percent of the males saw a physician (Table 10). The proportions of children 1–17 of each sex seeing a physician are quite similar (64 percent males vs. 62 percent females). However, beginning with the reproductive years (18–34) and continuing into old age, the proportion of women seeing a doctor during the year is considerably higher. For all persons 18 and over, the proportion of women seeing a doctor in 1963 was 72 percent compared to 61 percent for men.

Table 10 shows that not only are females more likely to see a doctor than males but also their mean number of visits is higher. In 1963 the mean number for females was 5.0 while it was 4.1 for males. Still, this difference of .9 visits is only one-half that found in 1958, when the mean number for females exceeded that for males by 1.8 visits, indicating that the difference is decreasing.

Children from low income families are less likely to see a physician during the year than are those from higher income families. However, these differences by income are not found for older adults. In Table 11 we see that the percentage of young children seeing a doctor during the survey year 1963 increased from 52 percent for those from low income families to 76 percent and 87 percent for those from middle and high income families. This direct relationship between family income and the percentage of people seeing a physician holds for all the age groups under 55 years of age. However, it becomes weaker as the age of the group increases. Thus, while 35 percent more of the children 1–5 with family incomes of $7,000 or more saw a physician than did children with family incomes of less than $4,000, the percentage difference between the income groups had decreased to 15 percentage points for adults 35–54. No consistent differences are found for persons 55 and over with respect to income.

The columns of Table 11 show that the proportions of people seeing a doctor in the various age categories vary considerably for the three income levels. Young children from families in the middle and upper income classes were more likely to have seen a doctor than were people of any other age group. To the contrary, young children 1–5 in the low income group were *less* likely to see a physician than any other age group with the exception of the 6–17 group.

Within the upper income class, the proportion of each age group seeing a doctor is similar except for the unusually high proportion of children 1–5 (87 percent). For the low and middle income classes, the percentage of children 6–17 seeing a physician is considerably lower than

TABLE 11
Percent of individuals seeing a physician during 1963 by age and family income[a]

	FAMILY INCOME					
AGE	Percent $0-3,999		Percent $4,000-6,999		Percent $7,000 and over	
1-5	52	(174)	76	(315)	87	(323)
6-17	41	(419)	53	(610)	70	(926)
18-34	57	(341)	67	(635)	70	(793)
35-54	54	(289)	64	(457)	69	(982)
55-64	69	(194)	70	(163)	66	(245)
65 and over	68	(428)	66	(139)	71	(127)
Total	56	(1845)	64	(2319)	71	(3396)

[a]Includes only persons in the sample for the entire 12-month period.

Table N	7560
Infants	158
Not in sample 12 months	85
Sample N	7803

any other age group. People 55 and over in the low income category, unlike those of similar ages in the other income categories, have considerably higher percentages seeing the doctor than any other age categories.

The doctor's office is by far the most frequent place of visit. Eighty-three percent of all outpatient visits in 1963 were in a doctor's office. Chart 2 shows the shift in visit site between 1958 and 1963. Home visits decreased as a proportion of all visits from 11 percent to 5 percent in this time period. Office and clinic visits each increased by 3 percentage points.

Traditionally, home visits have provided an important segment of care to those persons 65 and over. In 1963 the proportion of all visits taking place at home for the 65 and over age group was still over twice the proportion for all persons (Chart 2). Nevertheless, there was a major shift from home to office for the oldest group between 1958 and 1963. Home visits decreased by 14 percentage points in these five years while office visits increased by the same as a proportion of all visits.

The "physician visit" category for both the HIF-NORC and the NHS

studies has included "nurse visits." These are usually visits to a physician's office or clinic during which the patient never sees the doctor. In-
stead he is treated by a nurse. There is some question whether such visits
are really of the same nature as those when a patient is actually treated
by the physician. The importance of the question depends on the magnitude of these nurse visits. In the 1963 study an attempt was made to
separate out all nurse visits in physicians' private offices.

Almost one-tenth of all reported visits to physicians' offices were nurse
visits. That is, the patient was not treated or seen in a professional sense
by the doctor. Table 12 shows that the proportion of nurse visits is 9
percent for both males and females. The proportion of visits to a doctor's

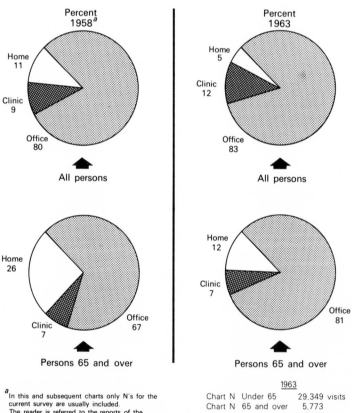

Chart 2   Percent of out-of-hospital physician visits by place
of visit for all persons, and for persons 65 and over:
1958 and 1963

Percent 1958[a]

Home 11
Clinic 9
Office 80

All persons

Percent 1963

Home 5
Clinic 12
Office 83

All persons

Home 26
Clinic 7
Office 67

Persons 65 and over

Home 12
Clinic 7
Office 81

Persons 65 and over

[a]In this and subsequent charts only N's for the
current survey are usually included.
The reader is referred to the reports of the
earlier surveys for the 1953 and 1958 estimates.
Generally, the N's from the earlier surveys are
slightly larger due to larger overall sample size.

1963

Chart N Under 65   29,349 visits
Chart N 65 and over   5,773

Sample N   35,122

office when only a nurse was seen is smaller for children 0–5 than for other age groups. Males age 6–17 have a greater proportion of nurse visits than any other male age group. For females the proportion of visits to doctors' offices in which only a nurse is seen increases with age. It increases from 7 percent for females 0–5 up to 14 percent for females 65 and over.

These data on physician visits indicate that the change in over-all use rates between 1958 and 1963 was minor. However, substantial differences were found in 1963 according to age, sex, and family income. In addition the site of visit continues to change from the home to office and clinic. Patient visits to a doctor's office when the doctor wasn't seen but the patient was treated by a nurse or technician amounted to a not inconsequential one-tenth of all visits to a doctor's office.

TABLE 12
Nurse visits to a physician's office as a percent of all visits to a physician's office by age and sex: 1963

AGE	NURSE VISITS AS A PERCENT OF ALL OFFICE VISITS					
	Percent male		Percent female		Percent all persons	
0-5	4	(1412)	7	(1451)	5	(2863)
6-17	14	(2061)	8	(1865)	11	(3926)
18-34	7	(2116)	9	(5438)	9	(7554)
35-54	12	(3104)	9	(4348)	10	(7452)
55-64	5	(1202)	10	(1553)	8	(2755)
65 and over	9	(2470)	14	(2185)	11	(4655)
Total	9	(12365)	9	(16840)	9	(29205)

2. Hospitalized surgery

Treatment by surgery[16] represents a substantial part of the total health picture in this country. Four out of every 100 Americans are hospitalized for surgery each year. These surgical admissions accounted for 35 percent of all admissions to short term hospitals in 1963.

The hospitalized surgical procedure rate remained stable over the ten-year period. For each study the rate was 5 per 100 person-years. Surgical admissions as a proportion of all hospital admissions declined slightly from 38 percent in 1953 to 36 percent in 1958 and 35 percent in 1963.

Table 13 shows the hospitalized surgical procedure rates according to basic socio-demographic characteristics of the population for 1958 and 1963. In both periods female rates exceeded those for males. Children had lower hospitalized surgical rates than adults in both 1958 and 1963. The rates by income apparently differed little in 1958. In 1963, however, by

16 See definition 38.

spreading the highest income category, a rather definite curvilinear pattern is seen. People with the lowest incomes have a low rate of 3 per 100 person-years.[17] The rate then rises with increasing income to a maximum of 7 for those with incomes of $7,500–9,999. The rate subsequently declines for higher income groups. As we shall see in a later chapter, lack of surgical insurance among people with the lowest incomes apparently decreases the over-all surgical rate of this group. In both surveys the hospital surgical rate for rural farm people was lower than for people with other residences. Again, lack of insurance among the rural farm population will be shown to be an important factor.

In handling the large surgical case load described above, heavy demands are made on the surgeon to keep abreast of new knowledge and to apply it effectively. Heart surgery, transplanting of organs, and similar

[17] See definition 30.

TABLE 13

In-hospital surgical procedures[16] per 100 person-years[17] by sex, age, family income, and residence: 1958 and 1963

CHARACTERISTICS	IN-HOSPITAL SURGICAL PROCEDURES PER 100 PERSON-YEARS		1963 PERSON-YEARS
	1958	1963	
Sex			
Male	4	4	3741
Female	5	6	3945
Age			
0-5	3	3	896
6-17	4	4	1965
18-34	5	5	1784
35-54	5	6	1732
55-64	5	6	603
65 and over	7	5	706
Family income			
Under $2,000	5	3	670
2,000-3,499	4	4	904
3,500-4,999	5	4	987
5,000-7,499	5	6	2139
7,500-9,999	}	7 }	1281
10,000-12,499	4	5 } 6	858
12,500 and over	}	4 }	847
Residence			
Large urban	5	5	1530
Other urban	5	5	3618
Rural non-farm	5	6	1777
Rural farm	3	4	761
Total	5	5	7686

procedures are dramatic examples of the intricacy of some modern day procedures. Surgical advances are directly related not only to new medical knowledge but to the long and arduous training presently necessary before a physician becomes a surgical specialist. Therefore, some characteristics of the physicians performing surgery in each of the studies are given below.

Forty-six percent of all hospitalized surgery in 1963 was performed by board-certified specialists—physicians who have had some seven years of training and practice beyond college and medical school. Table 14 shows that 28 percent were certified by a surgical examining board and an additional 18 percent were certified by other specialty boards which include surgery in the specialty.

The data indicate that with the passage of time a greater proportion

TABLE 14
Percent distribution of hospitalized surgical procedures by American Board certification of physician who performed the operation: 1953, 1958 and 1963

	HOSPITALIZED SURGICAL PROCEDURES[a]		
CERTIFICATION	Percent 1953	Percent 1958	Percent 1963
Certified by a surgical examining board	21[b]	25[b]	28
Orthopedic surgery	5	4	6
General surgery	13	18	15
Plastic surgery	1	1	3
Neurological surgery	1	1	1
Thoracic surgery	1	1	2
Colon and rectal surgery[c]	1	1	1
Certified by other specialty boards which include surgery in the specialty	16	17[b]	18[b]
Urology	2	2	1
Obstetrics and gynecology	4	4	8
Ophthalmology and otolaryngology	10	12	10
Not certified for surgery	63	58	54
Total	100	100	100
N	(338)	(552)	(339)

[a]Caesarean deliveries included in 1963 but excluded in 1953 and 1958.

[b]The sum of the components does not equal the total because a few operations were performed by physicians certified by more than one board.

[c]Classified as "Proctology" in the 1953 and 1958 surveys.

	1953	1958	1963
Table N	338	552	339
Physician not identified	36	43	36
Dentist	7	8	4
Osteopath	8	7	3
Sample N	389	610	382

of surgical procedures is being performed by board certified specialists.[18] In 1953 the percentage was 37. It rose to 42 percent in 1958 and to 46 percent in 1963. While slightly over half of all surgical procedures are still performed by physicians not certified for surgery, a large and growing proportion of all surgery, and probably most complicated surgery, is performed by physicians with extensive training and experience. Some evidence bearing on this point is presented later.

Involvement in surgery can also be assessed by considering the physician's own classification of his practice. The distribution in Table F shows

TABLE F

SPECIALTY REPORTED BY SURGEON FOR HOSPITALIZED SURGICAL PROCEDURES[19]	PERCENT
Surgical specialties only	72
Surgical specialties with other specialties[20]	7
Specialties not involving surgery	5
No specialty reported	16
Total	100
N	(339)

the type of practice reported by physicians performing surgery in 1963. This distribution shows that almost four-fifths of the surgical procedures in 1963 were performed by physicians reporting primary or secondary specialties involving surgery.

The proportion of hospitalized surgery performed by physicians reporting a special interest in surgery varies considerably according to the type of surgery. Table 15 shows that less than half of such common procedure as tonsillectomies, adenoidectomies, and appendectomies were per-

18 In the 1963 study, characteristics of physicians were obtained from the *American Medical Association Directory: 1963*, 22d ed., and the surgical procedures were performed in 1963. In the 1958 study the characteristics of physicians were obtained from the *AMA Directory*, 1958, 20th ed., while the surgical procedures were performed in 1957–58. In the earliest study, while the surgical procedures were performed in 1952–53, the data about physicians were obtained from the 1956 edition of the directory. As a result, in the 1953 study formal qualification which they did not actually have at the time of the surgery might be attributed to physicians, while in the latter two studies physicians may actually have had formal qualifications not ascribed to them in the directory.

19 Surgical specialties include general surgery, ophthalmology, otolaryngology, anesthesiology, colon and rectal surgery, neurological surgery, orthopedic surgery, plastic surgery, thoracic surgery, urology, and obstetrics and gynecology. Other specialties include all specialties recognized by the American Medical Association not included under surgical specialty above. Source: *AMA Directory*, 1963.

20 Surgeon reports both a primary and secondary specialty, one being a surgical specialty and the other being an "other" speciality as defined in footnote 19.

formed by physicians with special interest in surgery. However, these physicians performed 84 percent of all other operations.

These data on hospitalized surgical procedures show that the over-all rate remained the same from 1958 to 1963 and that differences among subgroups of the population continue to exist. There appears to be a gradual but consistent trend toward surgery by specialists. This is probably especially true for complicated surgery.

TABLE 15
Specialty interest of physician performing tonsillectomies, adenoidectomies, appendectomies, and other hospitalized surgical procedures: 1963

SURGICAL SPECIALTY REPORTED[a]	PERCENT OF SURGICAL PROCEDURES		
	Tonsillectomy, adenoidectomy, appendectomy	Others	All procedures
Yes	42	84	79
No	58	16	21
Total	100	100	100
N	(66)	(273)	(339)

[a]A surgical specialty as defined in footnote 19 is reported as either primary or secondary specialty by the physician performing the operation.

Table N	339
Physician not identified	36
Dentist	4
Osteopath	3
Sample N	382

3. Hospital use

Hospital care is the fastest growing major component of the health services system as measured in terms of both use and costs. The hospital admission rate has more than doubled since the CCMC study in the early thirties. The following chapter on expenditures will show that expenditures for hospital care are not only growing in absolute amounts but are increasing as a proportion of total expenditure for health services.

Some of this increase is attributed to the growing complexity of medical care and the physician's need of hospital services and personnel to provide the most up-to-date treatment for his patient. Some is attributed to the growth of health insurance and the improved economic conditions for the majority of families. Finally, the increase is most certainly related to greater consciousness of the value of hospital services as well as other types of health services among the general population.

Table 16 provides an over-all view of changes in hospital use over the ten years covered by the studies. The hospital admission rate of 13 per

100 person-years for 1963 is a slight increase over the rate of 12 in 1953.[21] Mean length of stay was 7.4 days for both studies.[22] Total number of hospital days per 100 person-years increased from 87 to 96 or by 10 percent in the ten-year period.[23]

Hospital admission rates and length of stay are lower for children than for other age groups (Table 16). The admission rate of 19 in 1963 for young adults 18–34 is the highest of any age group, primarily because of hospitalized maternity care. Following the reproductive years, admission rates drop sharply and then begin to rise again with age, reaching a

TABLE 16
Use of short term hospitals by age and sex: 1953 and 1963

AGE AND SEX	ADMISSIONS PER 100 PERSON-YEARS[21]			MEAN LENGTH OF STAY PER ADMISSION[22]			HOSPITAL DAYS PER 100 PERSON-YEARS[23]		
	1953	1963	1963 person-years	1953 days	1963 days	1963 admis-sions	1953	1963	1963 person-years
Age									
0-5	8	8	896	5.3	4.9	190	41	30	2861
6-17	8	6	1965						
18-34	16	19	1784	6.8	6.6	571	96	108	3516
35-54	12	14	1732						
55-64	12	17	603	11.9	11.9	230	148	208	1309
65 and over	13	18	706						
Sex									
Male	9	10	3741	8.3	8.0	391	71	83	3741
Female	15	15	3945	7.0	7.1	600	101	108	3945
Total	12	13	7686	7.4	7.4	991	87	96	7686

second peak for the oldest people in the population. Unlike admission rates, average length of stay rises consistently with age from a low for the youngest children to a high for the oldest group.

Table 16 shows for the period between 1953 and 1963 increases in hospital use for the adult groups 18–54 and 55 and over, but some decline for children 17 and under. The largest increase is found in admission rate and total hospital days of care for those 55 and over. During the ten-year period admissions increased by 5 per 100 person-years and hospital days per 100 person-years rose from 148 to 208.

The admission rate for females in 1963 was 15 compared to 10 for males (Table 16). Mean length of stay was higher for males than females (8.0 vs. 7.1), but because of higher admission rates, females used more hospital days per 100 person-years. Excluding obstetrical admissions still leaves

[21] See definition 13.   [22] See definition 26.   [23] See definition 14.

admissions and total hospital days about 10 percent higher for females than for males but length of stay shows little difference.[24]

Considering changes between 1953 and 1963, female admission rates remained the same while male rates showed an increase from 9 to 10 per 100 person-years (Table 14). The difference in mean length of stay for the sexes decreased during this time period. The mean decreased for

Chart 3   Percent distribution of the population, hospital admissions, and hospital days by age: 1963

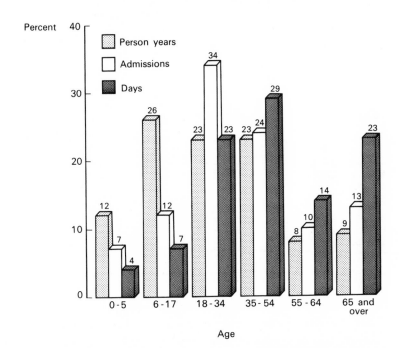

Percent

- ▦ Person years
- ☐ Admissions
- ■ Days

Age

Chart N 7686 person years
Chart N 7355 hospital days
Chart N   991 hospital admissions

males and increased slightly for females. Hospital days per 100 person-years increased for both groups. The increase was 17 percent for males and 6 percent for females.

Chart 3 indicates the extent to which the various age groups in 1963 contributed to the total of admissions and days in the hospital. The age group 65 and over, in relation to its proportion of the total population,

24 Hospital use statistics for females for general and special short term hospitals in 1963 were: 11 admissions per 100 person-years; 8.2 days per stay; and 92 days per 100 person-years.

was the greatest user of hospital days. The group 18–34 has an excessive proportion of hospital admissions, largely as a result of obstetrical care. However, these admissions are of relatively short duration and, consequently, percentage of hospital days used does not exceed percentage of person-years for this group.

The youngest age groups (especially those 6–17) use the smallest amount of hospital care in proportion to their numbers. In addition the percentage of days they use is less than the percentage of admissions they account for, owing to a low average length of stay. The middle-aged groups (35–54 and 55–64) account for proportions of all admissions slightly greater than their proportions in the population. Their share of hospital days is larger than their share of admissions because they have longer lengths of stay.

TABLE 17
Hospital admission rates by family income: 1953, 1958 and 1963

INCOME	ADMISSIONS PER 100 PERSON-YEARS			1963 PERSON-YEARS
	1953	1958	1963	
$0-$1,999	12	14	16	670
2,000-3,499	12	12	12	904
3,500-4,999	12	14	12	987
5,000-7,499	12	12	14	2139
7,500-9,999			14	1281
10,000-12,499	11	10	11 } 12	858
12,500 and over			10	847
Total	12	12	13	7686

Table 17 shows little variation in admission rates according to family income for the 1953 study. However, those with the highest family incomes did show a rate slightly lower than any other income group. By 1958 more differentiation was apparent. The lowest income group had a rate higher than the total population. The rate dropped for the next income class, rose again for the middle income groups and then dropped for those with the highest incomes. This same pattern was found in 1963, though the upward shift of income levels makes the pattern slightly more difficult to spot. The lowest income group ($0–1,999) again had a high rate, followed by a drop in the next classes ($2,000–4,999). The rates rose for the middle income groups ($5,000–9,999) and dropped once again for the upper income persons ($10,000 or more). The argument can apparently be made from both the 1958 and 1963 data that a bimodal distribution of admission rates by income level has developed, with the higher rates existing for the lowest and upper middle income groups and lower rates for the lower middle and upper income groups.

One possible explanation for the high rates among the lowest income group is that older people who have higher admission rates tend to cluster in the low income groups. However, when we look at the rates for various age levels in 1963 we see that this is not the entire answer. Among people 18–54 and 55 and over the rates for the lowest income group still exceed the rates for other income groups (Table 18). For children 0–17, on the contrary, the rates for those from families with very low incomes are lower than for any other income group.

It should also be noted that the bimodal pattern described for the sample as a whole held for the groups 18–54 and 55 plus. For each of these age groups the higher rates are found in the lowest and upper

TABLE 18
Hospital admissions per 100 person-years by age and family income: 1963

INCOME	AGE		
	0-17	18-54	55 and over
$0-1,999	5 (193)	20 (187)	21 (290)
2,000-4,999	6 (664)	15 (766)	14 (461)
5,000-9,999	7 (1405)	19 (1657)	19 (358)
10,000 and over	7 (599)	12 (906)	15 (200)
Total	7 (2861)	16 (3516)	18 (1309)

N 7686 person-years

middle income groups and the lower rates are found in the lower middle and upper income groups (Table 18). Again, children deviate from other age groups. Here the relationship seems to be a direct one with admission rates tending to increase as family income increases. The high rates for people 18 and over with low family incomes may indicate that hospitalization, especially for a family wage earner, sometimes reduces family income. The higher rate for persons with family incomes of $5,000–9,999 is in part a function of obstetrical admissions. Almost one-half of all obstetrical admissions are for women with family incomes in this range.

There appear to be definite differences in admission rates in each time period according to place of residence. In each study, people living in urban residences in the largest standard metropolitan statistical areas had the lowest admission rates (Table 19). At the other extreme, people with non-farm residences in rural areas had the highest rates in each period. In between these extremes are the "other urban" and rural farm populations, the latter having the higher rate in all except the first study (Table 19).

That the populations by types of residences have considerably different age distributions might be considered a factor here. For each age level, however, the rates appeared generally lower for the large urban and rural farm populations than for the other urban and rural non-farm populations (Table 20).[25] It will be shown in a later chapter that hospital insurance coverage is an important factor in understanding differences in admission rates by residence.

TABLE 19
Hospital admissions per 100 person-years by residence: 1953, 1958 and 1963

RESIDENCE	ADMISSIONS PER 100 PERSON-YEARS			1963 PERSON-YEARS
	1953	1958	1963	
Large urban	10	10	10	1530
Other urban	11	13	13	3618
Rural non-farm	14	14	15	1777
Rural farm	12	10	11	761
Total	12	12	13	7686

TABLE 20
Hospital admissions per 100 person-years by age and residence: 1963

RESIDENCE	AGE					
	0-17		18-54		55 and over[25]	
Large urban	5	(486)	14	(768)	12	(275)
Other urban	6	(1378)	17	(1637)	19	(603)
Rural non-farm	10	(689)	18	(810)	19	(278)
Rural farm	5	(308)	13	(300)	20	(153)
Total	7	(2861)	16	(3516)	18	(1309)

N 7686 person-years

In sum, hospital use increased over the decade from 1953 to 1963. The increase was accounted for in large part by higher admission rates of persons 55 and over. Females continue to use more hospital services than do

[25] Only in the case of rural farm persons 55 or over did the rate for a rural farm or large urban age group exceed the rate for an "other" urban or rural non-farm group and this slight difference could easily be accounted for by sampling error. The relatively low estimate for large urban residents 55 or over may also in part be a function of sampling error, in view of the small cell size. However, while the national health survey does not use exactly comparable age and residence categories, their data do indicate that among older persons urban residents do have the lowest discharge rate. See, National Center for Health Statistics, "Age Patterns in Medical Care, Illness and Disability: United States—July 1963–June 1965," ser. 10, no. 32 (June, 1966), p. 29.

males but the difference may be decreasing. A complex relationship was observed between income and hospital admission rates. People at the ends of the "urban-rural continuum," that is, urban residents in the largest standard metropolitan statistical areas and rural farm residents, generally have lower admission rates than do other residents.

4. Obstetrical care

One of the cornerstones of preventive medicine is health services for expectant mothers, before, during, and shortly after delivery. Optimum obstetrical care requires that the patient see the physician early and regularly. This section reports on changing use of medical and hospital services for obstetrical care for the recent ten-year period covered by the three studies.[26]

In the 1953 survey, 90 percent of the live births reported in the sample during the survey year had been attended by a physician in the hospital. An additional 5 percent had been attended by a physician, but not in a hospital. The remaining 5 percent were either attended by a midwife or were not attended by any professional help.

By 1958, the proportion of live births attended by a physician in a hospital had risen to 99 percent, while there were no reported instances in the sample of physicians attending a birth but not using hospital facilities. Only 1 percent of all live births in the 1958 survey were not attended by a physician. The data from the 1963 survey revealed that all live births in the sample were attended by a physician. The percentage of these births taking place in a hospital was 99.[27]

Considering only those women who saw a physician at least once during pregnancy or delivery, the proportion receiving care early in pregnancy increased markedly between 1953 and 1958 and began to level off by 1963. In 1953, 38 percent had seen a physician by the end of the second month of pregnancy. The proportion first seeing a physician by the end of their third month was 65 percent. In the 1958 survey the corresponding figures had risen to 51 and 77 percent respectively. They were 52 and 80 percent in 1963 (Chart 4).

26 The data presented in this section are based on 211 live births reported in 1953, 244 in 1958, and 158 in 1963. Because of the relatively small N's involved, caution should be exercised in the interpretation of the findings. The smaller number of births in 1963 is explained by the larger over-all sample sizes in 1953 (2809 families) and 1958 (2941 families); the double sampling technique used in 1958, which served to assign higher sampling probabilities to high expenditure families, which would include those with births; and the fact that the birth rate was higher in both 1953 and 1958 than it was in 1963.

27 Similar data from the National Health Survey are found in National Center for Health Statistics, "Natality Statistics Analysis, United States, 1963," ser. 21, no. 8 (March, 1966).

Considering the middle stages of pregnancy, the proportion seeing a physician by the end of the fourth month was 79 percent in 1953, 84 percent in 1958, and 88 percent in 1963. At the end of the sixth month the comparable figures were 92 percent, 96 percent, and 96 percent. Thus, when two-thirds of the pregnancy was completed, most of the women in each study had seen a doctor. Consequently, the percentage increase in proportion seeing a doctor by the sixth month between 1953 and 1963 is relatively small.

Chart 4   Month of initiation of prenatal care: 1953, 1958 and 1963

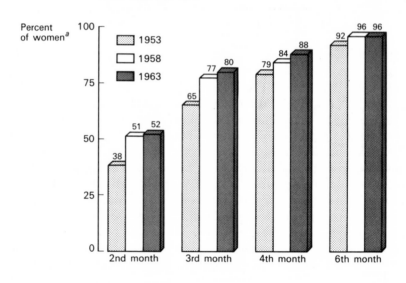

[a] Cumulative per cent receiving prenatal care from a physician by a determinate month.

Chart N   156 births
NA   2
Sample N 158

In each study the proportion of women from upper income and educational classes seeing a doctor early in the pregnancy was substantially greater than the proportion of those from lower income levels[28] and educational groups (Table 21). However, during the ten years covered by these studies, the differences between various income and educational groups became less pronounced. This happened because the proportion of the upper groups seeing a physician during the first trimester remained relatively constant over the ten-year period (approaching 90 percent). In con-

[28] See definition 9.

trast, the proportion of the middle and lower income groups seeing a doctor during the first trimester showed considerable increases over the decade. For example, the percentage of women with a grade school education seeing a doctor before the end of the third month of pregnancy increased from 42 to 68. In general, these increases appeared greatest among the lowest income and educational strata and the rate of increase was greater during the first five-year period than it was between 1958 and 1963.

TABLE 21
Percent of women having live births who saw a doctor in first trimester of pregnancy by family income level and education of mother: 1953, 1958 and 1963

INCOME AND EDUCATION	PERCENT SEEING PHYSICIAN BY END OF FIRST TRIMESTER			N 1963
	1953	1958	1963	
Income level [28]				
Lower	42	67	58[a]	36
Middle	66	77	86	72
Upper	89	86	88	48
Education				
Eight grades or less	42	57	68	31
Some high school	58	75	88	25
Completed high school	72	79	80	75
Some college	90	88	88	25
Total	65	77	80	156

[a]This estimate showing a decrease between 1958 and 1963 may in part reflect sampling error due to the small N upon which it is based and also lack of complete comparability between income categories. See footnote 28.

	1963
Table N	156
NA	2
Sample N	158

Improved prenatal care is indicated by the increasing number of prenatal visits from 1953 to 1963 as well as earlier initial exposure to a physician. In the 1953 study the median number of prenatal visits for women having a live birth was 8.4. By 1958 the comparable median had risen to 9.8 and in 1963 it was 10.5 (Table 22). Similarly, in the earliest survey, 43 percent had 10 or more visits, but the comparable figure had increased to 52 percent in 1958 and increased again to 61 in 1963.

Number of visits appears to be related to income and education, as were initial prenatal visits. Educated, higher income women went to the doctor earlier and saw him more often in each time period (Table 22). Thus, by 1963 median number of visits varied from a low of 6.5 for lower income women to a high of 11.1 for upper income women. The median number of visits according to education was from 8.0 for women completing eight grades or less to 10.8 for those who completed high school. However, these data on median visits also show, as did those on initial visit, that middle and lower income and educational groups are becoming more like the upper stratum with the passage of time. Thus, while median number of visits increased for lower income women from 4.8 to 6.5 between 1953 and 1963, the median for upper income women remained at about 11. By 1963, there appeared to be little difference in the amount of care received by the middle and high income and educational groups.

TABLE 22
Median number of prenatal physician visits by family income level and education of mother: 1953, 1958 and 1963

INCOME AND EDUCATION	MEDIAN NUMBER OF PRENATAL VISITS[a]			N 1963
	1953	1958	1963	
Income level				
Lower	4.8	6.3	6.5	36
Middle	9.6	9.5	10.9	74
Upper	10.5	11.7	11.1	48
Education				
Eight grades or less	5.1	5.4	8.0	31
Some high school	7.3	8.8	10.0	26
Completed high school	8.9	10.5	10.8	76
Some college	12.2	12.0	10.6	25
Total	8.4	9.8	10.5	158

[a]The median is that number of visits which exceeds the number of visits made by one-half of the mothers and is less than the number made by the other half.

While the first visit to a doctor tended to come sooner in the pregnancy in 1963 than in 1953 and number of prenatal visits increased over the decade, length of stay in the hospital for the delivery actually decreased. The number of women staying in the hospital 6 days or more decreased from 28 percent in 1953 to 12 percent ten years later. The median number of days per hospitalized delivery dropped from 4.5 in 1953 to 4.4 in 1958 and 3.7 in 1963 (Table 23).

Table 23 shows that in each survey median length of stay increased as income increased. Between 1953 and 1958 median stay for lower income women increased, while there was some decrease for the middle and upper income groups. Part of the increase for the lower income group resulted from the virtual elimination of out-of-hospital births by 1958; these had accounted for one-third of the births in this group in the 1953 sample. From 1958 to 1963, however, median stay for lower income mothers declined along with median stay for other income groups. Nevertheless, the difference in median stays between high income and low income women is still considerably smaller in 1963 than it had been in 1953.

In brief, women who had live births in 1963 sought medical care earlier in pregnancy and used more physician services, but stayed in the hospital fewer days for the delivery than they had 10 years earlier. Considerable differences exist in use of health services by expectant mothers according to income and education, but these studies indicate that the gap may be narrowing.

TABLE 23
Median[a] number of days for delivery admission for live births by family income level: 1953, 1958 and 1963

INCOME LEVEL	MEDIAN LENGTH OF STAY			N 1963
	1953	1958	1963	
Lower	2.2	3.6	3.1	36
Middle	4.8	4.5	4.0	74
Upper	5.0	4.8	4.2	48
Total	4.5	4.4	3.7	158

[a]This median calculation is based only on hospital days of the admission during which the delivery took place and excludes days during any prior admissions for prenatal complications or false labor. Non-hospitalized deliveries were coded "O" days and included in the calculation.

5. *Other health services*

Other types of health services besides hospital care and physician care are important parts of the total health system and are received by a large portion of the population during the year. Included in these services are dental care and eye care.

The proportion of people seeing a dentist at least once during the survey year increased from 34 percent in 1953 to 38 percent in 1963 (Table 24).[29] Older children 6–17 and young adults 18–34 are *most* likely to use dental services. The youngest and oldest age groups are *least* likely to see a dentist. During the 10 years covered by the studies, increases in the percentage of people seeing a dentist took place in all age groups. The increases were greater for older persons than for the younger ones. For instance, between 1953 and 1963 the increase was 7 percentage points for the groups 55–64 and 65 and over compared to 2 percentage points for those 1–5 and 18–34 and 3 percentage points for those 6–17. In both surveys females were more likely to see a dentist than were males.

The proportion of persons seeing an ophthalmologist, optometrist, or optician in 1963 was 20 percent.[30] Table 24 shows that the percentage

[29] See definition 3.   [30] See definition 6.

receiving eye care increased with each age group and reached a maximum of 31 percent for those 55–64 in 1963. People 65 and over were only slightly less likely to receive eye care than those 55–64. Females were more likely to receive eye care in both studies than were males.

Between 1953 and 1963 there was a 6 percentage point increase in the over-all proportion of people receiving eye care (Table 24). The increase was found among all age groups and both sexes but was especially pronounced for those 55 and over.

TABLE 24
Percent of people receiving dental care and eye care during survey year by age and sex: 1953 and 1963[a]

	PERCENT RECEIVING CARE					
	Dental[29]			Eye[30]		
AGE AND SEX	1953	1963	N 1963	1953	1963	N 1963
Age						
1-5	10	12	807	1	3	809
6-17	44	47	1950	11	18	1948
18-34	44	46	1766	14	18	1762
35-54	39	43	1724	20	25	1721
55-64	25	32	601	23	31	600
65 and over	13	19	691	18	29	691
Sex						
Male	31	36	3660	13	18	3657
Female	36	40	3881	16	21	3874
Total	34	38	7541	14	20	7531

[a] Includes only individuals who were members of the population for the entire survey year.

1963 Dental		1963 Eye	
Table N	7541	Table N	7531
NA	19	NA	29
Infants	158	Infants	158
Not in sample		Not in sample	
12 months	85	12 months	85
Sample N	7803	Sample N	7803

Among health services other than those provided by physicians and hospitals, dental care is of special interest because of its relationship to income. Table 25 shows that use of dental care is probably more closely related to family income than is any other major type of health care. The percentage of persons seeing a dentist rises consistently with increasing family income, from a low of 16 percent for those with incomes of less than $2,000 to 58 percent for those having family incomes of $10,000 or more in 1963 (Table 25).

The fact that older people, who are less likely to see a dentist, tend to have lower incomes can account for only part of this relationship. The percentage of people seeing a dentist increases with family income for all ages, whether the age group is a high or low user of dental services. For example, among children 6–17 (who are most likely to see a dentist) the proportion increases from 11 percent for the lowest income group to 30 and 48 percent, respectively, for the middle income groups (Table 25). This proportion reaches a maximum of 71 percent for the high income group. Substantial increases with income are also found in the age group 65 and over who, except for children 1–5, are least likely to see a dentist. For these older people the percentage rises consistently from 12 for the lowest income group to 39 for the highest income group.

TABLE 25
Percent of people receiving dental care during survey year by age and family income: 1963[a]

AGE	INCOME							
	Percent $0-1,999		Percent $2,000-4,999		Percent $5,000-9,999		Percent $10,000 and over	
1-5	0	(45)	4	(200)	13	(434)	23	(128)
6-17	11	(140)	30	(434)	48	(915)	71	(461)
18-34	31	(91)	33	(432)	49	(876)	57	(367)
35-54	23	(95)	28	(330)	42	(769)	58	(532)
55-64	16	(77)	25	(185)	32	(203)	52	(136)
65 and over	12	(211)	18	(268)	24	(150)	39	(62)
N	16	(659)	25	(1849)	40	(3347)	58	(1686)

[a] Includes only individuals who were members of the population for the entire survey year.

Table N	7541
NA	19
Infants	158
Not in sample 12 months	85
Sample N	7803

It may be that dental care is defined as less "necessary" and more "elective" than is physician or hospital care. Higher income people seem more likely to purchase such elective care than lower income persons. Also, the relationship between income and use of dental care is still virtually free of the complications caused by the presence of third-party purchasers of services, who are responsible for a large portion of physician and hospital care.

This section has shown a gradual increase in the proportion of people seeing a dentist and a somewhat more rapid increase in the proportion receiving eye care over the decade. These data indicate that dental care is probably less well distributed among the population than other major health services. Income appears to be a strong determinant of who sees the dentist among all age groups.

III

PERSONAL EXPENDITURES FOR
HEALTH SERVICES

The provision of health services described in the previous chapter requires a considerable investment of personnel and facilities. The health care system, to reiterate, includes some 7,000 hospitals; 250,000 practicing physicians; 95,000 practicing dentists; 600,000 active professional nurses; over 600,000 service workers; and additional thousands of technical health personnel including pharmacists, dietitians, physical therapists, and laboratory technicians. Behind these providers of services stand 88 medical schools, 53 dental schools, and 1,158 schools of professional nursing, along with the pharmaceutical, chemical, and drug industries, the hospital equipment and supply manufacturers, and the medical appliance manufacturers. This chapter considers the private expenditures of the population to support this large, complex system. These expenditures will be described separately on the national, family, and individual level. The three surveys permit detailed analysis of increasing expenditures—a trend which has been of major concern to the public and those who provide health services.

A. NATIONAL EXPENDITURES

Aggregate private expenditures for personal health services[1] are viewed here from two perspectives. First, they are considered in terms of their

[1] "Expenditure for personal health services" as used in this study refers to charges incurred by families for the medical goods and services used by family members during the survey year. These goods and services include physicians' services, general hospital care, prescribed and non-prescribed drugs and medications, dental care, and "other" goods and services for health such as use of non-physician health personnel, eyeglasses, and orthopedic appliances. These expenditures include amounts for which the family was reimbursed by health insurance but exclude health insurance premiums. They also include charges incurred by the family during the survey year which had not been paid at the time of interview. For detailed definitions of the components of total expenditure and estimates of these components for 1963 see definition 5 (Appendix II).

48

over-all magnitudes and increases in the magnitude from 1953 to 1963. The second views the consumer dollar used for the purchase of health service according to the proportion spent for each major type of health service. Changes in these proportions over the decade are examined.

1. *Total expenditures*

Americans spent privately almost $21 billion on all personal health services during the calendar year 1963, as estimated from the most recent study. During this same period, expenditures for direct personal health

TABLE 26
Estimated personal expenditures[1] for health services: 1953, 1958 and 1963

SERVICES	PRIVATE EXPENDITURE[a]		
	1953	1958	1963
Physicians	3.8	5.4	6.4
Hospitals[b]	2.0	3.7	5.4
Drugs and medicines	1.5	3.3	4.2
Dental care	1.6	2.4	2.7
Other medical goods and services	1.3	1.3	1.9
Total	10.2	16.2[c]	20.7[c]

[a] In billions of dollars.

[b] These estimates of private expenditures for hospital care include, but probably underrepresent, private expenditures for nursing home care. Nursing home expenditures more than doubled in the period 1958-1963, increasing from $200 million to $529 million. See Louis Reed, "Private Consumer Expenditures for Medical Care and Voluntary Health Insurance," 11, Social Security Bulletin, 27 (December 1964): 13, and Reed and Hanft, "National Health Expenditures," p. 15.

1963
N $875,000

[c] Because of rounding, components do not add to total.

services by government, private philanthropy, and other sources approached $7 billion.[2] In the following analysis we will consider only the former amount, which includes direct out-of-pocket payment by consumers and private health insurance benefit payments on behalf of these consumers.

Table 26 shows that aggregate personal expenditures for 1963 more than doubled the $10.2 billion spent in 1953. While the absolute amount

2 Louis S. Reed and Ruth S. Hanft, "National Health Expenditures, 1950–64," *Social Security Bulletin*, 29 (January, 1966): 13. This same source estimates total expenditures for personal health care in 1964 to be $31 billion of which 22 percent are government expenditures and 2 percent are expenditures by philanthropy and other sources. In a report such as this, emphasis cannot be placed on "last minute" information. Rather than stressing absolute magnitudes which are changing rapidly, emphasis is given to relationships and trends which have relevance for longer periods of time.

of spending increased substantially with each study, the rate of increase appeared to be smaller between the last two studies than it had been between 1953 and 1958. The expenditure of $16.2 billion for 1958 represented a 59 percent increase from the 1953 total, while the total expenditure for 1963 of $20.7 billion was 28 percent more than the amount 5 years earlier. There is no obvious reason for this deceleration.[3]

The order of magnitude of expenditure by type of service remained the same in 1963 as it had been in 1958 (Table 26). These studies differed from the 1953 study in that expenditures for drugs and medicines passed expenditures for dental care.

TABLE 27
Personal expenditures for types of physician services as a percent of total expenditures for physician care: 1953, 1958 and 1963

PHYSICIAN SERVICE	PERCENT OF TOTAL EXPENDITURE FOR PHYSICIAN CARE					
	1953		1958		1963	
Surgery	21		20		24	
Obstetrics	11		10		9	
Ophthalmologist[a]	—		2		2	
Other physician[b]	68		69		65	
Office		—	52		51	
Hospital		—	9		10	
Home		—	8		4	
Total	100		100		100	
Total expenditure (billions)	$3.8		$5.4		$6.4	

[a]Services of ophthalmologists were included with "other goods and services" in 1953.

[b]"Other physician charges" were not further separated in the 1953 study.

        1963
N $271,000

Physician services account for the largest proportion of personal expenditures, with $6.4 billion in 1963. Expenditures for other types of services in 1963 were $5.4 billion for hospitals, $4.2 billion for medicines, $2.7 billion for dental care and $1.9 billion for other goods and services.

[3] Data from the Social Security Administration also indicate a decreasing rate of increase for the second five-year period compared to the first. However, the difference between the two periods is considerably less according to Social Security data. Private consumer expenditures for the period covered by the second survey represented a 54 percent increase over expenditures for the first period while expenditures for 1963 were 46 percent more than 5 years earlier. Derived from Agnes W. Brewster, "Voluntary Health Insurance and Medical Care Expenditures: A Ten Year Review," *Social Security Bulletin*, 21, no. 12 (1958): 9, and Louis S. Reed, "Private Consumer Expenditures for Medical Care and Voluntary Health Insurance, 1948–1963," *Social Security Bulletin*, 27, no. 12 (1964): 13.

Expenditures for various types of physician services as a percentage of all physician expenditures are shown in Table 27. In 1963 surgery accounted for 24 percent of the total; obstetrical services were 9 percent. The 67 percent representing other physician services was made up in large part of expenditures for office visits. Between 1958 and 1963 the largest proportional change was in expenditures for home visits. These expenditures accounted for 8 percent of the total in 1958 but only 4 percent in 1963. With the exception of expenditures for home visits the proportions devoted to various types of physician services remained relatively stable for the ten-year period as a whole.

Expenditure components can also be examined for some other major categories of services. Hospital admissions in connection with obstetrical care account for 13 percent of all expenditures for hospital care. Prescribed drugs account for two-thirds of all expenditures for drugs and medicines, as was the case in 1958. About one-third of the total expenditure of "other medical goods and services" is for non-physician health personnel such as special duty nursing in the hospital or home, the services of optometrists or opticians, physical therapists, chiropractors, etc. The remaining two-thirds is spent primarily for medical appliances such as eyeglasses, hearing aids, and crutches.

2. Components of the consumer dollar for health services

While expenditures for all types of services are increasing, the rate of increase has varied by type of service over the ten years covered by these surveys. Consequently, the composition of the medical care dollar is changing.

Chart 5 shows the convergence of the two major categories of health services with the passage of time. Spending for physician care has been steadily decreasing as a proportion of total expenditure. The physician component dropped from 37 percent in 1953 to 34 percent in 1958 and to 31 percent in 1963. In contrast, payments to hospitals have increased from 19 to 23 percent between 1953 and 1958, and to 26 percent in 1963.

Among the other components, drug expenditures increased from 15 to 20 percent between the first two studies but appeared to stabilize at 21 percent in 1963.[4] Spending for dental care has shown a slight but consistent decline as a proportion of the consumer dollar, dropping from 16 percent in 1953 to 13 percent in 1963.

In sum, aggregate personal expenditures more than doubled between 1953 and 1963. However, these data indicate a slower rate of increase in

4 Some part of the relative rise in drug expenditures between 1953 and 1958 may have been due to improvement in the survey mechanism in 1958. The same technique was used in 1963 as had been used in 1958.

the second half of the decade than was observed in the first half. The components of the consumer dollar changed during this period with the proportion devoted to physician services decreasing while that devoted to hospital care increased.

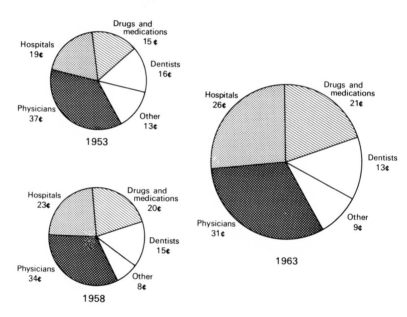

Chart 5   Composition of the medical care dollar: 1953, 1958 and 1963

B. FAMILY EXPENDITURES

The family[5] is a logical unit for discussing expenditures for personal health services. It is the primary earning, spending, and consuming unit in our society. In addition, trends over the ten-year period can be examined apart from family population increases, which account for some of the increases in total expenditure. Consideration will first be given to family total expenditure patterns. This will be followed by a breakdown of family expenditure according to type of service.

1. Total expenditures

The mean family expenditure for health services and goods in 1963 was $370 per year. The comparable amounts were $207 in 1953 and $294 in

[5] See definition 7.

1958. Although family expenditures increased $76 in the latest five-year period, the rate of increase was less than in the earlier period. The rate of increase from 1953 to 1958 was 42 percent compared to 26 percent between 1958 and 1963.[6]

In some respects it is more revealing to use median charges, indicating that one-half of the families incur charges less than a certain amount and one-half incur greater charges, than to use the arithmetic mean. This is because of the highly skewed distribution of family medical expenditures. A relatively few families have extremely high expenditures, making the mean considerably higher than the median. In such cases the median is a better measure of the central tendency of the sample.

Median charges per family increased from $110 in 1953 to $158 in 1958 and $209 in 1963. The percentage change in the median charge for the ten-year period is very similar to the percentage change in the mean. The percentage increase in the median from 1953 to 1958 was 44 percent while from 1958 to 1963 it was 24 percent. These similarities in percentage increase of the means and medians give some indication that the increases taking place represent increases for both high expenditure families and those with more modal expenditure patterns.

In each study mean expenditure increased with family income.[7] Table 28 shows that in every year families with incomes below $2,000 spent the least for health care, and expenditures increased with each succeeding higher income category to reach a maximum among families with incomes of $7,500 or more. For example, in 1963 families with incomes below $2,000, on average, spent $228 while those with incomes of $7,500 or more spent $480.

[6] The percentage increase per family in periods of expanding population is smaller than the percentage increase in aggregate expenditure because there are more families to include in the base in each succeeding time period.

[7] Income groups differ in each survey year because with the passage of time there was a decrease in the proportion of families in the lower brackets and an increase in the proportion of families in the higher brackets. Accordingly, there was some change with time in the makeup of the families constituting each income group. Taking this into account, it is still likely that gross comparisons can be made. See definition 8 regarding family income. The percentage of families in each income group by survey year is given below:

INCOME	PERCENT 1953	PERCENT 1958	PERCENT 1963
Under $2,000	21	17	13
$2,000-$3,499	22	17	14
3,500-$4,999	25	20	14
5,000-$7,499	20	26	25
7,500 and over	12	20	34
Total	100	100	100

There was considerable variation in the increases according to family income during the two five-year intervals bounded by these three studies. During the first five-year period the largest increases were by the lower middle income classes ($2,000–3,499 and $3,500–4,999). During the latter period the largest percentage increase was made by the lowest income group. In addition, the percentage increase in gross expenditure for the highest income classes ($5,000 or more) exceeded the increases for the lower middle income groups ($3,500–4,999 and $2,000–3,499). The latter groups, while having the greatest increases in the earlier five-year period, had the least increase in the latter period.

The pattern of increase in the first period was interpreted as indicating that the higher income groups had reached a relatively stable level of demand compared with the lower income groups.[8] The latter, despite in-

TABLE 28
Mean expenditure for all personal health services per family[5] by family income: 1953, 1958 and 1963

INCOME[7]	MEAN EXPENDITURE			PERCENT INCREASE		N 1963
	1953	1958	1963	1953-1958	1958-1963	
Under $2,000	$130	$165	$228	27	38	316
2,000-3,499	156	226	245	49	8	340
3,500-4,999	207	287	289	39	1	319
5,000-7,499	259	336	409	30	22	583
7,500 and over	353	411	480	16	17	809
Total	207	294	370	42	26	2367

creases in unit prices, were using more services than they had five years earlier. The pattern of increase in the last five-year period may reflect: (1) the increasing extent to which very low income indicates illness in the family which reduces the earning capacity of the family and forces them to spend increasing amounts for health services. In addition, relatively higher expenditures among low income families may in part be attributable to increased demand for services based on greater appreciation of the need for health services and increased insurance coverage. Finally, families making less than $2,000 in 1963 are more likely to be families with retired and disabled main earners and less likely to have main earners in the labor force than was true in 1958. Families with older and disabled heads tend to have high health expenditures. Consequently, the health expenditures for families with incomes of less than $2,000 might be expected to increase more rapidly through time than expenditures for other families. (2) the tendency of the higher income groups in the last period to spend

[8] Anderson, Collette, and Feldman, *Changes in Medical Care Expenditures*, p. 18.

more for "amenities" and "preventive care," which are reflected in their increased total expenditures.

In 1963 family spending for health services was higher for urban than for rural families. Thus, Table 29 shows that total expenditures for families living on farms in rural areas was $302. The total increased to $353 for those living in non-farm residences in rural areas, to $373 for families in urban areas, excluding the ten largest SMSA's, and to $404 for families living in urban areas of the largest SMSA's.[9] A number of factors probably contribute to these differences, including generally higher prices charged for services in urban areas and the tendency for urban people to use more services.

These relationships between expenditure and type of residence were also generally true in 1953 and 1958. The only exception was that ex-

TABLE 29
Mean expenditure for all personal health services per family by residence: 1953, 1958 and 1963

RESIDENCE[9]	MEAN EXPENDITURE			PERCENT INCREASE		N 1963
	1953	1958	1963	1953-1958	1958-1963	
Large urban	$237	$340	$404	43	19	533
Other urban	204	284	373	39	31	1111
Rural non-farm	197	297	353	51	19	522
Rural farm	178	211	302	19	43	201
Total	207	294	370	42	26	2367

penditures for rural non-farm families were slightly greater than those for "other urban families" in 1958 (Table 29). Larger percentage increases in total expenditure between 1953 and 1958 for large urban and rural non-farm families tend to be balanced by larger increases in the latter period for other urban and rural farm families. As a result, for the total ten-year period the percentage increases by residence are similar. From 1953 to 1963 percentage increases varied from a low of 70 percent for large urban and rural farm families to a high of 83 percent for other urban families.

Family expenditure for health as a percentage of average family income has remained relatively stable over the past five years. In 1953 family spending for health care represented 4.6 percent of average family income. The figure rose to 5.6 percent in 1958. However, it remained virtually unchanged at 5.5 percent in 1963.

Another measure of health expenditure used in previous studies is total

[9] See definition 35.

family outlay for health services.[10] Outlay is the family's actual cash allocation during the twelve-month survey year for personal health services and health insurance premiums. The primary difference between this measure and total expenditure is that family outlay includes health insurance premiums but excludes health insurance benefits, while total expenditure excludes premiums but includes benefits. Table 30 shows that the lower the family income, the greater the proportion of family income allocated to health. This relationship was consistent in each survey year. For example, in 1963 families with incomes under $2,000 were spending almost 16 percent of their income for health, while those with incomes of $7,500 and over were spending less than 4 percent.

TABLE 30

Aggregate family outlay[10] for personal health services as a percent of aggregate family income, by income group: 1953, 1958 and 1963

INCOME	AGGREGATE OUTLAY AS A PERCENTAGE OF AGGREGATE INCOME			N 1963[a]
	1953	1958	1963	
Under $2,000	11.8	13.0	15.7	$ 0.4
2,000-3,499	6.1	8.4	8.5	0.9
3,500-4,999	5.4	6.4	6.8	1.3
5,000-7,499	4.7	5.4	5.6	3.5
7,500 and over	3.0	3.9	3.8	9.7
Total	4.8	5.5	5.0	15.8

[a]Income in millions of dollars.

For all families we see that aggregate outlay has been around five percent of income in each survey. It measured 4.8 percent in 1953, rose to 5.5 percent in 1958 and dropped to 5.0 percent in 1963. The nature of health insurance premium payments provides one explanation for the apparent drop in outlay as a percentage of income between 1958 and 1963 with no corresponding drop in expenditure as a percentage of income. The proportion of employee group health insurance premiums paid by employers is steadily increasing. Since outlay includes families' own contributions but does not include employers' contributions, increasing employer contributions would tend to reduce family outlay. On the other hand, employer contributions would have no effect on expenditures since no premium costs are included in this measure.

For the ten-year period, outlay as a percentage of income increased for each income grouping except the highest. The increases were greatest among low income families and least among high income groups. It was

[10] See definition 29.

possible in 1963 for total outlay as a percentage of total income for all families to decrease from 1958 while the percentage for all except the highest income group increased. The reason was the shift of families into higher income groups where the allocation to health care as a percentage of total income is smaller. Families with incomes of $7,500 or over were 20 percent of the sample in 1958 but 34 percent of the sample in 1963. The proportion of income allocated to health services by this group is typically about one-fourth of that allocated by the lowest income group.

TABLE 31
Percent distribution of families by level of total expenditures for personal health services: 1953, 1958 and 1963

FAMILY TOTAL EXPENDITURES	PERCENT OF FAMILIES WITH TOTAL EXPENDITURES		
	1953	1958	1963
None ⎫	29.8	20.2 ⎰ 2.9	17.8 ⎰ 1.8
Under $50 ⎭		⎱ 17.3	⎱ 16.0
50-99	15.8	14.0	11.7
100-199	20.1	20.7	18.7
200-299	11.8	13.5	12.8
300-399	7.0	9.2	9.5
400-499	4.9	5.7	6.3
500-749	6.3	8.3	10.0
750-999	2.3	3.8	5.1
1,000-1,999	1.6	3.9	6.5
2,000 and over	0.4	0.7	1.6
Total	100	100	100

		1963
	N	2367

As in earlier surveys the magnitude of expenditures in 1963 varied sharply among families (Table 31). With each survey the proportions spending larger amounts increased. Thus the proportion spending $50 or less was 29.8 percent in 1953 compared to 20.2 percent in 1958 and 17.8 in 1963. However, the proportion spending $500 or more increased from 10.6 percent in 1953 to 16.7 in 1958 and to 23.2 in 1963.

This great variance in the distribution of expenditures means that the expenditures of the majority of families account for a relatively small proportion of the aggregate, while in contrast a relatively few families spend a large proportion of the total. Chart 6 shows that the 30 percent of the families spending less than $100 in 1963 accounted for only 3 percent of total spending for medical goods and services. At the other extreme, 8 percent of the families spent $1,000 or more and accounted for over one-third of the total spending.

Over the past three decades the proportion of total expenditures accounted for by the 10 percent of the families with the highest expenditure has been almost constant. This percentage in the C.C.M.C. study of 1928–1931 was 41 percent. It has also been 41 or 42 in each of the HIF-NORC studies.

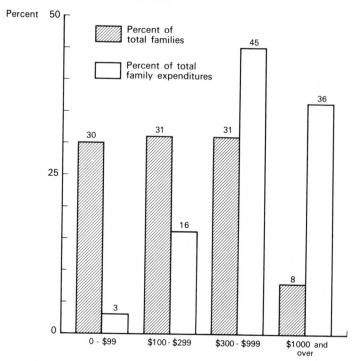

Chart 6   Percent of total family expenditures for health attributable to families with various levels of expenditures: 1963

Level of family expenditures

Chart N 2367 families
Chart N $ 875,000

In sum, total family expenditures for all health services rose from $207 in 1953 to $294 in 1958 to $370 in 1963. Family expenditures in urban areas tended to be higher than those in rural areas in each study. Aggregate outlay for health services as a percentage of family income varies inversely with income. Not only do the lowest income groups spend the largest proportion of their income for health services but the differences in percentage spent between low and high income families increased between 1953 and 1963. Considerable variance in family expenditure exists, as indicated by the finding that families spending $1,000 or more were only 8 percent of the population but accounted for 36 percent of all personal health spending.

2. *Expenditures by type of service*

The previous section showed family spending for all services. This section considers family spending for various types of services.

Total *family* expenditure divided according to type of service for each time period studied is shown in Table 32. In 1963 average family expenditures for physician care were $115 and expenditures for hospital care

TABLE 32
Mean expenditure per family, by type of service: 1953, 1958 and 1963

TYPE OF SERVICE	MEAN EXPENDITURE PER FAMILY			PERCENT INCREASE		
	1953	1958	1963	1953-1958	1958-1963	1953-1963
Physicians	$ 78	$ 98	$115	26	17	47
Hospitals	41	68	97	66	43	137
Drugs	31	60	75	94	25	142
Dentists	33	44	48	33	9	45
Other	26	25	35	−4	40	35
Total	207	294	370	42	26	79

1963
N   2367

approached $100. These two largest components of family expenditure were followed in order of magnitude by drugs ($75), dental care ($48), and other medical care ($35).

Over the ten-year period covered by the three studies the increase in family expenditures for all services was 79 percent. However, Table 32 shows that the rate of increase by type of service varied considerably. Family expenditures for hospital care and drugs increased much more rapidly over the ten-year span than did expenditures for the other components. For the former two components the increases between 1953 and 1963 were 137 percent and 142 percent respectively. In contrast, the percentage increases for physician care, dental care, and other medical care for the same span were under 50 percent. It should also be noted that the data indicate that family expenditures for drugs increased much more rapidly during the first five years (94 percent) than during the second five years (25 percent). The increase during the first five years was also considerably greater for dental care. For physicians and hospital care the rates of increase differed less, though they were also higher in the first five years. Only in the "other" category (which showed an absolute decrease between 1953 and 1958) was the increase greater in the latter period.

While there is a great deal of variation in mean family expenditure by type of service (from a high of $115 for physician care to a low of $35 for "other" medical care), for each type of service some families have considerable expense. Using $200 as an arbitrary amount indicating substantial expenditure, Table 33 shows the percentage of families in each survey having substantial expenditures for each type of service.

TABLE 33

Percent of families making expenditures of $200 or more for specified types of personal health services: 1953, 1958 and 1963

TYPE OF SERVICE	PERCENT OF FAMILIES MAKING EXPENDITURES OF $200 OR MORE		
	1953	1958	1963
All services	34	45	48
All physicians	11	14	18
Surgical	3	4	5
Obstetrical	a	1	1
Other physicians	6	8	9
Hospital	6	10	15
Drugs	2	6	8
Dental	4	6	6
Other	2	2	2

a Less than one-half of one percent.

	1963
N	2367

This table reflects the general increase of expenditures through time, as a larger percentage of families spent $200 or more for all services and each type of service in each succeeding period. More families have substantial expenditures for physician services and hospital care than for other types of care. However, 8 percent of all families spent $200 or more for medicines in 1963 and 6 percent spent this amount for dental care. The "other" medical care is the category in which families are least likely to spend $200 or more, but it still includes well over one million families in the country. Proportional increases over the ten-year period have been greatest for the categories of hospital care and drugs.

For our consideration of family expenditures by type of service, we have examined mean expenditures for each service and the proportion of families with expenditures over $200 for each service. Another important part of this picture is the change in the proportion spent for each type of

Chart 7 **Percent distribution of total expenditure for type of service for which expenditures were made, by level of total family expenditures: 1963**

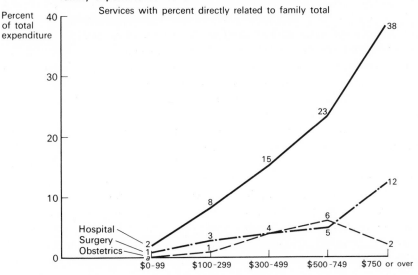

Percent of total expenditure

Services with percent directly related to family total

Hospital
Surgery
Obstetrics

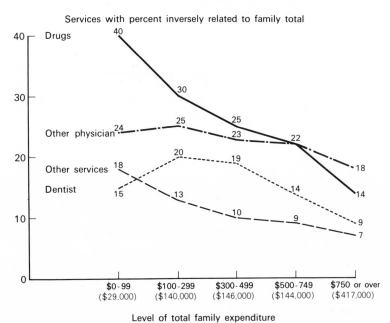

Services with percent inversely related to family total

Drugs

Other physician

Other services

Dentist

| | $0-99 ($29,000) | $100-299 ($140,000) | $300-499 ($146,000) | $500-749 ($144,000) | $750 or over ($417,000) |

Level of total family expenditure

a Less than one-half of one percent

Chart N $875,000

service as the magnitude of total expenditure per family increases. Each of the three studies has shown that the proportion spent for hospital and surgical services increases consistently with increased total expenditure. The proportion devoted to obstetrical care shows a curvilinear relationship increasing with increasing expenditure up to a certain level of expenditure but decreasing for families with extremely high expenditures. The proportion of total expenditures devoted to "other" physicians, drugs, and dental care tends to decrease with increasing total expenditure. The decrease is most prominent for the medicine category. The trends are graphically described for 1963 in Chart 7.

These findings on mean family expenditure by type of service show that the families were still spending more for physician services in 1963 than for any other service but that expenditures for hospital care and drugs increased more rapidly between 1953 and 1963. The proportions of families spending $200 or over for each major type of health service are highest for physician and hospital care, but for every service there is a considerable number of families who spend $200 or more. The proportion of total family expenditure devoted to each type of service varies considerably with level of expenditure. Low expenditure families spend the largest proportion for drugs and medicines while high expenditure families spend the largest proportion for hospital services.

C. INDIVIDUAL EXPENDITURES

While the family is a logical unit for discussing costs of personal health services, analysis on the individual level is necessary to show the substantial differences in expenditure patterns which exist for different age and sex groups. In addition, using the individual as the unit of analysis eliminates any effects of changes in family size on expenditure comparisons during the ten-year period.

1. *Total expenditures*

Mean expenditure per individual for all personal health services increased from $66 in 1953 to $94 in 1958 and $112 in 1963. The percentage increase dropped from 42 percent for the first five-year period to 20 percent between 1958 and 1963.[11]

Both spending per capita and increase over time varied considerably by sex. In each survey spending was higher for females than males. The averages per year for females in the three studies were $80, $111, and $131 respectively. The amounts for males were $51 in 1953, $77 in 1958, and

[11] The increase per individual is less than the increase per family between 1957–58 and 1963 because the average family size increased from 3.14 in the 1958 sample to 3.30 in the 1963 sample.

$92 in 1963. Over this ten-year period the increase has been proportionately greater for males than females. Male expenditures for health care have increased 80 percent, while the increase for females was 64 percent.

Expenditures increased with age in each survey as indicated in Chart 8. In 1953 average spending rose steadily from $28 for children under 6 to

Chart 8   Mean individual expenditures by age category: 1953, 1958 and 1963

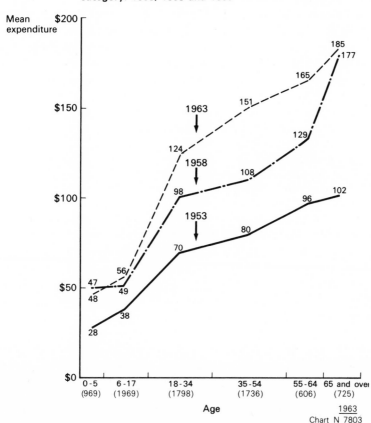

$102 for persons 65 and older. By 1958 each figure had increased, but the increases were greatest among children under 6 and elderly people 65 and over.[12]

Expenditures in 1963 ranged from $47 for children under 6 to $185 for those 65 and over. In contrast to the changes between 1953 and 1958, the

[12] The unique influence of the Asian flu epidemic during this period may have affected these relative increases by age group.

largest increases between 1958 and 1963 took place in the middle rather than at the extremes of the life cycle. Persons 35–54 showed the largest increase (40 percent) and the adjoining groups 18–34 and 55–64 had increases in expenditures of over one-fourth since 1958. Children under 6 showed no increase for the same period and the increase for those 65 and over was minimal.[13]

For the ten-year period as a whole, the large increases by the very young and the elderly during the first five years tended to be balanced by expenditure increases for the middle-aged groups in the latter period. Rates of increase for the entire ten-year period tended to be somewhat greater for the older groups, varying from a low of 47 percent for those 6–17 to highs of 89 percent for those 35–54 and 81 percent for those 65 and over. The average increase for all age groups was 70 percent. Health expenditures, then, are higher for females than for males and increase with age. Over the decade the differences according to sex have decreased while those according to age appear to be increasing.

2. Expenditures by type of service

Relative magnitudes of expenditures by type of service, as well as total expenditures, vary considerably by age. Chart 9 shows that physician care is the major component of expenditure for children under six, accounting for 45 percent of the total, and that drug expenditures are also an important part of the total. The largest components for young people 6–17 are dental care and physician care. The hospital component for the 18–34 age group (34 per cent) is larger than the hospital component for any other group. Obstetrical admissions for females 18–34 increase the relative magnitude of hospital expenditures for this age group.

Similar proportions of total expenditure are devoted to physician and hospital care for all age groups over 34. Consistent differences among the older groups are the increasing proportion of total expenditures going for medicines and the decreasing proportion spent on dental care as age increases. Components by sex are generally similar. Females spend a somewhat greater proportion for hospital care than do males.

Table 34 shows the actual mean dollar expenditures in 1963 of individuals for various types of services according to age and sex. Persons 65 and over spend more than other age groups for every service except dental

---

[13] This low rate of increase in expenditures by the private sector may in part reflect the increasing amount of medical care provided under public assistance which is concentrated in the older and younger age groups. Vendor medical care payments increased tenfold from $100 million in 1950–51 to over $1 billion in 1962–63. See "Medical Care under Public Assistance," *Progress in Health Services*, Health Information Foundation, vol. 13, no. 1 (1964).

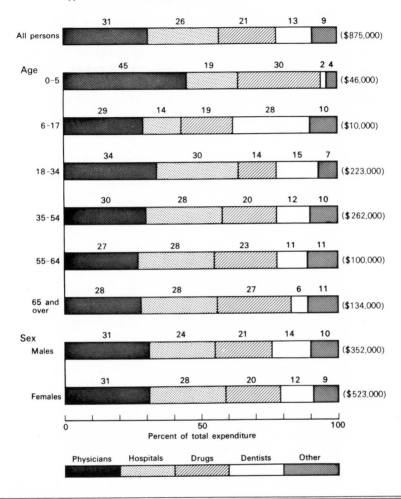

Chart 9   Percent of individual medical expenditures for type of service by age and sex:1963

All persons: 31 26 21 13 9 ($875,000)

Age

0-5: 45 19 30 2 4 ($46,000)

6-17: 29 14 19 28 10 ($10,000)

18-34: 34 30 14 15 7 ($223,000)

35-54: 30 28 20 12 10 ($262,000)

55-64: 27 28 23 11 11 ($100,000)

65 and over: 28 28 27 6 11 ($134,000)

Sex

Males: 31 24 21 14 10 ($352,000)

Females: 31 28 20 12 9 ($523,000)

0   50   100
Percent of total expenditure

Physicians   Hospitals   Drugs   Dentists   Other

TABLE 34
Mean expenditure per person for each type of service by age and sex: 1963

AGE AND SEX	MEAN EXPENDITURE						N
	Physician	Hospital	Drugs	Dentist	Other	All services	
Age							
0-5	$21	$ 9	$14	$ 1	$ 2	$47	969
6-17	16	8	11	16	6	56	1969
18-34	42	37	17	19	9	124	1798
35-54	46	42	31	18	15	151	1736
55-64	45	46	39	17	19	165	606
65 and over	51	52	50	11	20	185	725
Sex							
Male	29	22	20	13	9	92	3807
Female	41	36	26	16	12	131	3996
Total	35	29	23	15	10	112	7803

care, for which young adults have the highest expenditures. In general, expenditures for all types of services tend to increase as age increases. The major exceptions to this relationship are expenditures for dental care, discussed above, and higher expenditures for children 0–5 than for those 6–17 in the categories of hospital care, physician care, and drugs. Expenditures for females exceed those for males for every type of service. The differences are most pronounced for physician and hospital care, where expenditures for maternity care have the greatest impact.

TABLE 35
Percent increase in individual expenditures for various types of services from 1953 to 1963 by age and sex

AGE AND SEX	PERCENT INCREASE FROM 1953 TO 1963					
	Physician	Hospital	Drugs	Dentist	Other	All services
Age						
0-5	40	80	133	0	100	68
6-17	23	33	120	45	50	47
18-34	45	133	113	46	29	77
35-54	37	180	182	29	36	89
55-64	22	130	173	31	27	72
65 and over	42	108	127	175	18	81
Sex						
Male	53	144	186	44	29	80
Female	32	112	117	33	25	64
Total	40	123	130	50	25	70
N[a]	$271,000	$228,000	$178,000	$82,000	$15,000	$875,000

[a]Total expenditure of sample in 1963.

Table 35 indicates to what extent individual expenditures for various types of services in 1963 represent increases over the totals of ten years earlier. The greatest percentage increases in expenditure over the decade for children 0–5 and 6–17 were for drugs. For the age group 18–34 the greatest increase was for hospital expenditures. Middle-aged people 35–54 experienced large percentage increases in expenditures for both drugs and hospital care. Like children, adults 55–64 had the greatest increases in expenditures for drugs between 1953 and 1963. While, as a proportion of total expenditures for health, older people spend relatively little for dental care, their expenditures for this service rose more rapidly over the ten-year period than did any other component of their health services.

Expenditures for males increased at a faster rate than did expenditures for females. This was true for expenditures for all services combined and each type of service considered separately (Table 35).

The 1958 and 1963 studies permitted a breakdown of types of physicians' services and charges which was not possible in 1953. The later studies also allowed expenditures for drugs and medicines to be divided into prescribed and non-prescribed categories.

Table 36 shows mean expenditures for physicians' services for all individuals in the sample. It also shows the mean for those who actually had expenditures for various types of physician services. In 1963 mean expenditures for all individuals were highest for physician office visits ($18) with expenditures for in-hospital surgery ranking second ($7). These high-

TABLE 36
Mean expenditure for physicians' services, per individual and per individual
with expenses: 1958 and 1963

TYPE OF PHYSICIAN'S SERVICE	MEAN EXPENDITURE FOR SERVICE					
	Per individual			Per individual with expenses		
	1958	1963	N 1963	1958	1963	N 1963
In hospital surgery	$ 6	$ 7	7803	$158	$200	280
Non-hospitalized surgery	a	1	7803	37	39	205
Obstetrics	3	3	7803	114	142	166
Ophthalmologist	1	1	7803	14	14	420
Other physician, in hospital	3	4	7803	65	71	393
Other physician, home call	2	1	7803	19	20	556
Other physician, in office	16	18	7803	31	35	3971

a Less than 50 cents.

est mean expenditures for the total sample were followed in magnitude by hospital visits ($4), obstetrical care ($3), and non-hospitalized surgery, ophthalmological care, and home visits each accounting for mean expenditures of $1. Between 1958 and 1963 the rankings of these means remained roughly the same. During the five-year period, mean expenditures for most of the services increased. Only expenditures for house calls showed an actual decrease.

Mean expenditures among physicians' services for the entire sample are highest for office visits because a majority of the population have office visits in a given year, while a much smaller percentage are hospitalized or experience surgery. An even smaller proportion have obstetrical care.

A different picture emerges, however, if mean expenditures for only those people who receive a particular physician service in a given year are examined (Table 36). Thus, we see that for people with hospitalized surgery in 1963 the mean expenditure on physician services was $200 and that those who received obstetrical care had mean expenditures of $142. The mean expenditure for people with non-hospitalized surgery ($39) and hospital visits ($71) also exceeded the mean expenditure for physician office visits ($35) for people with such office visits. With each of the former services we find that people who do have expenditures for the service have high mean expenditures, especially for hospitalized surgery. The mean expenditure for office visits increased less when the base changed from all persons to those with expenditures for office visits, because one-half of the population have office visits.

TABLE 37
Mean expenditure for selected physician services per individual by age and sex: 1963

| | MEAN EXPENDITURE | | | | |
AGE AND SEX	In-hospital surgery	Hospital	Home	Office	N
Age					
0-5	$ 2	$1	$2	$15	969
6-17	3	1	1	9	1969
18-34	8	3	a	16	1798
35-54	11	5	1	25	1736
55-64	8	9	2	24	606
65 and over	11	7	6	25	725
Sex					
Male	6	3	1	16	3807
Female	8	4	1	19	3996
Total	7	4	1	18	7803

a Less than 50 cents.

Between 1958 and 1963 the rank of mean expenditures for various physician services among people with such expenditures remained the same. The largest increases in these mean expenditures were for in-hospital surgery and obstetrical care. The smallest increases were for ophthalmological care and physician home calls.

Expenditures for various types of physician services vary considerably by age and sex (Table 37). Mean expenditures for hospitalized surgery and hospital visits generally increase with age though some deviations are seen in the older age groups. Thus, mean expenditures for in-hospital surgery vary from a low of $2 for children 0–5 to a high of $11 for persons 35–54 and 65 and over. Mean expenditures for hospital visits vary from lows of $1 for children 0–5 and 6–17 to a high of $9 for persons 55–64.

A curvilinear relationship appears in Table 37 between age and expenditures for home visits. Mean expenditure for those 0–5 is $2. The mean expenditure drops to $1 for those 6–17 and reaches a low of less than fifty cents for those 18–34. It then increases in the older age groups, reaching a maximum of $6 for those 65 and over.

Mean expenditures for office visits for children 0–5 are considerably greater than for children 6–17 ($15 vs. $9). Expenditures then increase to $16 for the 18–34 age group and are $24 or $25 for all older age groups (Table 37).

Mean expenditures for females are greater than expenditures for males for each type of physician service given in Table 37 except home visits. The mean for females is 33 percent more than the mean for males for in-hospital surgery and hospital visits and 19 percent more for office visits.

TABLE 38
Mean expenditure for prescribed and non-prescribed drugs per individual and per individual with expenses: 1958 and 1963

	MEAN EXPENDITURE					
	Per individual			Per individual with expenses		
TYPE DRUGS	1958	1963	N 1963	1958	1963	N 1963
Prescribed drugs	$13	$15	7803	$32	$36	3373
Non-prescribed drugs	6	7	7803	12	11	5501

The division between mean gross expenditure for prescribed and non-prescribed drugs is given in Table 38. Mean expenditure for prescribed drugs per individual increased from $13 to $15 between 1958 and 1963 and the mean expenditure for non-prescribed drugs increased from $6 to $7. Considering only people with such expenditures, the mean in 1963 was $36 for prescribed drugs and $11 for non-prescribed drugs.

Mean gross expenditures for prescribed and non-prescribed medicines according to age and sex are shown in Table 39. The pattern for both pre-scribed and non-prescribed medicines shows expenditures for children 0–5 higher than for those 6–17, followed by continual increases with age and reaching maximums for persons 65 and over. Mean expenditures for pre-scribed medicines vary from a low of $6 for persons 6–17 to a high of $38 for persons 65 and over. The latter is considerably higher than the next highest expenditure of $27 for persons 55–64. Expenditures for non-prescribed medicines vary from a low of $5 for children 6–17 to a high of $12 for persons 65 and over.

It is interesting to note that while the direction of the relation of age to mean expenditure is similar for prescribed and non-prescribed drugs, the differences between expenditures of the younger and older age groups are much greater in the case of prescribed medicines. Using the mean expenditure for children 6–17, the age group with the lowest drug expenditures, as a base, we find that the mean expenditure for prescribed medicines for the age group 35–54 is 2.5 times greater, and the age group 65 and over has a mean expenditure over 6 times as high as the 6–17 group. By comparison, mean expenditure for non-prescribed drugs for persons 35–54 is 80 percent higher than mean expenditures for persons 6–17 and the increase for persons 65 and over is 140 percent.

TABLE 39
Mean expenditure for prescribed and non-prescribed drugs per individual
by age and sex: 1963

AGE AND SEX	MEAN EXPENDITURE		N
	Prescribed	Non-prescribed	
Age			
0-5	$ 8	$ 6	969
6-17	6	5	1969
18-34	11	6	1798
35-54	21	9	1736
55-64	27	11	606
65 and over	38	12	725
Sex			
Male	12	7	3807
Female	18	8	3996
Total	15	7	7803

Table 39 shows that mean expenditure for females is higher than for males for both prescribed and non-prescribed medicines. However, the difference is greater for prescribed than for non-prescribed medicines. Mean expenditures for prescribed medicines for females are 50 percent more than for males but for non-prescribed medicines they are only 14 percent more.

The focus of this section has been on individual expenditures for various types of medical services. Substantial variation was found in the proportion of total expenditures devoted to each type of service according to age and sex. In absolute terms people over 65 spend more than other age groups on every type of service except dental care and females spend more than males for every service. In general, the greatest percentage increase in expenditures for all age and sex groups for the period from 1953 to 1963 was for hospital services and drugs. However, people 65 and over showed a large percentage increase for dental expenditures. While mean expenditures for physician office visits were highest among all physician services for the total population, mean expenditures for in-hospital care and obstetrical care were much higher if only people with each type of expenditure were considered. For most types of physician services, mean expenditures were higher for children 0–5 than for those 6–17 but increased with age thereafter. The means for females were higher than those for males. Similar age and sex patterns with regard to mean expenditures were found to exist for prescribed and non-prescribed medicines as were found for physician services.

D. EXPENDITURES FOR OBSTETRICAL CARE

Expenditures for live births pertain to private expenditures only. They do not include estimates for the value of free maternity care received by some families.[14] Per live birth, the mean of total expenditures increased from $193 reported in the 1953 survey to $272 in 1958 and to $316 in 1963 (Table 40) or by 61 percent between 1953 and 1963.

TABLE 40
Mean expenditure per live birth by type of service: 1953, 1958 and 1963

TYPE OF SERVICE	1953		1958		1963	
	Mean expenditure	Percent of all services	Mean expenditure	Percent of all services	Mean expenditure	Percent of all services
Hospital[16]	$ 82	43	$128	47	$162	51
Physician[15]	91	47	118	44	133	42
Drugs and medicines[17]	10	5	17	6	16	5
Laboratory fees[18]	3	1	2	1	3	1
Other medical care[19]	7	4	6	2	2	1
Total	193	100	272[a]	100	316	100

[a]Components do not add to total because of rounding.

1963
N 158 live births

Part of the increase between 1953 and 1958 was due to the rise in proportion of births occurring in the hospital. When only hospitalized births are considered, the corresponding increase during this five-year period was from $213 to $274. Since, by 1958, nearly all births were occurring in the hospital, the increase from 1958 to 1963 was not influenced by this factor.

14 The expenditures exclude items unrelated to the medical aspects of having a baby, such as layettes and cribs. This total expenditure for live births should also be differentiated from the "obstetrics" component of total health expenses considered earlier which includes only physician care.

As proportions of total annual private expenditures on health by type of service, the categories of hospital, physicians, drugs and medicines, laboratory fees, and other medical expenditures remained fairly stable over the ten-year period (Table 40). In terms of expenditures per confinement, physicians' services were $91 in 1953, or 47 percent of total spending on health services per confinement.[15] Although the comparable figure rose to $133 in 1963, its proportion of the total dropped to 42 percent. For hospitals, on the other hand, the average figure rose from $82 per confinement in 1953 to $162 in 1963, and the proportion of the total also rose from 42 to 51 percent.[16]

Spending on drugs and medicines rose from $10 to $17 during the five-year interval between 1953 and 1958 and was approximately the same in 1963 as in 1958.[17] In all three surveys the expenditures for drugs and medicines as a percentage of all expenditures remained quite stable, varying between 5 and 6 percent. For each time period, laboratory fees[18] and "other medical expenditures"[19] accounted for relatively small amounts.

For the over-all ten-year interval, the increase in expenditures was largest for hospitals, amounting to 98 percent. The increase in average expenditures for physicians' services was 46 percent. For drugs and medicines the increase was 60 percent.

In each survey there was considerable variance in total expenditure per live birth. In 1963, for example, 12 percent of the births involved costs of less than $100. Thirty-four percent had total expenditures from $100–299 and 54 percent amounted to $300 or more.

Part of this variance is related to income. Not only did women receive

[15] Includes charges by physicians for prenatal care and delivery, plus anesthesiologists' fees for delivery when the bill for that service was submitted independently of the hospital bill. These expenditures also differ from the physician's obstetrical component of all expenditures. The earlier estimates included expenditures for all obstetrical care while the present data are limited to such care in connection with live births.

[16] Includes charges incurred by the mother while a patient in the hospital during the course of the delivery admission, plus hospital charges during prior admissions for false labor. These figures also include charges incurred by the baby for nursery care and for such extra services as oxygen and incubator and operating room charges for circumcision. Special hospital expenses such as ambulance charges, not billed by the hospital, were allocated to "other medical expenses."

[17] Includes expenditures for prescribed and non-prescribed medicines purchased directly by the mother. Drugs administered in the hospital or by the physician and included in the hospital or doctor bill are excluded from this category.

[18] Includes expenditures for laboratory services such as diagnostic tests and X-rays for which the mother was billed directly from the laboratory.

[19] Includes expenditures for the services of practical nurses, midwives, chiropractors, and ambulance charges.

more services as family income rose, as was indicated in Chapter II, but mean total expenditures also rose with income. However, the differential in spending by income would undoubtedly have been smaller if dollar estimates for the value of free care, received mainly by low income families, had been included and if account had been taken of the traditional physicians' practice of varying fees according to the patient's income.

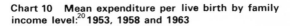

Chart 10   Mean expenditure per live birth by family income level:[20] 1953, 1958 and 1963

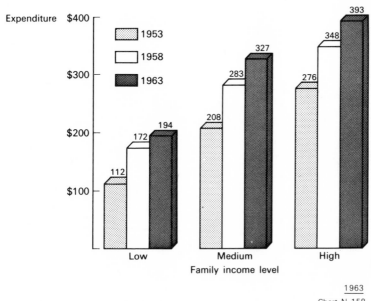

1963
Chart N 158

In 1953, mean expenditure per mother in low income families was $112, in middle income families it was $208, and in the high income families it was $276 (Chart 10).[20] In 1958 the corresponding figures were $172, $283, and $348, and in 1963, $194, $327, and $393.

The increases in dollar spending for these income groups between the surveys of 1953 and 1963 are $82, $119, and $117 respectively. When these sums are expressed as a percentage of 1953 spending, however, the increases are much larger among low income families—73, 52, and 42 percent. As a result, the relative differences between low income and high income families narrowed somewhat. In 1953 high income families were

20 See definition 9.

spending nearly 2.5 times as much as the low income families, but in 1963 they were spending only about twice as much. In general, patterns of expenditure for obstetrical care are similar to over-all expenditure patterns found in this study. Expenditures for care in connection with live births appeared to increase more rapidly between 1953 and 1958 than between 1958 and 1963, while by type of services hospital costs were increasing faster than those for physician care. Considerable differences in total expenditure were found according to income but the relative size of these differences appears to be decreasing.

IV

METHODS OF PAYING FOR PERSONAL HEALTH SERVICES

Essential parts of the total picture of provision of personal health services include type and amount of services used, expenditures for these services, and how people pay for the services they use. Use and expenditure have previously been considered. This chapter deals with method of payment.

Method of payment is important because expenditures for health care account for a sizable proportion of personal income (5 or 6 percent). It is even more important because of the unique characteristics of health service use and expenditure. Medical expenditures are often unexpected. They are unequally distributed among the population. They are incurred by all families regardless of income. Therefore, they are difficult to plan and budget for. In addition, some families experience extraordinary medical expenses which cause severe economic hardship. For example, in 1963, 8 percent of the families interviewed had medical expenditures of $1,000 or more and 2 percent had expenses of $2,000 or more.

An important method of paying for personal health services in the United States is voluntary health insurance. By 1963 three-fourths of all families had some health insurance. This health insurance covered 69 percent of all personal expenditures for hospital care and one-fourth of the expenditures for physician care. Important issues regarding voluntary health insurance are the extent and type of coverage and nature of benefits provided. These issues are treated in the first two parts of this chapter.

The final section considers briefly other methods of paying for personal health services. These include use of income and savings, care received at no direct cost to the consumer, payments for family health services made by non-family members, personal debts incurred for health services, and loss-of-income insurance, which might be considered a source of medical funds to cover expenses as well as a means to pay for family living expenses.

A. VOLUNTARY HEALTH INSURANCE COVERAGE

The modern era of health insurance in the United States started in the 1930's and has grown rapidly since that time. In 1940 about one person in ten had some type of health insurance. By 1963 the proportion was seven in ten. No other country in the world has had this rapid growth of privately sponsored health insurance. Consideration of coverage is divided into sections covering extent of enrollment, type of insurers, and method of enrollment.

1. *Extent*

Table 41 shows the increase in health insurance[1] coverage for families[2] and individuals for the ten-year period spanned by the three studies. The

TABLE 41
Percent of families[2] and individuals with health insurance by type of coverage: 1953, 1958 and 1963

	PERCENT COVERED		
TYPE OF COVERAGE	1953	1958	1963
Family:[3]			
Any health insurance[1]	63	69	74
Major medical[4]	a	7	24
Individual:[6]			
Hospital[7]	57	65	68
Surgical-medical[8]	48	61	66

[a]Less than one-half of one percent.

1963
N 2367 families
N 7803 individuals

proportion of families with some health services covered by insurance[3] increased from 63 percent in 1953 to 74 percent in 1963. While major medical insurance[4] is still held by only a minority of families, expansion of this type of coverage has been rapid, especially between 1958 and 1963. From practically no representation in 1953 the proportion of families covered by a major medical type of contract increased to 7 percent in 1958 and to almost one-fourth of all families in 1963.

1 See definition 12.

2 See definition 7.

3 See definition 18.

4 See definition 25.

Sixty-nine percent of all individuals were estimated to have some health insurance in 1963.[5] The proportion of individuals covered by insurance[6] is somewhat lower than the proportion of families because not every person in an insured family is necessarily covered. Data from Table 41 indicate that the difference in the proportions of the population with hospital[7] and surgical-medical[8] coverage narrowed between 1953 and 1963.

The trend in extent of basic[9] coverage among families with different characteristics is indicated in Table 42. In each period, coverage was substantially greater among higher income groups.[10] Between 1953 and 1958,

TABLE 42
Percent of families with health insurance by selected family characteristics: 1953, 1958 and 1963

| FAMILY CHARACTERISTIC | PERCENT INSURED | | | N |
	1953	1958	1963	1963
Income level[10]				
Lower	41	42	51	753
Middle	71	79	78	688
Upper	80	86	89	926
Residence[11]				
Urban	70	73	77	1644
Rural non-farm	57	73	74	522
Rural farm	45	44	54	201
Main activity of main earner[12]				
Working full-time	69	78	82	1667
Not working full-time	25	39	56	700
Total	63	69	74	2367

increases in coverage were made among these families of the middle and upper income brackets. There was practically no change in over-all coverage among low income families.

In the last five-year period the pattern changed. The lowest family income group shows the greatest increase in basic coverage. As we shall see, higher income families, which were largely covered by hospitalization and

5 The Health Insurance Council estimates that 156 million persons had health insurance at the close of 1965. This amounts to about 82 percent of the civilian non-institutionalized population. The difference between HIC's estimate for 1965 and the estimate made in this report for 1963 should not be taken as an indication of increased coverage over the two-year period since HIC's estimates have consistently exceeded those made from social surveys. See Appendix I concerning the comparability of such estimates.

6 See definition 21.

7 See definition 15.   9 See definition 1.

8 See definition 37.   10 See definition 9.

surgical-medical insurance by 1958, purchased major medical insurance in the next five years (Table 43). Lower income families, which were less likely to have any health insurance in 1958, purchased basic hospital and surgical insurance.

A similar pattern emerges when other family characteristics included in Table 42 are related to basic coverage. Groups with the largest proportions covered in 1953 had large percentage point increases between 1953 and 1958. Between 1958 and 1963, however, the greatest increases are made by those groups least likely to have any health insurance. Thus, according to residence,[11] families in urban dwellings and rural non-farm dwellings, which had the highest levels of coverage in 1953, showed the greatest gains during the next five years (the increase of 16 percentage points by rural non-farm families was especially high). However, between 1958 and 1963 rural farm families, which are least likely to have coverage, showed a percentage point increase of 10 (from 44 to 54 percent) while the proportion of urban families covered increased by 4 percentage points and rural non-farm families in the sample showed an increase of only 1 percentage point.

Considering the activity of the main earner,[12] families most likely to be covered are those with the main earner working full time. Between 1953 and 1958 these families showed a sizable increase of 9 percentage points (from 69 to 78) in the proportion with some coverage. However, the increase was only 4 percentage points between 1958 and 1963. Among families with a main earner not working full time (including main earners who are working part time, unemployed, retired, disabled, students, housewives, etc.) the percentage covered increased from 25 percent in 1953 to 39 percent in 1958. Rather than slowing down, this increase continued at a rapid rate between 1958 and 1963. By the end of the latter year, 56 percent of the families with main earners not working full time had some health insurance coverage.

A different pattern of increased coverage is developing in the field of major medical insurance. Apparently major-medical is being purchased largely by groups of families that already have extensive basic coverage. Thus, in 1958, 11 percent of the upper income families had major medical insurance compared to 7 percent of the middle income group and only 1 percent of the lowest income families (Table 43). By 1963 the proportion covered in the highest income families had increased by 29 percentage points to 38 percent while the increase in the middle income group was 15 percentage points to 22 percent, and still only 6 percent of the low income families had major medical insurance.

Table 43 shows that according to family residence, the percentage of

11 See definition 35.   12 See definition 24.

urban families (which are most likely to have basic coverage) with major medical coverage increased by 19 percentage points. The corresponding increase for rural non-farm families was 12 percentage points and for rural farm families 9 percentage points. The percentage of families with the main earner working full time that had major medical insurance increased from 8 to 30 percent between 1958 and 1963. Coverage for families with the head not working full time reached only 8 percent in 1963.

Each of the three studies has shown a strong relationship between characteristics of the family head[13] and extent of health insurance coverage.

TABLE 43
Percent of families with major medical insurance by selected family characteristics: 1958 and 1963

FAMILY CHARACTERISTIC	PERCENT WITH MAJOR MEDICAL INSURANCE		N
	1958	1963	1963
Income level			
Lower	1	6	753
Middle	7	22	688
Upper	11	38	926
Residence			
Urban	7	26	1644
Rural non-farm	7	19	522
Rural farm	1	10	201
Main activity of main earner			
Working full-time	8	30	1667
Not working full-time	a	8	700
Total	7	24	2367

[a]Less than one-half of one percent.

Chart 11 shows some of these relationships for 1963. Percentage of families with some insurance increases with increasing age, reaching a peak of 80 percent among families with heads in the 30–44 group. The percentage covered drops off slightly for families with heads 45–54 and more sharply for those with heads 65 and over. It is of special interest to further divide those 65 and over. A sharp decrease in the percentage covered between families with heads 65–74 and those with heads 75 or more is noted. Seventy-three percent of the families with heads 65–74 had some health insurance in 1963 compared to 52 percent of the families with heads 75 or over.[14]

13 See definition 11.

14 The relationship of age and health insurance status has been altered considerably by Medicare. Practically all persons 65 and over are eligible for coverage and the vast majority of those eligible have enrolled themselves in the program.

Over three-fourths of the families with male heads had health insurance compared to 65 percent of the families with female heads (Chart 11). The 1958 study showed that this difference was largely accounted for by the clustering of families with female heads in the youngest and oldest age categories, both of which, we have just seen, are less likely to have health insurance than families with heads of middle age.[15]

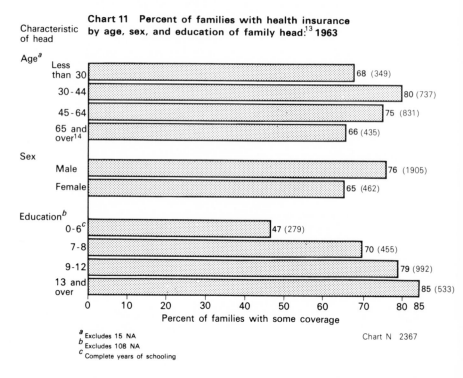

Chart 11   Percent of families with health insurance
Characteristic   by age, sex, and education of family head:[13] 1963
of head

Chart 11 illustrates that the percentage of families with insurance increases as the education of the household head increases. The greatest increase shown in the chart occurs between families where the head has completed 6 grades or less and those where he has completed 7 or 8 grades. The percentage covered is 47 percent for the former compared to 70 percent for the latter group. Coverage reaches a peak of 85 percent for families with a head who has completed some college.

Another family characteristic which shows considerable association with health insurance coverage, both basic and major-medical, is industry[16] of the main earner. Chart 12 shows that the percentage of families with

[15] Anderson, Collette, and Feldman, *Changes in Medical Care Expenditures*, p. 173.

[16] See definition 17.

basic coverage varies from a low of 62 percent for those families where the head is employed in agriculture, forestry and fisheries to a high of 92 percent where the head is employed in public administration. However, families with the main earner in agriculture have shown the greatest increase since 1958, with a 21 percentage point gain. Other families whose

Chart 12   Percent of families with health insurance and major medical insurance by industry[16] of family's main earner:[a] 1963

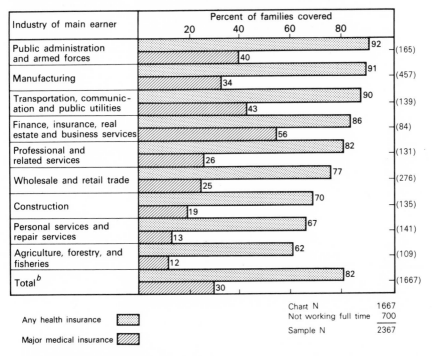

Industry of main earner	Percent of families covered	
Public administration and armed forces	92 / 40	(165)
Manufacturing	91 / 34	(457)
Transportation, communication and public utilities	90 / 43	(139)
Finance, insurance, real estate and business services	86 / 56	(84)
Professional and related services	82 / 26	(131)
Wholesale and retail trade	77 / 25	(276)
Construction	70 / 19	(135)
Personal services and repair services	67 / 13	(141)
Agriculture, forestry, and fisheries	62 / 12	(109)
Total[b]	82 / 30	(1667)

Any health insurance ▨
Major medical insurance ▧

Chart N   1667
Not working full time   700
Sample N   2367

[a] Includes only families with main earner working full time
[b] Includes 11 NA, 11 mining, and 8 entertainment and recreation services

main earners are employed in manufacturing, transportation, finance, and the professions are equal to or above the mean percentage coverage of 82 percent for all families with the main earner working full time. Other groups of families falling below this mean coverage include those whose main earners are employed in trade, construction, and personal services.

The rank coverage by industry is somewhat similar for major medical insurance and any health insurance. The extent of major medical coverage is, as expected, considerably less for any given industry. Family coverage by industry of main earner varies from a low of 12 percent in agriculture to a high of 56 percent in finance.

Turning from family to individual coverage, Chart 13 reveals the pattern for hospital insurance coverage according to age. Through the first five-year period spanned by these studies the pattern of coverage remained much the same. In 1953 and 1958, relatively high coverage for children

Chart 13   Percent of persons insured against costs of hospital care by age: 1953, 1958 and 1963

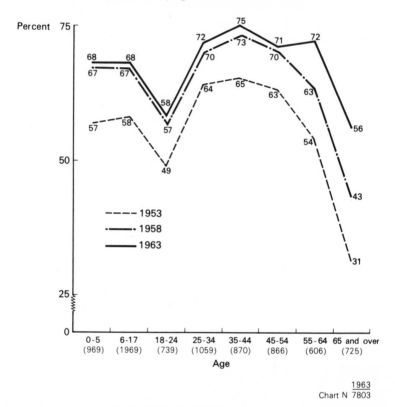

1963
Chart N 7803

17 and under was followed by a drop for the age group 18–24. Highest coverage was attained between 25 and 54, followed by decreasing coverage in the 55–64 age bracket and lowest coverage for those 65 and over. The largest increases in percentage covered between 1953 and 1958 were for the youngest and oldest age groups.

The 1963 study reveals that significant increases were made by the two oldest age groups. The percentage of persons covered in the 55–64 age bracket increased from 63 to 72. An even larger increase—from 43 percent to 56 percent—occurred in the 65 and over age group.[17] Gains among other age groups between 1958 and 1963 were small.

In each study the proportion of persons with some coverage has been similar according to sex. In 1963, 68 percent of all males and 69 percent of all females were covered by health insurance.

In sum, three-fourths of all American families were covered by voluntary health insurance in 1963. The proportion with insurance has increased by 11 percent since 1953 and by 5 percent since 1958. The increase since 1958 has been primarily among families formerly least likely to be covered such as those with low incomes, rural-farm residence, or where the head of the family is older. Major medical coverage increased more rapidly between 1958 and 1963 than did other types of health insurance coverage. Over three times as many families had major medical insurance in 1963 as five years earlier. These gains were mostly among upper income, urban families. Considerable differences in coverage were shown to exist according to industry of main earner and, in individual coverage, according to age. No difference in individual coverage was found according to sex.

As we have seen in this section, a large and growing proportion of the population has health insurance. This pattern of coverage serves to set apart two "deviant" groups who are sometimes considered "problems" by planners and providers of health services. On the one hand, there was a substantial number of people who were still uncovered in 1963. How they differ from the rest of the population and why they did not have health insurance are important questions. On the other hand, 11 percent of the individuals with hospital insurance had more than one hospital policy in 1963 and 9 percent of those with surgical insurance had more than one surgical policy. When a large proportion of the population has hospital and surgical insurance, and health insurance for the family can often be obtained from more than one source, some degree of multiple coverage can be expected. In insurance circles, multiple coverage is regarded as a problem if such duplication leads to overinsurance, i.e., insurance in excess of the costs of services insured. An analysis of the characteristics of the uninsured, those with one policy, and those with multiple coverage in the 1963 study is found in another publication.[18] This analysis shows that these groups differ from one another in basic socio-demographic characteristics and also in use of health services. These findings seem to indicate that multiple coverage is in part a function of back-

17 See footnote 14.

18 Ronald Andersen and Donald C. Riedel, "People and Their Hospital Insurance: Comparisons of the Uninsured, Those with One Policy, and Those with Multiple Coverage," Health Information Foundation Research Series No. 23, 1967.

ground characteristics such as number of wage earners in the family. In addition, however, there are indications that some users of large quantities of medical care seek out additional coverage more actively than do people with lower use rates.

2. Type of insurer[19]

The main types of insurers for the civilian population over the ten-year period covered by the studies were Blue Cross and Blue Shield plans, sponsored by hospital and medical associations respectively; private insurance companies; and a number of independent group practice plans which are generally physician service plans.[20]

TABLE 44
Percent of individuals insured against the costs of hospital and surgical care
by type of insurer: 1953, 1958 and 1963

	TYPE OF COVERAGE					
	Hospital			Surgical-medical		
INSURER[a]	1953	1958	1963	1953	1958	1963
Blue Cross or Blue Shield	27	31	31	19	28	29
Private insurance	29	32	36	27	33	36
Independent	6	7	5	7	5	6
Dependents' Medical Care Program of the U. S. Armed Forces	b	1	1	b	1	1

[a] An individual may be counted in two or more categories.

[b] Category not used in 1953.

	Hospital 1963		Surgical 1963	
	Table N	7764	Table N	7764
	NA insurer	39	NA insurer	39
	Total N	7803	Total N	7803

The private insurance companies in each period covered a somewhat larger proportion of the population against hospital and surgical-medical costs than did the Blue Plans (Table 44). The proportion of the total population insured by private insurance companies against costs of hospital care increased from 29 to 36 percent between 1953 and 1963. The proportion covered by Blue Plans increased from 27 to 31 percent in the same period, though none of the increase occurred in the last five years. Five percent of the population was covered by independent plans in 1963 compared to 7 percent in 1958 and 6 percent in 1953. One percent re-

[19] See definition 22.

[20] In addition, a category was provided for coverage under the Dependents' Medical Care Program of the U.S. Armed Forces in 1958 and 1963.

ported coverage under the Dependents' Medical Care Program of the U.S. Armed Forces in 1958 and 1963.

By 1963, 36 percent of the population had surgical or medical coverage provided by a private insurance company (Table 44). The proportions covered by the Blue Plans and the independent plans for surgical or medical expense were 29 percent and 6 percent respectively.

Coverage by insurer can also be considered as a proportion of the insured population only, rather than as a proportion of the total population, as discussed above. Of all persons with some hospital insurance, 54 percent

TABLE 45
Percent of families insured against the costs of hospital care by Blue Cross and private insurance by family income level and residence: 1958 and 1963

	PERCENT OF INSURED FAMILIES[a]				
	Blue Cross[21]		Private insurance		N
INCOME AND RESIDENCE	1958	1963	1958	1963	1963
Income level					
Upper	51	52	51	60	805
Middle	45	48	52	57	530
Lower	38	47	51	55	376
Residence					
Urban	51	52	51	57	1228
Rural non-farm	46	45	50	56	376
Rural farm	32	36	64	68	107

[a]All duplication within type of insurer is eliminated. However, a family covered by two types of insurer is included in the proportion covered for each. The increases in percent covered by both Blue Cross and private insurance between 1958 and 1963 provided some indication of the increasing extent to which members of the population are covered by more than one hospital policy.

	1963
Table N	1711
NA insurer	19
Not insured	637
Sample N	2367

had some private insurance hospital coverage. Forty-six percent had some Blue Cross coverage[21] and an additional 8 percent of all insured persons had hospital insurance through an independent plan.[22]

In each study the proportion of families with hospital insurance covered by Blue Cross and private insurance varied according to family income and type of residence. Table 45 shows these relationships for 1958 and 1963.

In 1963 Blue Cross continued to insure a greater proportion of upper income families than of the lower brackets. However, since 1958 the pro-

21 Includes Blue Shield plans providing hospital benefits.

22 The sum of these percentages exceeds 100 because some persons had hospital coverage through more than one type of insurer.

portion of insured low income families covered by Blue Cross rose from 38 to 47 percent. The percentage of insured families covered by private insurance companies did not vary by income group in 1958. Between 1958 and 1963 the greatest gain in private insurance coverage appears to be among the higher income brackets.

Blue Cross coverage by residence remained virtually unchanged with the exception of a 4 percentage point increase in the proportion of rural-farm residents covered. A larger proportion of families with each type of residence was covered by private insurance in 1963 than in 1958, with the greatest increase appearing to be among non-farm residents. Thus, in 1963 private insurance was insuring a somewhat greater proportion of the population against the costs of hospital and surgical services than was Blue Cross-Blue Shield and also appeared to make greater gains in enrollment between 1958 and 1963. These data indicate that in 1963 Blue Cross was insuring a larger proportion of insured lower income and rural-farm residents than in 1958, while private insurance made its greatest gains in proportions of insured higher income, non-farm residents.

3. Method of enrollment

The distribution of health insurance by method of enrollment (group or individual)[23] is of significance because of the greater ease and lower administrative costs in selling through groups. In addition, more comprehensive benefits are generally offered through group contracts. Chart 14 shows that while the percentage of the population covered by group hospital insurance grew during the decade covered by the studies, the proportion of the population with non-group hospital coverage has remained about the same. Between 1953 and 1963 the percentage of the population with group hospital insurance increased from 42 percent to 53 percent.

We have seen that the percentage of the total population covered by group hospital insurance increased and the proportion covered by non-group insurance remained stable. Table 46 shows us what these changes mean in terms of the composition of the insured population according to type of insurer. The proportion of all insured persons with Blue Cross group hospital insurance has been 35 or 36 percent in each study. While the Blue Cross group proportion remained stable, the private insurance group proportion increased from 30 to 40 percent in the ten-year period. The proportion with independent group coverage dropped from 10 percent to 7 percent of all persons with hospital insurance.

Turning to individual coverage, we again find a relatively stable pat-

[23] See definition 4.

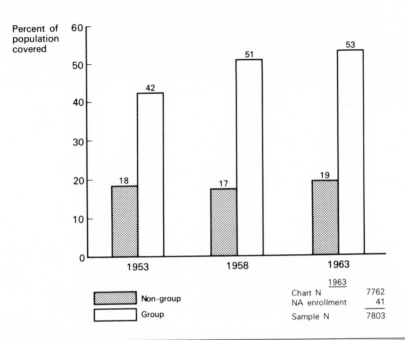

Chart 14   Percent of the total population covered by hospital insurance by type of enrollment:[23] 1953, 1958 and 1963

Percent of population covered

Non-group
Group

1963	
Chart N	7762
NA enrollment	41
Sample N	7803

TABLE 46
Percent of individuals covered by hospital insurance by type of enrollment and type of insurer: 1953, 1958 and 1963

TYPE OF ENROLLMENT AND INSURER	1953	1958	1963	N 1963
Group	73[a]	78[a]	79[a]	5257
Blue Cross	36[b]	35[b]	36[b]	5218
Private	30	36	40	5218
Independent	10	8	7	5218
Dependents' Medical Care Program of the U.S. Armed Forces	c	2	1	5218
Non-group	32[a]	26[a]	26[a]	5257
Blue Cross	10	12[b]	11[b]	5218
Private	21	14	15	5218
Independent	1	1	1	5218

[a]Components exceed 100 percent because some insured persons held both group and non-group policies.

[b]Subcomponents exceed group or non-group total because some persons held policies from more than one type of insurer.

[c]Category not used in 1953.

1963 Enrollment	
Table N	5257
NA enrollment	41
Uninsured	2505
Sample N	7803

1963 Enrollment Insurer	
Table N	5218
NA enrollment	41
NA insured	39
Uninsured	2505
Sample N	7803

tern for Blue Cross, which covered 10 to 12 percent of all insured persons in each study. However, the proportion of all insured persons who had non-group private insurance policies decreased from 21 percent in 1953 to 14 percent in 1958, but appeared to stabilize at 15 percent in 1963.

Each study revealed that groups of individuals least likely to have health insurance were most likely to have non-group insurance if they

TABLE 47

Percent of individuals covered by hospital insurance who had group or non-group coverage by age, income and residence: 1953 and 1963

CHARACTERISTIC	1953[a]		1963		N
	Group	Non-group	Group	Non-group	
Age					
0-5	75	28	84	18	658
6-17	69	32	83	20	1321
18-24	68	32	82	24	423
25-34	74	27	86	17	758
35-44	73	29	84	20	648
45-54	73	32	79	26	614
55-64	61	50	70	41	430
65 and over[24]	47	67	35	70	405
Family income					
$0-1,999	41	62	31	68	197
2,000-3,499	67	37	54	50	364
3,500-4,999	79	25	68	37	562
5,000-7,499	79	25	82	21	1677
7,500-9,999	} 73	} 36	89	17	1046
10,000 and over			83	22	1411
Residence					
Urban	76	29	81	23	3689
Rural non-farm	75	30	76	27	1230
Rural farm	52	53	56	49	338

[a]Based only on individuals with Blue Cross and/or private insurance coverage for 1953.

	1963
Table N	5257
NA enrollment	41
Uninsured	2505
Sample N	7803

had any at all. This means that such groups had fewer people enrolled to begin with, and that those persons with insurance in such groups probably had less comprehensive benefits. Table 47 shows that these groups included the older age groups, the low income groups, and those living in rural farm residences. In contrast, younger people, high income groups, and non-farm residents were more likely to have group insurance. The only exceptions to these general trends are: 1) Very young insured adults (18–24) are more likely to have non-group coverage (probably because some of them are no longer covered by their parents' group plans and obtain non-group coverage before they are covered through their own employee groups). 2) The highest income people who have insurance appear more likely to have non-group coverage than the middle income groups.

Table 47 also allows us to examine changes over the decade in proportions with group and non-group hospital insurance according to certain individual characteristics. Between 1953 and 1963 the proportion of insured people with group coverage increased while the proportion with non-group coverage decreased for every age group except persons 65 and over. For the oldest age group the reverse was true, as a greater proportion of older insured people had non-group coverage in 1963 than in 1953 but a smaller proportion had group coverage.[24] Among insured people with family incomes under $5,000 the percentage with group coverage decreased while the percentage with non-group coverage increased in a pattern similar to the changes for those 65 and over. However, for insured persons with family incomes of $5,000 or more, group coverage increased while non-group coverage decreased. Over the decade the percentage of insured persons with group coverage increased for all places of residence while the percentage with non-group coverage decreased for people with urban and rural farm residences and remained the same for people with rural non-farm residences.

The most common method of enrollment for health insurance is through some group. Most of this coverage is through employee or union groups which provide health insurance for employees and their dependents. In 1963, 70 percent of all families with health insurance coverage had some work group insurance of this type. Five percent had some insurance through some "other" group such as a farmer's, tradesman, professional, fraternal, social, or cooperative organization, and 36 percent purchased some coverage individually.

In addition to providing a means for enrollment, employers are paying an increasing portion of the premium for work group health insurance. In 1953, 59 percent of all families with some work group insurance had all or part of the premium for this insurance paid for by the employer (Table 48). By 1963 four-fifths of all such families were receiving wage supplements in the form of employer contributions for their work group health insurance. The proportion of families carrying work group insurance with the employer paying the entire premium increased from 10 percent to 27 percent over the decade.

These data show that in 1963 over half the population was enrolled in group health insurance while one-fifth was covered by non-group insur-

24 See footnote 14.

ance. Between 1953 and 1963 the proportion covered by group insurance increased while that covered by non-group remained about the same. Over the decade the proportion of the insured persons covered by Blue Cross (both group and non-group) remained about the same while for private insurance the group proportion increased and the non-group proportion decreased. In general, older, low income, and farm people were more likely to have non-group insurance while younger, higher income, and non-farm people were more likely to have group. The trends between

TABLE 48
Employer contribution toward family's premiums for health insurance policies carried through a work group or union: 1953 and 1963

EXTENT OF CONTRIBUTION	PERCENT OF FAMILIES CARRYING ONE OR MORE HEALTH INSURANCE POLICIES THROUGH WORK GROUP OR UNION	
	1953	1963
Employer pays some of family's work group health insurance premiums	59	79
Employer pays all[a]	10	27
Employer pays part	49	52
Employer pays none of family's work group health insurance premiums	41	21
Total	100	100

[a] Includes premium for any dependents covered under policy. If family has more than one work group policy, employer must pay entire premium for each policy for family to be included in this category.

1963	
Table N	1219
"Other group" only	66
Non-group/NA	466
Uninsured	616
Sample N	2367

1953 and 1963 tended to magnify these differences. Seventy percent of all insured families were covered through a work group in 1963 and employer contributions to premium costs of this insurance increased during the ten-year period.

B. HEALTH INSURANCE BENEFITS

A major issue in voluntary health insurance is the proportion of the public's expenditures for health covered by health insurance benefits. Although enrollment growth has continued, a more decisive trend found in these studies is the increasing ability of prepayment to pay a higher percentage of the average insured person's total health bill. Criteria have not been established as to the exact proportions that are "practical" or "desirable." This is true for all personal health services and also for the individual components such as hospital and physician services. One school of thought would have insurance primarily reimburse families for most, if not all, of infrequent, high magnitude health expenditures. Another school would have insurance cover all health expenditures regardless of magnitude or frequency of occurrence. At any rate, the following data show that between 1953 and 1963 families with unusually high costs for health services in a given year have benefited most by the recent increases in health insurance reimbursements. Considered separately are benefits related to type of service, type of insurer, and method of enrollment.

TABLE 49
Estimated aggregate health insurance benefits[25] by type of service: 1953, 1958 and 1963

SERVICE[26]	BENEFITS IN BILLIONS OF DOLLARS					
	1953		1958		1963	
Hospital	1.0		2.2		3.7	
Physician	0.5		1.0		1.6[b]	
Surgery		.3		.5		.9
Obstetrics		.1		.2		.2
Other		.1		.3		.6
Drugs	a		a		0.1	
Dentists	a		a		a	
Other medical care	a		a		0.1	
Total	1.5		3.1[b]		5.5	

[a] Less than .05 billion.
[b] Components do not add to total due to rounding.

	1963
N	$233,000

1. *Type of service*

Families in the U.S. received an estimated total of $5.5 billion in benefits[25] to cover expenditures for personal health services[26] during 1963. The amount was 77 percent more than the $3.1 billion reported in 1958 and close to 4 times the $1.5 billion reported in 1953.[27] Table 49 shows that over the ten-year period, aggregate benefits increased for each service covered. The increase for hospital services was from $1.0 billion to $3.7 billion, or 270 percent, between 1953 and 1963. The increase for all physician services during this same period was from $0.5 billion to $1.6 billion, or 220 percent.

25 See definition 2.

26 See definition 5 for a detailed description of the various health service components.

27 Of the total benefits provided in 1963 it is estimated that 7 percent were provided through a major medical benefit structure.

Aggregate health insurance benefits were increasing more rapidly than aggregate health expenditures between 1953 and 1963. Consequently, the proportion of aggregate expenditures for all personal health services covered by health insurance benefits increased during the ten-year period from 15 percent in the earliest study to 19 percent in 1958 and 27 percent in 1963. Table 50 indicates that for each separate service there was also a gain during the decade. However, benefits continued to be provided primarily for hospital care and physician care. Thus, by 1963, 69 percent of all hospital expenditures were covered by voluntary health insurance.

TABLE 50
Percent of aggregate expenditures for personal health services covered by aggregate health insurance benefits: 1953, 1958 and 1963

| SERVICE | PERCENT OF EXPENDITURES COVERED BY INSURANCE BENEFITS | | | N[b] |
	1953	1958	1963	1963
Hospitals	50	58	69	$228,000
Physicians	13	18	25	271,000
Surgery	38	48	58	66,000
Obstetrics	25	30	32	24,000
Other physicians	4	7	13	182,000
Prescriptions and other medicines	a	1	1	178,000
Dentists	a	a	a	115,000
Other medical goods and services	1	1	5	82,000
Total	15	19	27	875,000

[a]Less than one-half of one percent.
[b]Sample expenditures.

One-quarter of personal expenditures for physician services were covered but the proportion varied a great deal according to type of physician service.

In 1963, 58 percent of all surgical expenses and one-third of expenditures for obstetrical care were covered. In contrast, only 13 percent of "other physician" care was covered. Most of the benefits in the latter category were for physician visits in the hospital while home and office visits remained largely uncovered. While some small increases were indicated, expenses for medicines, dentists, and other care remained mostly uninsured in 1963.

Up to this point the discussion of insurance benefits has been related to the expenditures of the *total* population. Of primary importance is what these changes in benefit patterns mean to people with insurance.

Benefits as a proportion of expenditures increased for insured families[28] as well as for the population as a whole. These increases indicate that benefits are increasing more rapidly than expenditures for insured families. In addition, the increase during the second five-year period exceeded that during the first. Average benefits increased from 19 percent in 1953 to 24 percent in 1958, and to 31 percent in 1963. The mean benefit per insured family rose from $45 in 1953 to $80 in 1958 and $131 in 1963.

One of the stated goals of voluntary health insurance is to release the

TABLE 51
Mean benefits by level of expenditure for health services for insured families:[28] 1953, 1958 and 1963

| LEVEL OF EXPENDITURE FOR HEALTH SERVICES | MEAN BENEFITS[a] | | | N |
	1953	1958	1963	1963
$1-49	$ 2	$ 1	$ 1	214
50-99	4	1	2	191
100-199	16	10	7	320
200-299	33	28	32	228
300-399	67	64	49	179
400-499	100	94	103	122
500-749	147	156	171	200
750-999	204	257	291	109
1000 and over	362	572	748	177
Total	45	80	131	1751[b]

[a]These mean averages include all insured families in the specific expenditure category whether or not they actually received any benefits.

[b]Includes 11 families with no expenditure.

	1963
Table N	1751
Uninsured	616
Sample N	2367

family of financial burdens associated with large "catastrophic" costs of illness. It is thus important to examine the benefits of insured families according to their level of expenditure.

In each survey the magnitude of average family benefits increased as expenditures increased, as shown in Table 51. However, with the passage of time, insured families with low expenditures received fewer benefits while high expenditure families received larger amounts. For example, average benefits for families with expenditures of $100–199 decreased from $16 to $7 between 1953 and 1963.[29] In contrast, benefits for those

28 See definition 18.

29 One explanation for this shift is that families at comparable expenditure levels were very likely not buying the same goods and services in 1963 as in earlier periods. For example, a family spending $100–199 in 1953 may have paid for a hospital stay and received insurance benefits. In 1963, with the rise in prices the same expenditure was more likely to have paid only for outpatient or dental care, which is generally not insured.

with expenditures of $750–999 increased from $204 to $291 in the same period.

Chart 15 shows average benefits as a percentage of expenditure for insured families at each level of expenditure. At all levels of expenditure below $400, average benefits were greater in 1953 than in the later periods. However, average coverage in 1953 reaches a maximum of 25 percent for families with expenditures of $500–749 and declines slightly thereafter.

Chart 15   Aggregate benefits as a percent of aggregate expenditures for insured families by level of family expenditure: 1953, 1958 and 1963

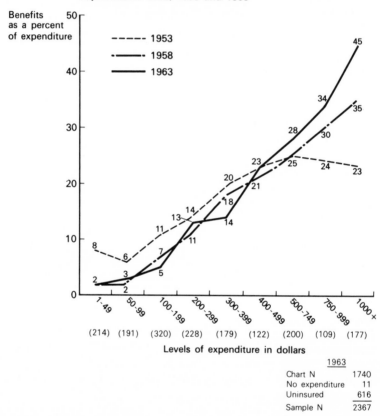

Levels of expenditure in dollars

	1963
Chart N	1740
No expenditure	11
Uninsured	616
Sample N	2367

In contrast, average benefits as a percentage of expenditure increase in the later periods with each expenditure level and reach their maximum for families with expenditures of $1,000 or more. The graph indicates that the proportion paid in 1963 was substantially greater than in 1958 for families at high expenditure levels. Thus, average benefits for families in the $1,000 and over expenditure category were 45 percent in 1963 compared to 35 percent in 1958.

Average benefits alone are not sufficient to describe benefit patterns, since some 57 percent of insured families with some medical care expenditures in 1963 received no benefits. Furthermore, there was considerable variation in the extent of coverage among those who did receive benefits. Table 52 shows the extent of coverage for families with selected levels of expenditure.

TABLE 52
Percent of insured families with specified levels of coverage by selected
magnitudes of expenditure: 1953, 1958 and 1963

SELECTED MAGNITUDE OF EXPENDITURE	PERCENT OF FAMILIES WITH EACH LEVEL OF COVERAGE[a]		
	20 percent or more	50 percent or more	80 percent or more
All insured families			
1953	24	9	3
1958	24	10	2
1963 (1751)	30	14	3
Low ($100-199)			
1953	20	6	2
1958	13	4	1
1963 (320)	11	3	b
High ($500 or more)			
1953	49	19	2
1958	56	24	4
1963 (486)	64	34	12

[a] "Level of coverage" is annual health insurance benefits per insured family as a percent of their annual health expenditure.

[b] Less than one-half of one percent.

1963	
Table N	1751
Uninsured	616
Sample N	2367

For all insured families there was very little change between 1953 and 1958. There was some increase at the lower levels in 1963. Thus, in 1953 and 1958, 24 percent of all insured families had 20 percent or more of their medical expenditures covered by insurance while 30 percent of the families had such coverage in 1963. However, as many insured families had 80 percent or more of their expenses covered in 1953 as in 1963 (3 percent).

The picture changes considerably if levels of coverage are examined according to magnitude of expenditure. At a relatively low magnitude of expenditure ($100–199), the percentage of families at each level of coverage in 1963 is *lower* than in 1953. In contrast, the degree of coverage of insured families with expenditures of $500 or more *increased* in each time period for each level of coverage.

While the proportion of personal expenditures that *should* be covered by voluntary health insurance is debatable, 80 percent is taken here arbitrarily as an indicator of "comprehensive" coverage. No inference is intended as to the desirability of such coverage in all circumstances. It should be remembered that the base for this percentage includes expenditures for such items as non-prescribed drugs, eyeglasses, wheelchairs, and crutches, which are generally not considered part of the "insurable package" today.

In 1963 only 8 percent of all insured families with expenditures had 80 percent or more of their expenses covered. However, if we look at the proportion of expenditures covered according to type of service, as revealed in Chart 16, a somewhat different picture emerges. The percentage of insured families having 80 percent or more of their expenses paid by insurance was much higher for those services for which families are more likely to incur larger expenses. In each study the percentage was highest for hospital care, followed by surgical care and obstetrical care, in that order. In 1963 two-thirds of all insured families receiving benefits for hospital care had 80 percent or more of their bill paid by insurance. Over one-half had 80 percent of their surgical bill paid and the fraction was slightly over one-quarter for obstetrical care. Between 1953 and 1963 the proportion of families receiving benefits of 80 percent or more for hospital care has increased, while it has fluctuated around 50 percent for surgical care and decreased for obstetrical care.[30]

In a previous section it was shown that higher income families are more likely to have insurance coverage than lower income families. A subsequent question in considering all families that do have insurance is how the benefits of the higher and lower income families compare.

Table 53 allows us to examine benefits as a proportion of expenditure by family income in 1963 and also make comparisons with the situation ten years earlier. First of all, we see that benefits as a percentage of expenditures have increased for all family incomes. However, the increases have been considerably greater for the upper income groups. The result is that, while in 1953 families with the lowest incomes had the greatest proportion of their expenditures covered, by 1963 families with incomes from $5,000 to $10,000 had the largest proportion of their expenditures covered.

However, examining Table 53 more closely, a roughly similar pattern

[30] The estimate for obstetrical care is subject to considerable sampling error due to the small sample size.

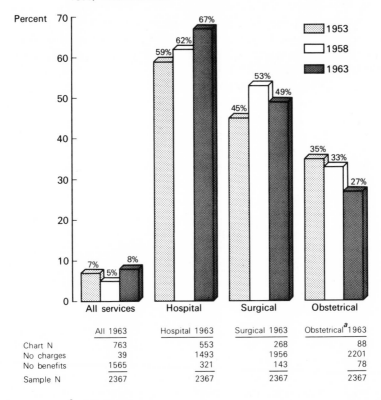

Chart 16   Percent of families receiving benefits who had
80 percent or more of charges covered, by type of service:
1953, 1958 and 1963

	All 1963	Hospital 1963	Surgical 1963	Obstetrical[a] 1963
Chart N	763	553	268	88
No charges	39	1493	1956	2201
No benefits	1565	321	143	78
Sample N	2367	2367	2367	2367

[a]Limited to physician charges

TABLE 53
Total health insurance benefits as a percent of total expenditures for all
insured families: 1953 and 1963

FAMILY INCOME	BENEFITS AS A PERCENT OF EXPENDITURES		N 1963
	1953	1963	
Under $2,000	26	30	137
2,000-3,499	20	30	179
3,500-4,999	22	24	224
5,000-7,499	18	36	491
7,500-9,999		36	312
10,000-12,499	15	26 } 29	203
12,500 and over		23	205
Total	19	31	1751

	1963	
Table N	1751
Uninsured	616
Sample N	2367

may be seen in the two time periods. First, it is necessary to remember the over-all increase in income over the ten-year period, which causes the same income categories to represent somewhat different segments of the population in terms of relative income. In each time period the lowest income groups, as represented by those insured families with incomes of $2,000 or less in 1953 and $3,499 or less in 1963, have a relatively high proportion of their expenses covered. Coverage then declines for the lower middle income families, including those making $2,000–3,499 in 1953 and those making $3,500–4,999 in 1963. In each study coverage then increases for the next income groups ($3,500–4,999 in 1953 and $5,000–9,999 in 1963). From these maximums, benefits as a proportion of expenditure then taper off considerably for the highest income families.

It is of particular interest that in both studies insurance carried by the low income families appears at first glance to be more "adequate" than that carried by upper income families. In fact, low income families are less likely to use and have charges for services other than hospital care and surgery, such as dental care and "preventive" medical care. The latter services were not generally covered by health insurance in 1963.[31] Thus, the expenditures that insured low income families do have are more likely to be reimbursed. Probably upper income families carry insurance with greater benefits, but they are not reflected in a measure of benefits as a proportion of total health expenditures. Upper income families also tend to use more expensive facilities such as private hospital rooms and receive treatment from specialists with higher fee schedules. Thus, even though these services might be covered in part by insurance, the use of more expensive services might tend to reduce the proportion paid by insurance benefits.

In Table 54 we have isolated benefits as a percentage of charges for hospital care and surgery to see if upper income families do receive benefits which cover a larger proportion of charges for such services. As family income increases, the proportion of families receiving benefits to cover 80 percent or more of their gross hospital bill also increases, with the exception of the highest income group. A smaller proportion of families with incomes of $10,000 or more than of those between $5,000 and $10,000 receives comprehensive hospital benefits. It may be that use of amenities such as private rooms accounts for this finding.

Table 54 shows, for surgical expenses, a reversal of the relationship between income and benefit coverage found for hospital expenses. Here, the proportion of families receiving benefits to cover 80 percent or more

---

31 While coverage of such services as drugs, dental care, and home care is still, in 1966, provided to a very small proportion of the total population, such coverage is now being written at an increasing rate.

of their surgical expenditures *decreases* as family income increases.[32] Alternatives to the hypothesis that surgical coverage held by low income families is more adequate include the following: (1) High income people are more likely than low income people to use the services of physicians whose fees exceed coverage provided by insurance. (2) Physicians may charge high income persons more than low income persons for a given surgical procedure, thus reducing the proportion covered by insurance for the latter.

In the past there has been considerable discussion regarding whether or not charges for maternity care should be covered by insurance. Several objections were raised to such insurance: (1) The insured have some

TABLE 54
Percent of families receiving insurance benefits which covered 80 percent or more of hospital or surgical expenditures by family income: 1963

FAMILY INCOME	PERCENT OF FAMILIES RECEIVING BENEFITS WHO WERE REIMBURSED FOR 80 PERCENT OR MORE OF CHARGES	
	For hospital charges	For surgical charges
Less than $3,500	49 (70)	65 (26)
3,500-4,999	58 (59)	54 (26)
5,000-7,499	71 (193)	52 (89)
7,500-9,999	76 (110)	48 (62)
10,000 or more	67 (121)	37 (65)
All families	67 (553)	49 (268)

	Hospital	Surgical
Table N	553	268
No charges	1493	1956
No benefits	321	143
Sample N	2367	2367

choice as to whether they will have children. (2) In contrast to most other insured occurrences, having children is frequently considered a boon. (3) The occurrence is known months in advance and, since the expenses for uncomplicated obstetrical care are usually moderate, most families could budget for them.

Nevertheless, in response to increasing consumer demand, most hospital and surgical contracts provide some maternity care coverage. This coverage generally covers only a portion of the charges. Frequently, the partial coverage is intended to act as a mild utilization deterrent, rather similar

[32] Recent findings from the National Health Survey do not show such a decided inverse relationship between income and proportion of the surgical bill paid by insurance. However, these data do show that surgically treated discharges with family incomes from $2,000 to 3,999 were most likely of all income groups to have three-quarters or more of the surgeon's bill paid by insurance. National Center for Health Statistics, "Proportion of Surgical Bill Paid by Insurance," ser. 10, no. 31 (September, 1966).

to the coinsurance feature of major medical expense insurance. However, as we shall see, in the flow of private financing for maternity care, the proportion coming through voluntary health insurance continues to rise.

In 1953, insurance benefits for maternity care had been received by 45 percent of the families in which a live birth occurred. By 1958 this proportion had risen to 55 percent. In 1963 it was 58 percent. Between 1953 and 1958, average benefits per maternity case for families receiving benefits increased from $129 to $187. Benefits had expanded to $236 in 1963.

Chart 17   Health insurance benefits as a proportion of expenditures for live births: 1953, 1958 and 1963

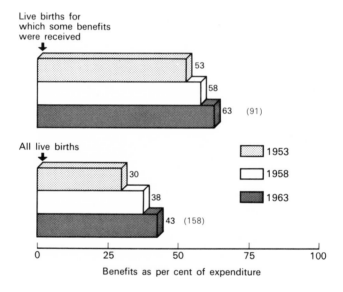

Since benefits increased more rapidly than expenditures,[33] the proportion of expenditures covered by insurance benefits rose from 53 percent in 1953 to 58 percent in 1958 and 63 percent in 1963 (Chart 17). Considering all families having a live birth during the survey year, whether or not they were insured and whether or not they received any insurance benefits, the proportion of their total expenditure for maternity care covered by insurance benefits increased from 30 percent in 1953 to 38 percent in 1958 and 43 percent five years later.

In review, health insurance benefits as a proportion of gross expenditure for health services increased from 15 percent to 27 percent between

[33] For definitions of types of expenditures included for live births see footnotes 14–19, Chapter 3.

1953 and 1963. In each study much larger proportions of the total charges for hospital and surgical services than for other services were covered by insurance. Among insured families in 1963, the proportion of aggregate charges covered by insurance was directly related to family expenditure (Table 54). Compared to ten years earlier, low expenditure insured families were having a *smaller* proportion of their expenditures covered, while high expenditure families were having a *larger* proportion covered. In 1953, among families receiving benefits, the lowest income group had the largest proportion of its expenses covered by insurance. By 1963 it was the middle income group with the largest proportion covered. However, in both periods the lowest income families receiving benefits had greater proportions of their expenditures covered than did the highest income families. Benefits as a percent of charges were found to be *directly* related for hospital care but *inversely* related for surgical care. If higher income families do tend to have more comprehensive insurance coverage, then it appears that surgical charges are much more likely to vary with family income level than are hospital charges. Among families receiving benefits in connection with live births, benefits as a proportion of expenditures increased from 53 percent in 1953 to 63 percent in 1963.

2. Type of insurer

While some inroads are being made in providing benefits for other services, the dominant pattern of voluntary health insurance benefits is coverage of general hospital services and physicians' services in the hospital. Blue Cross and Blue Shield plans and private insurance companies have developed this pattern. Since Blue Plans and the insurance companies are in competition for subscribers, some gross comparisons between the benefits of the two types of insurance are presented here.

In interpreting these data, it is necessary to remember that private insurance plans sometimes differ more within themselves than they do with Blue Plans and that there are also substantial differences among Blue Plans. In addition, premiums, administrative costs,[34] and quality of service are not taken into account. The comparisons are limited to the extent to which various agencies paid for the total expenditures for hospital and surgical services.

Chart 18 shows that in each study Blue Cross[35] paid a high percent-

[34] Operating expense as a percentage of premium income varies considerably according to type of insurer. In 1964 this percentage was 5.9 percent for Blue Cross-Blue Shield plans, 7.6 percent for independent plans, 12.9 percent for private insurance group plans and 45.4 percent for private insurance non-group plans. Louis S. Reed, "Private Health Insurance in the United States: An Overview," *Social Security Bulletin*, 28, no. 12 (1965): 18.

[35] Includes Blue Shield plans providing hospital benefits.

age of the hospital bill more often than did private insurance companies. Thus, in 1963, 64 percent of the admissions insured by Blue Cross had 90 percent or more of the bill paid, compared to 53 percent for admissions insured by private insurance. Private insurance paid less than 70 percent of the bill for 24 percent of their admissions, compared to 13 percent for Blue Cross.

Chart 18   Percent of hospital bill covered by insurance, for admissions[a] insured by Blue Cross and private insurance: 1953, 1958 and 1963

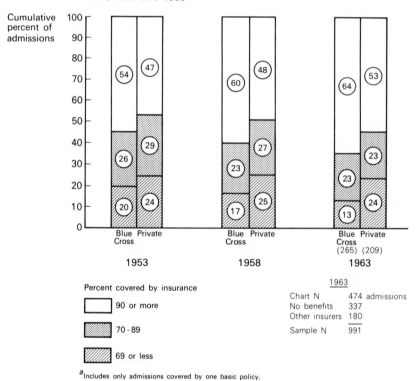

The trend over the decade is for both types of insurer to pay greater proportions of the hospital bill more often (Chart 18). Thus, the percentage of admissions for which Blue Cross pays 90 percent or more increased by 10 percentage points between 1953 and 1963. The increase for private insurance companies was 6 percentage points. Blue Cross also decreased the proportion of its insured admissions for which it paid less than 70 percent, but this proportion remained the same for private insurance.

The decrease for Blue Cross was from 20 percent to 13 percent while it was 24 percent for private insurance in both periods.

The admissions covered by Blue Cross and private insurance differ not only in the extent to which they are insured but also in terms of daily room and board rate and type of accommodation.

TABLE 55

Type of hospital accommodation and daily room and board charge for admissions[a] insured by Blue Cross and private insurance: 1963

ACCOMMODATION AND DAILY CHARGE	PERCENT BLUE CROSS	PERCENT PRIVATE INSURANCE
Accommodation[b]		
1 bed	19	25
2 beds	54	47
3 or more beds	27	28
N	(262)[d]	(205)[e]
Daily charge[c]		
$14 or less	15	26
15-19.99	34	37
20 or more	51	37
N	(228)[f]	(186)[g]
Total	100	100

[a]Includes only admissions covered by one basic policy and for which some hospital benefits were received. Excludes all admissions for which the patient was insured by two or more basic policies, whether or not both policies actually provided benefits, and all admissions for which major medical benefits were received.

[b]If more than one type of accommodation was used during one admission, the accommodation with the fewest beds was coded.

[c]Basic charge for room and board.

[d]Excludes 3 NA.

[e]Excludes 4 NA.

[f]Excludes 37 NA.

[g]Excludes 23 NA.

Table N	474 admissions
No benefits	337
Other insurers	180
Sample N	991

A greater proportion of patients insured by private insurance had private (1 bed) accommodations while Blue Cross patients were more likely to have semi-private (2 bed) accommodations, and the proportion in wards (3 or more beds) was similar for the two types of insurance. In 1963, 24 percent of the admissions covered by private insurance had 1 bed accommodations compared to 19 percent of those covered by Blue Cross (Table 55). In contrast, 54 percent of all Blue Cross admissions were in two-bed rooms compared to 47 percent for private insurance.

In each period it was found that Blue Cross admissions tended to have higher room and board charges. Table 55 shows that over one-fourth of all private insurance admissions had daily room and board charges of $14 or less compared to 15 percent of Blue Cross admissions in 1963. However, over one-half of all Blue Cross admissions had daily charges of $20 or more while the corresponding proportion for private insurance was 37 percent.

Consideration of hospitalized surgical coverage showed that Blue Shield[36] plans were more likely to pay 90 percent or more of the bill than were the private insurance companies in 1963.[37] Blue Shield paid this proportion for 52 percent of their procedures compared to 41 percent for private insurance (Table 56).

TABLE 56
Percent of surgical bill covered by insurance for hospitalized procedures[a]
insured by Blue Shield and private insurance: 1963[40]

PERCENT OF BILL COVERED BY INSURANCE	PERCENT OF PROCEDURES	
	Blue Shield[36]	Private
1-69	35	39
70-89	15	20
90 or more	52	41
Total	100	100
N	(105)	(83)

[a]Excludes all procedures in connection with obstetrical care. Includes only hospitalized procedures covered by one basic policy and for which some hospital benefits were received.

Table N	188 procedures
No benefits	132
OB surgery	23
Other insurers	39
Sample N	382

This section indicates that Blue Cross was more likely to pay 90 percent or more of the hospital bill for an insured admission in each period than was private insurance. Over the ten-year period the proportion of all insured admissions for which 90 percent or more of the bill was paid by insurance increased for both types of insurer. In 1963 patients receiving benefits from private insurance appeared more likely to have a private room while Blue Cross patients were more likely to have semi-private accommodations. Daily room and board charges for Blue Cross patients tended to be higher than those for private insurance patients.[38] Regarding coverage of hospitalized surgical costs, Blue Shield seemingly paid 90 percent or more of the total cost more often than did private insurance.

36 Includes Blue Cross plans providing surgical benefits.

37 These estimates are subject to considerable sampling error due to the relatively small number of procedures involved.

38 The concentration of Blue Cross patients in densely populated regions where hospital costs tend to be highest may be reflected by this finding. See Table 45.

3. Method of enrollment

This section compares benefits provided under group enrollment with those provided under non-group enrollment. In addition, group and non-group enrollment are further subdivided according to type of insurer and are related to benefit patterns.

Chart 19 shows that group insurance has generally paid a considerably larger proportion of the hospital bill than has non-group coverage. For example, in 1963, 35 percent of admissions covered by non-group policies had less than 70 percent of the hospital bill paid compared to only 13 percent of those covered by group contracts. In contrast, for two-thirds of the admissions covered by group insurance, 90 percent or more of the bill was paid compared to about one-third of the admissions covered by non-group insurance.

The reimbursement pattern for group insurance changed little between 1953 and 1958. However, between 1958 and the latest study, the proportion of admissions with 90 percent or more of the bill covered rose from 59 percent to 66 percent.

Between 1953 and 1958, benefits from non-group insurance actually appeared to be growing less comprehensive (Chart 19); the proportion of admissions covered by non-group insurance for which 90 percent or more of the bill was paid decreased from 39 percent to 34 percent, while the proportion with 70 percent or less covered increased from 34 to 44 percent. However, the 1963 study did not indicate a continuation of this trend. In fact, the proportion of admissions for which benefits were 70 percent or less of charges decreased from 44 percent in 1958 to 35 percent in 1963, while the proportion with benefits of 70–89 percent increased from 22 percent in 1958 to 32 percent in 1963. The proportion with 90 percent or more covered remained about one-third.

Previous data have shown that benefit patterns differ according to type of insurer and type of enrollment. A further refinement in Table 57 allows us to examine benefits in terms of insurer and enrollment simultaneously. In the last two studies Blue Cross group insurance was providing the most "liberal" benefits, followed in order by private group insurance, Blue Cross non-group, and private non-group. Thus, 90 percent or more of the expenditures for an admission were covered for 73 percent of the admissions insured by Blue Cross group insurance. Comparable proportions were 59 percent for private group insurance, 35 percent for Blue Cross non-group, and 31 percent for private non-group.

Looking at the changes through time we find that the proportion of Blue Cross group admissions reimbursed for 90 percent or more of the charges has increased with each study (Table 57). The percentage increased from 55 percent in 1953 to 63 percent in 1958 and 73 percent in 1963. Private group insurance has shown relatively little change in benefit patterns for the ten-year period as a whole. Private group benefits covered 90 percent or more of the charges for 59 percent of the admissions in 1953 and the percentage was the same in 1963. The proportion with *under* 70

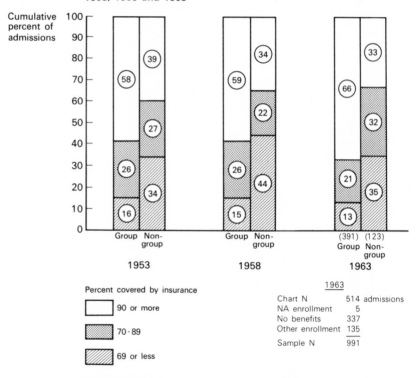

Chart 19   Percent of hospital bill covered by insurance for admissions[a] insured through group and non-group enrollment: 1953, 1958 and 1963

Percent covered by insurance

☐ 90 or more

▦ 70-89

▨ 69 or less

1963
Chart N   514 admissions
NA enrollment   5
No benefits   337
Other enrollment 135
                  ───
Sample N   991

[a]Includes only admissions covered by one basic policy, with some benefits received.

percent covered by private group benefits actually increased from 11 percent in 1953 to 18 percent in 1963.

Turning to non-group coverage we find indications that levels of coverage were generally lower in 1963 than they had been ten years earlier for Blue Cross (Table 57). The proportion of admissions with 90 percent or more of the bill covered decreased from 50 percent in 1953 to 46 percent in 1958 and 35 percent in 1963. For private insurance, non-group benefits appeared to be considerably less comprehensive in 1958 than they had been in 1953. For example, the proportion of admissions with 70 percent or less of the bill covered increased from 44 percent to 63 percent. However, the data for 1963 show benefit levels very similar to those found in the 1953 study, and, consequently, more liberal than those shown in 1958.

While benefit levels differ considerably according to type of enrollment, accommodations and daily room charges for admissions covered by different types of enrollment are very similar (Table 58). It appears that admissions with non-group coverage are slightly more likely to have private

TABLE 57
Percent of hospital bill covered by insurance for admissions[a] insured through group and non-group enrollment: 1953, 1958 and 1963

PERCENT OF HOSPITAL BILL COVERED BY INSURANCE		PERCENT GROUP		PERCENT NON-GROUP	
Year	Percent	Blue Cross	Private	Blue Cross	Private
1953	1-69	20	11	20	44
	70-89	25	30	30	26
	90 or more	55	59	50	30
	Total	100	100	100	100
1958	1-69	15	16	27	63
	70-89	22	30	27	15
	90 or more	63	54	46	22
	Total	100	100	100	100
1963	1-69	8	18	26	42
	70-89	19	23	39	26
	90 or more	73	59	35	32
	Total	100	100	100	100
1963 N		(197)	(154)	(65)	(53)

[a] Includes only admissions covered by one basic policy with some benefits received.

1963	
Table N	469 admissions
NA enrollment	5
No benefits	337
Mixed enrollment or other insurance	180
Sample N	991

accommodations and room charges of $20 a day or more than are admissions covered by group insurance. Thus, of all non-group enrollment admissions 26 percent were in private rooms and 47 percent had daily charges of $20 or more. The comparable proportions for group enrollment were 21 percent and 42 percent.

These data show that in each period group insurance provided considerably more comprehensive benefits than non-group insurance, and the differences appeared to be greater in 1963 than in 1953. In 1963 Blue

Cross group insurance was most likely to pay 90 percent or more of the hospital bill, followed by private group, Blue Cross non-group, and private non-group in that order. While patients with non-group insurance had less comprehensive coverage, they still appeared more likely to have private hospital rooms and higher daily room and board charges.

TABLE 58
Type of hospital accommodation and daily room and board charge for insured admissions[a] by method of enrollment: 1963

ACCOMMODATION AND ROOM CHARGE	METHOD OF ENROLLMENT	
	Percent group	Percent non-group
Room accommodation		
1 bed	21	26
2 beds	50	50
3 or more beds	29	24
N	(387)[b]	(120)[c]
Daily charge		
$14 or less	21	19
15-19.99	37	34
20 or more	42	47
N	(328)[d]	(103)[e]
Total	100	100

[a]Includes only admissions covered by one basic policy and for which some hospital benefits were received.

[b]Excludes 4 NA.

[c]Excludes 3 NA.

[d]Excludes 63 NA.

[e]Excludes 20 NA.

Table N	514 admissions
NA enrollment	5
No benefits	337
Other enrollment	135
Sample N	991

C. OTHER METHODS OF PAYING FOR PERSONAL HEALTH SERVICES

In the first two parts of this chapter on methods of paying for personal health services, the coverage and benefits provided by voluntary health service have been considered. Of course, since these data were collected, government-sponsored health insurance in the form of Medicare has begun to provide coverage for our older population. While future studies of expenditure and use patterns under Medicare will be of considerable value, the Medicare program in terms of benefit patterns is in many respects similar to a good program under voluntary insurance providing hospital, sugical, and medical coverage. Thus, we might expect health care patterns for the elderly under Medicare to resemble those for older persons with relatively comprehensive voluntary coverage in the past.

However, insurance today, both voluntary and Medicare, still provides for less than 50 percent of personal expenditures for health. In addition, a considerable amount of personal health services is provided at no expense to the patient. In the remainder of this chapter we will view briefly other methods by which personal health services are financed.

Among the methods families employ to pay for health service expenditures not covered by health insurance are using current income, drawing from savings, receiving financial help from someone outside the family, using loss-of-income and disability insurance benefits, and borrowing from a financial institution.

1. *Income and savings*

In 1963, 27 percent of all private personal expenditures for health services were covered by voluntary health insurance. Much of the remainder was paid for directly by the families receiving the services, using current income and savings.[39] Direct payment, then, is still an important method of paying for health services.

Because health insurance benefits have been generally limited to certain types of services, the pattern of mean expenditures by type of service, excluding health insurance benefits, looks considerably different from the pattern for total mean expenditures according to type of service. In addition, since expenditures for various types of services do not fall evenly across the entire population, the mean charges for persons experiencing charges provide a different view from mean charges for the total population. Table 59 attempts to show how much the individual must pay directly, taking the above factors into account.

The highest mean expenditures for the total sample by type of service are for non-obstetrical hospital inpatient care ($24), physician office visits ($18), and prescribed drugs and dental care ($15 each). However, the means for persons actually experiencing expenditures show a different pattern because of the extreme variance in the proportion of people with expenditures for particular types of services, as shown in the first column of Table 59. These proportions vary from 2 percent for obstetrical hospital care and physicians' services to 70 percent for non-prescribed medicines.

As a result, the rank order of means for persons with expenditures changes considerably from the rank order of means for all persons. Non-

39 However, this proportion decreased considerably between 1950 and 1964. Direct out-of-pocket payments by consumers accounted for about two-thirds of all expenditures for personal health care in 1950 and slightly over one-half in 1964. The remainder was accounted for by third-party payers including government, health insurance, and philanthropy. See Louis S. Reed and Ruth Hanft, "National Health Expenditures, 1950–1964," *Social Security Bulletin*, 29, no. 1 (January, 1966): 13–14.

obstetrical hospital inpatient charges are still first ($325). However, following in order are hospitalized surgery ($200), obstetrical inpatient care ($175), physician obstetrical care ($142) and physician hospital visits ($71). Meanwhile, physician office visits and prescribed drugs, which ranked second and third in the ranks of means for all persons, increased to only $35 and $36 dollars respectively because such expenditures are experienced by a much larger proportion of the population.

The last column in Table 59 shows the mean for all persons with expenditures, excluding health insurance reimbursements, for each service. Health insurance has the greatest impact in reducing direct payments for non-obstetrical hospital inpatient services and hospitalized surgery. The mean charges not covered by insurance are $84 and $75 respectively for

TABLE 59
Mean expenditure per person by type of service including and excluding health insurance benefits: 1963

TYPE OF SERVICE	PERCENT OF SAMPLE WITH EXPENDITURE FOR SERVICE	MEAN EXPENDITURE PER PERSON		
		All persons	Persons with expenditure	Persons with expenditure excluding insurance benefits
Hospital				
Non-obstetrical hospital inpatient	7	$24	$325	$84
Obstetrical hospital inpatient	2	4	175	77
Hospital outpatient	7	2	23	17
Physician				
Hospital surgery	4	7	200	75
Non-hospitalized surgery	3	1	48	33
Obstetrics	2	1	142	96
Ophthalmologist	5	3	14	14
Other hospital visits	5	4	71	44
Other office visits	51	18	35	31
Other house visits	7	1	20	19
Drugs				
Prescribed	43	15	36	35
Non-prescribed	70	7	11	11
Dental care	35	15	41	41
Other medical care				
Non-physician practitioners	15	4	23	22
Other	22	7	32	30

N 7803

these services. Considerably lower means are also found for obstetrical hospital inpatient care ($77), physician obstetrical care ($96), and physician hospital visits ($44). In contrast, health insurance benefits reduce direct payments very little for physician office visits ($31) and prescribed drugs ($35) and have no effect on dental care ($41).

In general, the mean charges for persons with expenditures show much less variance after health insurance benefits are taken into account, since the latter are generally provided for services costing the most. Mean expenditures including costs covered by health insurance benefits vary from $325 for hospital inpatient care to $11 for non-prescribed drugs. After insurance benefits are excluded the highest net mean is $96 for obstetrical physician services while the lowest remains $11 for non-prescribed drugs.

TABLE G

SAVINGS[40]	PERCENT OF FAMILIES
Less than $200	47
200-499	13
500-999	11
1,000-2,999	11
3,000-4,999	4
5,000 or more	9
NA	4
N	(2367)

In this study we were unable to distinguish between payments made from current income and those taken from savings.[40] However, we did get some idea of savings that families had at the time of the interview which they might use "to meet heavy medical costs in an emergency." The distribution of the families according to level of savings is shown in Table G.

This distribution shows that almost half of all families in 1963 had less than $200 which they might draw on to meet the expenses of a medical emergency. On the other hand, almost one quarter had savings of $1,000 or more. It might be remembered that in 1963, 8 percent of all families experienced personal health expenditures of $1,000 or more. However, among insured families the large, infrequent expenditures are the ones most likely to be covered by insurance, as shown previously in Chart 15.

Despite the growth of health insurance, use of current income and savings remains the most important method of paying for personal health services. These data show that "out-of-pocket" expenditures for people actually having expenditures, excluding health insurance benefits, differ

[40] See definition 36.

considerably from mean expenditures for the total population, and from mean expenditures for persons with expenditures *not* excluding health insurance benefits. These differences result from the magnitudes and prevalences of expenditures for different types of services and health insurance benefit structures. These out-of-pocket expenditures must be carefully evaluated when examining the financial impact of health service expenditures on families. While many families have substantial savings, data for 1963 reveal that about one-half do not have savings sufficient to meet the expenses of even a relatively moderate medical bill (less than $200).

2. Interfamily transfer of funds for medical care

Interfamily transfers are another method used to pay for health services. Families in this study both received financial help from non-family members and provided funds to pay for health services for persons not members of the immediate family.

TABLE H

AMOUNT RECEIVED FROM NON-FAMILY MEMBER	PERCENT OF ALL FAMILIES RECEIVING FINANCIAL HELP		
$1-24	33	Table N	80
25-99	37	Not received	2263
100 or more	30	NA received	20
		NA amount	4
Total	100	Sample N	2367

Four percent of all families reported that "a friend or relative" not in the family paid something toward the medical expenses of some family member during 1963. The mean amount received by these families was $94 and the median was $50. The distribution of amounts received is shown in Table H.

Thirty-two families in the sample reported that during 1963 they paid some of the expenses of someone staying in "a nursing home, convalescent home, old people's home, sanatorium, or other place like that."[41] In slightly over half of these cases the institutionalized person was the parent of the family head or his spouse. The remaining individuals were about equally divided as aunts, uncles, or children of the head or his spouse. In only one case was the person not related to the family. The median family expenditure for these institutionalized persons was $200 in 1963.

In addition to the costs for institutionalized persons reported above, 5 percent of the families paid some hospital, medical, or dental bills for some other non-family person in 1963. The relationship of these persons

[41] These families constitute 1.4 percent of all sample families.

who received financial help to the household head or his spouse is shown in Table I.

A large proportion of *institutionalized* persons receiving financial help from the families were from an older generation than the head or his spouse. In contrast, the distribution above shows that the *non-institu-*

TABLE I

RELATION OF PERSON TO HEAD OR SPOUSE	PERCENT OF ALL PERSONS RECEIVING MONEY FROM FAMILY
Parent	33
Child	23
Sibling	14
Spouse	8
Grandchild	7
Other relative	4
Not related	11
Total	100
N	(124)

Table N   124 persons receiving help
NA relation   6
130

TABLE J

EXPENDITURE BY FAMILY FOR MEDICAL CARE OF NON-INSTITUTIONALIZED NON-FAMILY MEMBERS	PERCENT OF FAMILIES
$1-24	27
25-99	32
100-299	28
300 or more	13
Total	100

Table N   114
No expenditure   2245
NA expenditure   8
Sample N   2367

tionalized persons receiving financial help for medical care were more likely to be of the same generation or of a younger generation than the head of the family providing the help.

The mean amount provided by the families for the medical care of non-institutionalized non-family members was $140, while the median was $70. A breakdown of the amounts provided is given in Table J.

Some comparisons are made in Table 60 of characteristics of all families in the sample with families receiving money from and those giving money to non-family persons for medical care. This table shows that families receiving funds are more likely to have heads either under 29 or over 64, while those giving funds resemble all families in age distribution of heads. Families receiving funds include large proportions that have main earners not working full time and that are uninsured. Families providing funds again resemble "all families" in these characteristics. The racial compositions of all groups appear similar. There is a tendency for both families giving and receiving to have higher gross expenditures for health services than do all families. Families receiving funds include a large proportion

TABLE 60
Characteristics of families providing to, and receiving from, non-family members financial help to pay for medical expenses: 1963

CHARACTERISTIC	PERCENT OF FAMILIES		
	All families	Families giving funds[a]	Families receiving funds
Age of head			
29 or less	15[b]	12[c]	40
30-44	31	30	13
45-64	35	40	18
65 and over	19	18	29
Major activity of main earner			
Work full time	70	79	38
Other	30	21	62
Hospital insurance status			
Insured	73	73	56
Uninsured	27	27	44
Race			
White	86[d]	86[e]	88
Non-white	14	14	12
Mean medical expenditures			
$99 or less	30	24	27
100-299	31	30	24
300 and over	39	46	49
Family income			
Less than $3500	28	20	62
3500-7499	38	37	29
7500 and over	34	43	9
Total	100	100	100
N	(2367)	(134)	(84)

[a]Includes families providing funds for both long term institutionalized care and other medical care of non-family members.

[b]Excludes 15 NA.

[c]Excludes 1 NA.

[d]Excludes 29 NA.

[e]Excludes 2 NA.

Giving		Receiving	
Table N	134	Table N	84
Not given	2217	Not received	2263
NA given	16	NA received	20
Sample N	2367	Sample N	2367

with low incomes while those providing funds are somewhat more likely to have higher incomes than are all families in this study.

Four percent of the families in the sample reported receiving funds from non-family members to pay for health services and 6 percent reported providing such funds to non-family members. As compared to all families in the study, those receiving funds were more likely to have either young or aged heads, a main earner not working full time, no hospital insurance, high expenditures for health services, and low family income. Those providing funds to non-family members were more like all families in the sample though they tended to have more main earners working full time and higher family incomes.

3. Debts for health services

Another method of financing the costs of personal health services if some more satisfactory means is not available requires the family to borrow or go into debt to meet their financial obligations. Medical debt is generally considered an "unsatisfactory" method of financing health services because of the unique characteristics of health services. If they could be purchased like other goods and services—when desired and of the quantity and quality the family could afford—perhaps the problem of medical debt could be dismissed as of no more concern than the balance owed by a family on its automobile or television set. The cost of these items is known in advance and the consumer determines the time of purchase. The costs of health services cannot be so predetermined and the consumer usually has no choice but to purchase these services at the particular time they are necessary. Systematic saving is only a partial solution, since families do not know how much should be saved annually.

At the time of the interview for the last study, 20 percent of the families owed something to providers of health services or were still paying on loans they obtained to cover medical expenses incurred in 1963 or earlier.[42] The mean average obligation for these families was $157 and the median was $71. The distribution of families according to level of medical debt is shown below in Table K.

A comparison of families with no medical debt and those with various levels of debt is shown in Table 61. Families with medical debts are more likely to have heads under 45 than are those with no debt. Families with high levels of debt have the same proportion of main earners working full time as families with no debt, but families with lower levels of debt appear to have a larger proportion of main earners working full time. Small differences are found regarding hospital insurance, but it does appear that families with large debt are less likely to have insurance. A disproportion-

42 See definition 27.

TABLE K

AMOUNT OF FAMILY MEDICAL DEBT	PERCENT WITH DEBT
Less than $50	36
50-99	23
100-299	26
300 or more	15
Total	100

Table N	445
No debt	1893
NA debt	11
NA amount	18
Sample N	2367

TABLE 61
Selected family characteristics by level of medical debt: 1963

CHARACTERISTIC	PERCENT NO DEBT	PERCENT WITH DEBT[42]		
		Lower third ($1-39)	Middle third ($40-119)	Upper third ($120 or more)
Age of head				
29 or less	14[a]	15	24[b]	19
30-44	29	45	40	36
45-64	36	33	30	37
65 and over	21	7	6	8
Major activity of main earner				
Work full time	72	78	81	72
Other	28	22	19	28
Hospital insurance status				
Insured	73	75	74	68
Uninsured	27	25	26	32
Race				
White	85[c]	80[d]	82[d]	88[e]
Non-white	13	18	17	11
Mean medical expenditures				
$99 or less	34	20	9	9
100-299	32	46	25	15
300 and over	34	34	66	76
Family income				
Less than $3500	28	28	25	24
3500-7499	37	44	49	41
7500 and over	35	28	26	35
Total percent	100	100	100	100
Total number of families	(1893)	(138)	(155)	(152)

[a]Excludes 13 NA.
[b]Excludes 2 NA.
[c]Excludes 24 NA.
[d]Excludes 2 NA.
[e]Excludes 1 NA.

Table N	2338
NA debt	11
NA amount	18
Sample N	2367

ately large number of non-white families are found among families with lower levels of debts compared to their representation among families without debt but they are less likely to be found among families with a large medical debt.

As might be expected, families with debt tend to have higher gross medical expenses than those with no debt, and families with large debts have higher expenditures than those with low debts. The income relationships shown in Table 61 seem to indicate that families with lower levels of debt are clustered in the middle income category while those with high level debt are more likely to be in the upper income categories.

4. Loss-of-income insurance

Expenditure for health services is only one of the major "costs" of illness. Another is the loss of productivity to society, and wages to the family, resulting from absenteeism of wage earners due to illness or injury. In some instances the absent worker does not lose income because of sick leave or other similar benefits provided directly by the employer. In other instances wages are lost but the worker receives workmen's compensation[43] or cash benefits from an insurance company, union, fraternal order, or some other source to help cover loss of income.[44] In other instances the worker does suffer a loss of income because he receives no benefits or is only partially compensated for his lost income.

"Loss-of-income insurance" is included here because the benefits received under these programs may be used to pay for health services in connection with the accident or injury as well as for current living expenses. While we are unable to determine the proportion of these funds actually used to pay for health services, they are certainly an important general source of income for the families with wage earners incapacitated because of illness or injury. This source takes on added importance since the family is faced with the double financial burden caused by added health care expenses and loss of income.

Thirty-nine percent of all families reported that one or more wage earners lost time from work during 1963 because of illness or injuries in the family. Slightly over one-half (52 percent) of the workers involved did not lose wages because they were off work. Of the remainder, 37 percent lost wages and did not receive compensation for the loss, while 11 percent were compensated in full or in part.

[43] For a discussion of national aggregate statistics regarding workmen's compensation, see Alfred M. Skolnik, "Twenty-five Years of Workmen's Compensation Statistics," *Social Security Bulletin*, 29, 10 (October, 1966): 3–26. In addition see Saul Waldman, "Income-Loss Protection Against Short-Term Sickness, 1948–1964," *Social Security Bulletin*, 29, no. 1 (January, 1966): 20–28.

[44] See definition 23.

Table 62 shows the relationship between amount of time the worker lost and compensation received. As the length of work loss increases, the percentage of workers losing wages also increases. Thus, 38 percent of those losing one week or less lost wages compared to 70 percent of those losing five weeks or more. However, the percentage of workers receiving compensation for lost wages also increases as time lost increases. Short term disability insurance plans commonly provide payments after waiting periods of 3 days to a week. Only 3 percent of all workers losing one week or less were compensated compared to 29 percent of those off work five weeks or more.

The mean wage loss during 1963 for workers losing income because of illness was $367 as shown in Table L.

TABLE 62
Loss of income benefits[44] to worker for work loss due to sickness or injury according to length of work loss period: 1963

	TIME LOST		
LOSS OF INCOME BENEFITS	Percent 1 week or less	Percent 2-4 weeks	Percent 5 weeks or more
No wages lost	62	48	30
Wages lost without benefits	35	39	41
Wages lost but benefits received	3	13	29
Total	100	100	100
N	(565)	(250)	(228)

Table N	1043
NA	16
No loss/not employed	6744
Sample N	7803

TABLE L

ALL WORKERS LOSING INCOME	WORKERS NOT RECEIVING COMPENSATION	WORKERS RECEIVING COMPENSATION	
		Gross loss	Net loss
$367 (493)[a]	$260 (382)[b]	$739 (110)[c]	$346 (107)[d]

[a] Excludes 10 NA
[b] Excludes 8 NA
[c] Excludes 3 NA
[d] Excludes 6 NA

Table N	503
NA	12
No wage loss	544
No loss/not employed	6744
Sample N	7803

Workers not receiving compensation are seen to have a much lower mean loss than those receiving compensation ($260 vs. $739). However, if compensation received is subtracted from wages lost for workers receiving compensation, the resulting net loss, $346, is only about one-half of the gross loss. Still, this mean net loss was considerably higher than the mean loss for workers who were not compensated. These data show that loss-of-income insurance is more likely to be provided for workers experiencing the larger income losses due to illness. On average, however, such insurance provided for only about half of the lost income and still left these workers with a net loss exceeding the amount for workers who lost income but were not compensated. While loss-of-income insurance provides an important source of income to the disabled worker, its use as a supplementary source to pay for health services appears limited, since it replaces only about one-half of the lost income.

5. *Free care*

A significant proportion of personal health services used by American families is provided at no direct cost to the family or at substantially reduced rates. Such services are in large part provided by government agencies on the federal, state, and local levels. Other services are provided through Workmen's Compensation and employers' liability insurance, school and employer facilities, private charitable organizations, and through physicians' practices of differential pricing according to ability to pay and "professional courtesy."

In this study no attempt was made to determine the monetary value of "free care" or to estimate the exact quantity of such services received by the sample. However, an attempt was made to find out the number of families benefiting from such services.

A large number of persons receive free services such as chest X-ray examinations, polio vaccinations, flu shots, etc., in mass screening programs. Others receive incidental free goods and services, such as free drug samples, from their doctors. An effort was made to separate families with members who received these relatively minor free services from families with members who received larger amounts of care at no direct cost. This was done by considering only patients having terminated pregnancies,[45] hospitalized illnesses,[46] and other major illnesses.[47] Families with one or more members receiving "all or most of the care" free or at substantially reduced rates for these major conditions were classified as benefiting from "substantial free, or reduced rate care."

[45] See definition 39.

[46] See definition 16.   [47] See definition 28.

Six percent of all families in the sample received substantial free or reduced rate care.[48] Fifty-six percent of all families in the population had one or more members with a terminated pregnancy, hospitalized illness, or other major illness during the survey year 1963. Thus, 10 percent of all families with one or more major conditions received substantial free care for at least one of these conditions.

Of special interest is the proportion of these families receiving free care (or care at sharply reduced rates) because they were unable to pay for it themselves as opposed to those receiving such care for other reasons, such as "professional courtesy," the patient being a member of a group which entitled him to free care (e.g., a veteran or serviceman), or the patient having a particular disease which qualified him for certain free benefits through some private charitable organization. Of all families receiving substantial care for a major condition, 54 percent received such care primarily because they were unable to pay for it themselves.

In the last three sections of this chapter medical debt, loss-of-income insurance, and free care were considered as methods by which families pay for, or are relieved of the obligation of paying for, health services. In 1963, 20 percent of the families reported some medical debt. Families in debt tended to be younger families with high medical expenditures. Thirty-nine percent of all families reported that one or more wage earners lost time from work during 1963 due to illness or injury. For about one-half of the workers no wages were lost, while 11 percent received some form of loss-of-income insurance benefits. Ten percent of all families with one or more conditions requiring considerable medical care received substantial free care. Over one-half of these families received such care because they were unable to pay for it themselves.

48 See definition 10.

V

RELATIONSHIPS OF USE, EXPENDITURE, AND METHODS OF PAYMENT

The thesis of this report has been that at least three components are central to a description of how people use the health care system and how interaction of the people with the system changes through time. These components are utilization patterns, personal expenditures for health services, and how people go about paying for these services. Each of the topics has been treated separately in a previous chapter. However, these components are not independent of one another. This chapter will point out some of the interrelationships among them.[1]

[1] The analyses of each of these components presented in previous chapters and the interrelationships presented in this chapter are primarily in terms of simple rates and the cross tabulations of basic variables. The advantages of this approach as compared to a "multivariate approach" involving simultaneous consideration of many variables include: (a) The methods used are comparable with those used in the earlier reports. (b) Results can be presented in a less complex, more readily understood manner with some basic relationships more apparent to a larger proportion of the readership. (c) It is not necessary to make certain assumptions about the nature of the data associated with many of the multivariate models.

However, there are also disadvantages to the methods used in this report. Fewer variables can be considered than with a multivariate approach. While we have tried to include what appear to be some of the most basic and important relationships, certainly valid arguments can be made that more attention should have been paid to such variables as race, education and family size. In addition, cross tabulations sometimes leave the reader with less understanding of relative "importance" of a number of explanatory variables than is apparently provided by a multivariate approach.

While no multivariate analyses are presented in this report, data from the studies have been, and are being, subjected to such analysis. For application of a multiple regression analysis to use and expenditure data from the 1958 study, see Paul Feldstein, "The Demand for Medical Care," *Report of the Commission on the Cost of Medical Care,* vol. 1 (American Medical Association, 1964), pp. 57–76. Data from the 1963 study are presently being used in connection with a computer program for studying the inter-

A. USE AND EXPENDITURES

The previous chapters have documented considerable increase in individual use of health services and expenditure for these services over the decade from 1953 through 1963. Part of the expenditure increase related to "price" increases, or increases in the cost per unit of service to the consumer. The remainder can be accounted for by the increased amount of services used. The relative contribution of each of these components to expenditure increase is considered in the following paragraphs.

1. *Changes through time*

The survey of 1963 showed an increase in mean expenditure for health services per person of 70 percent over the mean in 1953 (Table 63). During the period between the surveys of 1953 and 1963 the medical care component of the United States Department of Labor's Consumer Price Index, or the "price" of medical care, increased by 42 percent.[2] The remaining expenditure increase of 20 percent not accounted for by "price" increases was attributed to increases in "use."[3] Since these figures are at best an approximation, they should be used with caution. However, in general it appears that the relative contribution of "price" to the expenditure increase has been about twice that of "use" for the ten-year period.

The contribution of each of these factors to the total increase varied

---

relationships among a set of variables from social survey data. Preliminary findings from this work are found in Ronald Andersen and Odin W. Anderson, "Family Life Cycle and Use of Health Services," a paper presented at the meetings of the American Sociological Association, September 2, 1965. Additional findings from these analyses will be published at a later date.

[2] This percentage was computed by averaging annual figures for 1952 and 1953 since the "1953" survey covered expenditures for a one-year period beginning in 1952 and ending in 1953. These limitations to the use of the Consumer Price Index should be remembered: (a) Although based on measures of average changes in prices of goods and services usually bought by city families of wage earners and clerical workers, the Index is used here to adjust the expenditure data for all families in the surveys. (b) The Index makes no attempt to measure, along with changes in prices, changes in the quality of items purchased. For example, a day of hospital care or a physician's visit may change radically, yet still be compared as uniform.

[3] The proportionate increase in constant dollars is here taken to approximate an increase in "use"; that is, all remaining increase in expenditure not accounted for by increases in the medical care component of the Consumer Price Index. An increase in "use" in this context may not necessarily mean an increase in the quantity or volume of goods and services. It may mean a more expensive type of service within the same general category, e.g., consultation with a specialist, a private room in a hospital, or a more complex form of medication. Despite such qualifications, it is likely that this method does indicate the general direction of trends, if not their precise amounts.

sharply according to type of service.[4] For physician services, most of the increase was due to price rises; 37 percent against a 2 percent increase in use (Table 63). Price rises also contributed much more than use to hospital expenditure increases (90 percent price, 17 percent use), but the over-all magnitude of the increase makes the use component of some significance. The picture appears totally reversed for drugs, with use accounting for a 110 percent increase and price only 9 percent. For the period

TABLE 63
Percent increase per person in "price,"[2] "use"[3] and expenditure by type of health service from 1953 to 1963

TYPE OF SERVICE[4]	PERCENT INCREASE 1953-1963			1963 MEAN EXPENDITURE
	Price	Use[a]	Expenditure	
Physicians	37	2	40	$ 35
Hospitals	90	17	123	29
Dentists	26	19	50	15
Drugs and medications	9	110	130	23
All services	42	20	70	112[b]

[a]For all services and for each type of service the residual increase in expenditure not accounted for by "price" increase was defined as increase due to "use." For example, consider all services:

increase in expenditure = 70 percent
increase in "price"   = 42 percent

$$\text{increase in use} \left(\frac{1.70}{1.42} \right) - 1 = 20 \text{ percent}$$

1963
N   7803 persons

[b]Components do not add to total because "other goods and services" component is not included in subcomponents.

1953–63 the components of dental care expenditure increase were more evenly divided than for any of the other services (26 percent price vs. 19 percent use).

Up to this point we have considered increases in expenditure for all medical care and for each of the services separately. But what do these increases for each type of service contribute to the over-all increase in ex-

[4] Subcomponents of the Medical Care Price Index were used to convert increased expenditures in current dollars to constant dollars, or use. These subcomponents were physicians' fees, dentists' fees, hospital rates, and prescriptions and drugs. There is no subcomponent of the Consumer Price Index which corresponds to the expenditure category "other medical goods and services." One criticism of the Medical Care Price Index is that its accurate reflection of prices varies from one subcomponent to another. For a discussion of this and other problems regarding the Medical Care Price Index and proposed solutions see Anne A. Scitovsky, "An Index of the Cost of Medical Care—A Proposed New Approach," and Margaret G. Reid, "Comment," in *The Economics of Health and Medical Care* (Ann Arbor, Mich.: The University of Michigan Press, 1964), pp. 128–47.

penditure per person? Table 64 shows that in current dollars[5] increases in expenditure for physicians' care accounted for 23 percent of total increases in expenditure per person. Increases in hospital expenditures accounted for the largest proportion of the total increase (36 percent). Increases in drug expenditures accounted for an additional 30 percent and dental expenditure increases for 11 percent. However, when we allow for price increases by using constant dollars, the drug component contributes by far the largest proportion of the total increase.[6] In constant dollars (use), drugs account for 71 percent of the total increase. The physician and hospital components fall to 3 percent and 14 percent respectively. Dental care accounts for about the same proportion of the increase in both current and constant dollars.

TABLE 64
Percent of the increase in expenditure per individual by type of service in current and constant dollars from 1953 to 1963

| | PERCENT INCREASE | |
SERVICE	Current dollars[5]	Constant dollars[6]
Physicians	23	3
Hospitals	36	14
Dentists	11	12
Drugs and medications	30	71
All services[a]	100	100
Dollar increase 1953-1963	($44)	($15)

[a]Excluding "other goods and services" component.

1963
N   7803 persons

By age group, price accounts for more of the expenditure increase for older persons than for children under 18 (Table 65). This is in part explained by proportionately high hospital expenditures for adults, coupled with the large price increase in hospital care.[7] Children, however, have proportionately higher expenditures for services which have not experienced such large price increases.

[5] The reported proportional expenditure increase with no consideration of price changes.

[6] Prices for 1952–53 were used as the standard for this computation of percentage increase in "constant" dollars. Expenditures for 1963 were deflated to 1952–53 price levels.

[7] Since proportion of total expenditure for each type of service varies substantially by age group, the total price increase for each group was computed using the subcomponents listed in footnote 4. The subcomponent, "medical care less hospital rates and group hospitalization," was used to compute the price increase portion of the "other medical goods and services" expenditure category.

Use contributions are less than price for every age group. They vary from a low of 10 percent for the 6–17 age group to 32 percent for those 35–54. All other age groups showed use increases of 20 percent or more for the ten-year period.

Price increases are similar for males and females (Table 65). However, percentage increase due to use is almost twice as high for males as for females (28 percent vs. 15 percent). These findings are consistent with use data presented in Chapter II which showed that while females continue to use more of most kinds of services, the differences according to sex are narrowing.

TABLE 65
Percent increase per person in price, use and expenditure for all health services by age and by sex from 1953 to 1963

AGE AND SEX	PERCENT INCREASE 1953-1963[7]			1963	
	Price	Use	Expenditure	Mean expenditure	N
Age					
0-5	36	24	68	$ 47	969
6-17	34	10	47	56	1969
18-34	45	22	77	124	1798
35-54	43	32	89	151	1736
55-64	42	21	72	165	606
65 and over	41	28	81	185	725
Sex					
Male	40	28	80	92	3807
Female	42	15	64	131	3996
All individuals	42	20	70	112	7803

These data have shown that increases in price have contributed more than increases in use to over-all expenditure increases for health services between 1953 and 1963. The relative contributions of these components vary considerably by type of service. At one extreme, practically all the expenditure increase for physician services appears to be attributable to price increase while at the other extreme most of the increase in drug expenditures appears to be related to use increase. Price increases were greater for adults than for children under 18. Use contributions to expenditure increase were fairly similar for all age groups with the exception of children 6–17 who showed less increase because of use for the ten-year period. While price contributions to expenditure increases were similar for males and females, use contributed more to increases for males than females.

2. A cross-sectional view

The previous section showed relationships of changes in expenditures to changing use patterns through time. This section considers some relationships between levels of expenditure and use pattern for the survey year 1963.

Given a specified illness or condition to be treated, a number of factors are related to the resulting expenditure for treatment. These factors include a measure of the quantity of services used, the price or cost per unit of service, and the level of services provided. Level of service has two sub-categories. One is the technological level of the treatment provided and the "skill level" of the provider of services. The other includes the "amenities," or extra comforts and services provided to the patient more or less external to "essential" treatment. We might expect that expenditure level will increase as quantity, price, technological skill, and amenities increase.

No detailed analysis of expenditure level will be attempted here. However, we do wish to give an example of how the various characteristics of treatment listed above do relate to expenditures. For this example total expenditure for maternity care associated with live births was selected. This selection provides some standardization of the condition or "level of illness," and the population at risk cuts across all classes of society.

Measures of quantity of care used are number of prenatal visits and length of stay for delivery. As a gross measure of price, percentage of women reporting free or reduced rate care is used. To get some idea of the technological level of the treatment provided, the degree of specialization of the attending physician is used. Finally, to represent amenities the sample is divided according to whether or not the mother had private or semi-private, as opposed to ward, accommodations in the hospital.

The relationships between levels of expenditure for live births and characteristics of use described above are shown in Table 66. Live births at the highest expenditure level involve more care and are less likely to include any free care than are births at the lowest expenditure level. There also appears to be a direct relationship between level of expenditure and the technological level of care and amenities provided to the mother and child.

Thus, for 79 percent of the births with expenditures of $400 or more the mother had 10 or more prenatal visits, compared to 31 percent for births with expenditures of less than $200. Also, four-fifths of the births at higher expenditure levels included no free care, compared to less than one-half of those with the lowest expenditures. Considering level of care, mothers

TABLE 66
Total expenditure for live births by selected characteristics of maternity services received: 1963

| TOTAL EXPENDITURE | Quantity | | Price | Level | | N |
| | | | | Technological | Amenities | |
	Percent 10 or more prenatal visits	Percent 4 days or more delivery admission[a]	Percent no free or reduced rate care	Percent attending physician OB specialist[b]	Percent non-ward accommodations[a]	
$0-199	31	31	47	28	44[c]	36
200-399	63	49	81	47	69	73
400 and over	79	62	80	63	79	49

CHARACTERISTIC OF SERVICES

Sample N 158

[a]Excludes 1 delivery outside hospital.
[b]Physician certified by American Board of Obstetrics and Gynecology or reports special interest in OB.
[c]Excludes 1 NA.

with maternity care costing $400 or more were more likely to have a specialist attending and to have private or semi-private accommodations in the hospital than were other mothers.

This table shows the possibility of separating factors contributing to differences in expenditure. It indicates how measures of quantity, price, and level of care may contribute to expenditure differences. Refining the measures and studying their relative contribution to expenditure differences is an important task for research in this area.

B. USE AND METHODS OF PAYMENT

The method of paying for health services most often studied for its relation to use patterns is voluntary health insurance. The use patterns of the insured and the uninsured vary considerably. This variance has important implications for the planning of health services and for understanding health service use. In this section we will look at some of the differences in use of health services between the insured and uninsured.

While there can be little doubt that the presence of health insurance has some influence on use, not all the differences found should be directly attributed to health insurance. The chapter on methods of payment showed that the insured and uninsured populations differ in other important characteristics which can also influence use. For instance, families with higher incomes, urban residences, and main earners working full time are more likely to have health insurance than are families with lower incomes, farm residences, and main earners not working full time. Such characteristics, independent of health insurance coverage, may have important effects on use patterns.

Attention will be given to three types of services: hospitalized surgery, hospital care, and dental care. The first two are the most heavily insured services. The third, while practically uninsured, is included to show that use patterns of the insured differ from those of the uninsured even for those services not covered by health insurance.

1. *Hospitalized surgery*

In 1958 the hospitalized surgical procedure rate per 100 person-years[8] was 5 for insured persons[9] and 4 for the uninsured. In 1963 the rates were 6 for the insured and 3 for the uninsured. Table 67 shows that in the latest survey the rates are higher for insured people than for uninsured people for every age, sex, family income, and residence category.

The rates according to sex of patient show a greater difference between the insured and uninsured for females than for males. Similarly, there is

---

[8] See definition 30.   [9] See definition 20.

a greater difference between the rates of the insured and the uninsured for people 54 and under than there is for those 55 and over.

For the total population, hospitalized surgical rates showed a curvilinear relationship with family income[10] in Chapter II. The lowest and highest income patients had lower rates than middle income patients. In Table 67 we see that the low rates for the low income patients as a whole are actually indicative of the practices of the uninsured only. In fact, the rates for the low income ($3,499 or less) patients with insurance are

TABLE 67
Insured and uninsured in-hospital surgical procedures per 100 person-years[8]
by sex, age, family income and residence: 1963[a]

CHARACTERISTIC	IN-HOSPITAL SURGICAL PROCEDURES PER 100 PERSON-YEARS			
	Insured[9]		Uninsured	
Sex				
Male	5	(2438)[b]	3	(1303)[c]
Female	7	(2595)	3	(1350)
Age				
0-5	4	(612)[d]	2	(284)[d]
6-17	4	(1298)	2	(667)
18-34	7	(1129)	3	(655)
35-54	8	(1219)	2	(513)
55-64	6	(416)	6	(187)
65 and over	7	(360)	3	(346)
Family income[10]				
Less than $2000	7	(165)[d]	2	(505)[d]
2,000-3,499	7	(323)	2	(581)
3,500-4,999	5	(533)	2	(454)
5,000-7,499	6	(1630)	4	(509)
7,500-9,999	8	(1008)	4	(273)
10,000-12,499	5	(699)	2	(159)
12,500 and over	5	(676)	3	(171)
Residence[11]				
Large urban	7	(1076)[d]	2	(454)[d]
Other urban	5	(2440)	3	(1178)
Rural non-farm	7	(1194)	3	(583)
Rural farm	6	(324)	1	(437)
All persons	6	(5033)	3	(2653)

[a]The small N's associated with some of these estimates may lead to considerable sampling error.

N 7686 person-years

[b]Surgically insured person-years.

[c]Surgically uninsured person-years.

[d]Components do not add to total due to rounding.

10 See definition 8.

higher than the rate for all insured persons. However, since 72 percent of all person-years for people with family incomes of less than $3,500 are uninsured, the over-all surgical rate is closer to the uninsured than to the insured rate. For both insured and uninsured persons the rates are seen to be higher for those from middle income families ($5,000–9,999) than for upper income families ($10,000 or more).

The low hospitalized surgical rate for rural people living on farms shown in Chapter II is also related to level of surgical coverage.[11] Table 67 shows that the surgical rate for insured rural farm people is 6 or just as high as the rate for all insured persons. However, a large portion of the farm people (57 percent of all person-years) do not have surgical coverage and the surgical rate for these people is very low. Consequently, the over-all rate of 3 for rural farm residences is considerably lower than the rate of 5 for persons with other residences.

The relationship of surgical insurance to surgical rates is strongest where "elective" procedures are involved. Tonsillectomies are one of the most frequently performed surgical procedures, and many of them are thought to be elective in nature. In each of the three surveys the tonsillectomy rate for children 17 years of age or under with insurance was considerably higher than for children without insurance. In 1963 the rate for children with insurance was 24 per 1000 person-years compared to a rate of 7 for uninsured children.

Data presented here show that in 1963 hospitalized surgical procedure rates were higher for insured than for uninsured persons (6 vs. 3). Differences remained when comparisons were made according to age, sex, income, and residence categories.

2. Hospital use

Differences in hospital use patterns between the insured[12] and uninsured populations are pronounced and varied. In each survey the admission rate and total hospital days per 100 person-years have been higher for insured than for uninsured people. In contrast, the mean length of stay per admission has been longer for the uninsured in each instance. These relationships according to age and sex of patient for 1963 are shown in Table 68.

In 1963 the admission rate[13] for insured persons was 15 per 100 person-years compared to a rate of 9 for uninsured persons. For every age group the rate for insured people exceeded that for the uninsured. The difference was greatest in the 18–54 age group, where the insured rate was 19

[11] See definition 35.

[12] See definition 19.   [13] See definition 13.

and the uninsured rate was 11. Insured males had 12 admissions per 100 person-years and insured females had 17. The corresponding rate was 7 for uninsured males and 12 for uninsured females.

The mean length of stay[14] for the uninsured (8.8 days) was almost 2 days longer than the mean length of stay for those with insurance (7 days). This general pattern is followed for age groups 0–17 and 55 and over. In these groups the mean length of stay was at least 3 days longer for the uninsured than for the insured. However, a reversal of this relationship has been found in the middle age group (18–54) in each of the three studies. In 1963 the mean length of stay was 6.9 days for those in this age group with hospital insurance and 5.7 days for the uninsured (Table 68).

TABLE 68
Use of short term hospitals by insured[12] and uninsured persons by age and sex: 1963

AGE AND SEX	ADMISSIONS PER 100 PERSON-YEARS[13]				MEAN LENGTH OF STAY PER ADMISSION[14]				HOSPITAL DAYS PER 100 PERSON-YEARS[15]	
	Insured		Uninsured		Insured		Uninsured		Insured	Uninsured
Age										
0-17	7	(1955)	5	(906)[a]	3.5	(143)[b]	7.3	(47)[b]	26	38
18-54	19	(2419)	11	(1097)	6.9	(452)	5.7	(119)	129	62
55 and over	19	(831)	14	(478)	10.4	(161)	15.4	(69)	199	222
Sex										
Male	12	(2516)	7	(1225)	6.6	(304)	12.7	(87)	79	91
Female	17	(2689)	12	(1256)	7.3	(452)	6.6	(148)	122	77
Total	15	(5205)	9	(2481)	7.0	(756)	8.8	(235)	101	84

[a]Person-years
[b]Admissions

N 7686 person-years
N   991 admissions

In each time period the mean length of stay for uninsured males has exceeded that for insured males. The greatest difference was found in the 1963 study. While there has been a considerable difference in length of stay between insured and uninsured males, the corresponding mean lengths of stay for females have shown more similarity. In 1953 and 1958 the mean was higher for uninsured women. In 1963 it was higher for insured women (7.3 days vs. 6.6 days for uninsured women).

While uninsured persons have an over-all mean length of stay somewhat higher than the insured group, their admission rate is considerably lower. Consequently, their total hospital days[15] per 100 person-years (which is a product of admissions and length of stay) is also lower. Thus, in 1963 total

14 See definition 26.   15 See definition 14.

hospital days were 84 for the uninsured compared to 101 for the insured. Despite the fact that the over-all rate is lower for the uninsured, the rate is actually higher for the uninsured in the age categories 0–17 and 55 and over. However, in the 18–54 age group the insured population used over twice as many hospital days per 100 person-years as did the uninsured population. Uninsured males used more hospital days per 100 person-years than did insured males, but the rate for insured females was considerably higher than that for uninsured females.

The difference in mean length of stay between insured and uninsured patients can be further examined through the distribution of length of stay given in Table 69. From this distribution it does not appear that the

TABLE 69
Length of stay by insurance status of admission:[a] 1963

LENGTH OF STAY[b]	PERCENT INSURED ADMISSIONS	PERCENT UNINSURED ADMISSIONS	PERCENT ALL ADMISSIONS
2 or less	23	20	23
3-5	35	37	35
6-9	21	18	20
10-19	15	16	15
20 or more	6	9	7
Total	100	100	100
N	(749)	(230)	(979)

[a]Excludes all stays which began in 1962 or extended into 1964.
[b]In days.

Table N	979
Partly outside 1963	12
Sample N	991

longer mean for the uninsured is a consequence of generally longer lengths of stay for the uninsured population. Rather, the difference is more a function of the greater proportion of very long stays exceeding 20 days in the uninsured group. Such stays amount to 9 percent of uninsured admissions compared to 6 percent of insured admissions.

Admission rates for the insured population exceed those for the uninsured for every family income group and type of residence (Table 70). Within both populations the rate is highest for persons with family incomes of less than $2,000. It is especially high for insured low income persons (25 per 100 person-years). The rate for both the insured and uninsured drops considerably for persons with incomes above $2,000 and remains relatively stable for all incomes up to $10,000. Admissions then show a considerable drop for the highest income class among both insured and uninsured persons.

Table 70 shows that by type of residence there is least difference in admission rate between the insured and uninsured among urban residents in the largest metropolitan areas. There are greater differences between the insured and uninsured for "other" urban and rural non-farm residents, and the greatest difference is for the rural farm population.

It should be remembered that the over-all rates are lowest for the large urban and rural farm population (Chapter II). In Table 70 we see that the rates are generally low for both the insured and uninsured groups in

TABLE 70
Hospital admissions by family income and residence: 1963

INCOME AND RESIDENCE	NUMBER OF ADMISSIONS PER 100 PERSON-YEARS			
	Insured		Uninsured	
Income				
$0-1,999	25	(196)[a]	12	(474)[b]
2,000-4,999	15	(906)	9	(985)
5,000-9,999	15	(2705)	10	(715)
10,000 and over	11	(1398)	6	(307)
Residence				
Large urban	11	(1130)[c]	9	(400)
Other urban	15	(2515)	10	(1103)
Rural non-farm	17	(1227)	11	(550)
Rural farm	16	(332)	7	(428)
All admissions	15	(5205)	9	(2481)

[a] Insured person-years.   N   7686 person-years
[b] Uninsured person-years.
[c] Components do not add to total due to rounding.

large urban areas. However, for rural farm residents, those with insurance have admission rates among the highest. In contrast, the uninsured rural population has the lowest rate among the uninsured. Since a large portion of the rural farm population had no insurance in 1963, this low admission rate for the rural farm uninsured brings down the over-all rate for the rural farm population.

In general, admission rates and hospital days were higher for insured persons than for the uninsured, but average length of stay was longer for the latter in each study. These observations hold for all age groups, with two exceptions. First, the length of stay for those 18–54 who were uninsured is *shorter* than for the insured. People in this age group are most likely to be employed or responsible for child care. It may be that the pressures to return to these obligations are greater for the uninsured than for the insured and more than compensate for the other factors which tend to result in longer lengths of stay for uninsured people in general. The other exception is that number of hospital days for persons 65 and over is *higher* for uninsured persons than for insured persons as a consequence of the long mean length of stay of the former group.

Admission rates for insured persons exceed those for the uninsured at every income level and for every type of residence. The generally low admission rate for rural farm people is related to low levels of coverage in rural farm areas. However, the relatively low admission rate for persons in the large urban areas appears to be characteristic of both insured and uninsured living in these areas.

Chart 20 Percent of persons receiving dental care by family income and hospital insurance status: 1963[a]

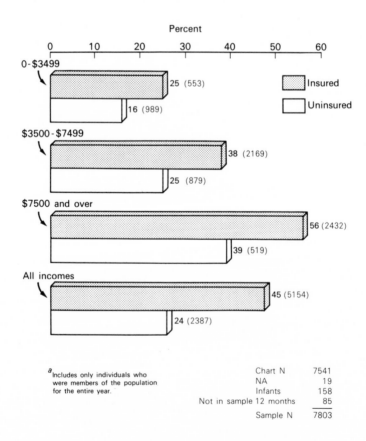

[a]Includes only individuals who were members of the population for the entire year.

Chart N	7541
NA	19
Infants	158
Not in sample 12 months	85
Sample N	7803

3. Dental care

Even though dental care is generally not covered by health insurance, insured people are more likely to see a dentist than are the uninsured.[16] Forty-five percent of the insured persons saw a dentist in 1963 compared to 24 percent of those without insurance. The insured population is more likely to see a dentist at every income level (Chart 20). For example, among persons with a family income between $3,500 and $7,499, 38 percent of those with hospital insurance saw a dentist compared to 25 percent of those without hospital insurance.

TABLE 71
Percent of persons with and without hospital insurance visiting a dentist during 1963 by age and family income[a]

AGE	FAMILY INCOME											
	$0-3,499				$3,500-7,499				$7,500 and over			
	Insured		Not insured		Insured		Not insured		Insured		Not insured	
1-5	3	(31)	2	(106)	12	(308)	8	(106)	21	(222)	3	(34)
6-17	26	(87)	16	(257)	47	(566)	30	(238)	69	(667)	48	(135)
18-34	38	(86)	27	(196)	47	(559)	35	(248)	61	(533)	38	(144)
35-54	34	(80)	25	(157)	39	(441)	23	(167)	55	(747)	43	(134)
55-64	23	(82)	18	(85)	28	(162)	15	(48)	48	(186)	45	(38)
65 and over	19	(187)	10	(188)	26	(133)	13	(72)	39	(77)	15	(34)
Total	25	(553)	16	(989)	38	(2169)	25	(879)	56	(2432)	39	(519)

[a]Includes only individuals who were members of the population for the entire survey year.

Table N	7541
NA	19
Infants	158
Not in sample 12 months	85
Sample N	7803

As we have seen in Chapter II, seeing a dentist is also highly related to age of individual. Since age is correlated with insurance coverage, the relationship between hospital insurance status and seeing a dentist is examined for each age *and* income group in Table 71. For every group defined by age and family income, a greater percentage of people with hospital insurance than of those without saw a dentist during 1963. Thus, apart from the effects of age and income, a strong relationship remains between having hospital insurance and using dental services. Since insurance is very unlikely to pay for dental services, it appears that there are other characteristics which differentiate insured from uninsured indi-

16 "Insured" and "uninsured" refer to hospital insurance status.

viduals and contribute to the different patterns of use observed in the two groups.[17]

C. EXPENDITURE AND METHODS OF PAYMENT

A prime consideration involving the relationship of expenditure and method of payment is the difference in expenditure patterns between people with and without health insurance. This section will show that insured people spend considerably more, and the difference is apparently growing as an increasing proportion of the population becomes insured. In addition, the expenditures of families with medical debt and those receiving free care are examined briefly.

1. *Expenditures of the insured and uninsured*[18]

Chart 21 shows that in each study over the decade expenditures of insured families have been greater than expenditures of uninsured families. In 1953 the mean expenditure for the uninsured families was $154 compared to $237 for the insured. By 1963 the corresponding amounts were $201 and $429. Large differences between insured and uninsured families are also found when median expenditures are considered.

Through the decade expenditures for insured families have been growing faster than expenditures for the uninsured. In 1953 mean expenditure for the uninsured families was 64 percent of mean expenditure for the insured. By 1958 this percentage had dropped to 57 percent and further declined to 47 percent in 1963.

One reason for the higher expenditure of insured families is that these families also tend to have higher incomes than the uninsured families and income is directly related to expenditure. However, Table 72 shows that the expenditure of insured families is higher at every income level. This is true using either the mean measure, which reflects to a greater extent the high expenditure families, or the median measure, which is more representative of the distribution of all families.

Insured families spend more in absolute amounts than do uninsured families, and they also spend a larger percentage of their income on health. Again looking at Table 72, we see that at every income level aggregate outlay[19] as a percentage of family income for insured families exceeds that for uninsured families. The percentage difference is greatest among low income families. Insured families with incomes below $3,500

---

[17] Among these characteristics are most likely residence and education of head. People from rural areas and with little education have fewer dental visits and are also more likely to be uninsured. See: National Center for Health Statistics, "Volume of Dental Visits, United States—July, 1963–June, 1964," ser. 10, no. 23 (October, 1965).

[18] See definition 18.   [19] See definition 29.

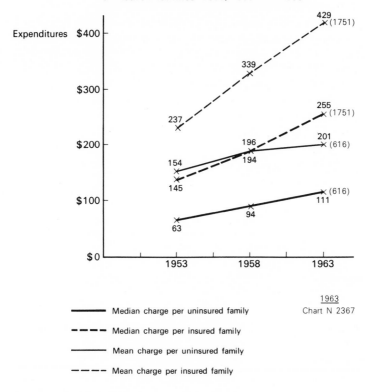

Chart 21 Mean and median expenditures for all personal health services for insured and uninsured families: 1953, 1958 and 1963

Expenditures

429 ✕(1751)

339

237 ✕

255 ✕(1751)

201 ✕(616)

196 ✕ 194

154

145

111 ✕(616)

94 ✕

63 ✕

1953   1958   1963

1963
Chart N 2367

—————— Median charge per uninsured family

- - - - Median charge per insured family

—————— Mean charge per uninsured family

- - - - Mean charge per insured family

TABLE 72
Mean and median family expenditures for health and family outlay for health[19]
for insured[18] and uninsured families by income: 1963

FAMILY INCOME	MEAN EXPENDITURE		MEDIAN EXPENDITURE		AGGREGATE FAMILY OUTLAY PERCENT[a]	
	Insured	Uninsured	Insured	Uninsured	Insured	Uninsured
Under $2,000	$292 (137)	$162 (179)	$100	$ 72	23.7	10.0
2,000-3,499	337 (179)	144 (161)	149	79	11.5	5.1
3,500-4,999	322 (224)	212 (95)	186	115	7.7	4.6
5,000-7,499	438 (491)	253 (92)	265	168	6.1	3.1
7,500 and over	501 (720)	317 (89)	333	201	3.9	2.5
All families	429 (1751)	201 (616)	255	111	5.2	3.9

[a]Percent of aggregate family income.   N 2367

spend more than twice as large a proportion of their income on health services as do low income uninsured families. Among families with incomes of $7,500 or more those with insurance have an aggregate outlay for health which is 3.9 percent of their income compared to 2.5 percent for the uninsured.

Contributing to this difference in expenditure between insured and uninsured families is the greater amount of free care received by uninsured families. Twelve percent of the uninsured families received "substantial amounts of free care"[20] compared to only 4 percent of the insured families.

Differences in expenditures according to insurance status[21] are substantial, as would be expected, on the individual level as well as the family level. The large and growing differences in mean individual expenditure are illustrated in Chart 22. Mean expenditure per uninsured person as a

Chart 22   Mean expenditures for health services for insured[20] and uninsured individuals: 1953, 1958 and 1963

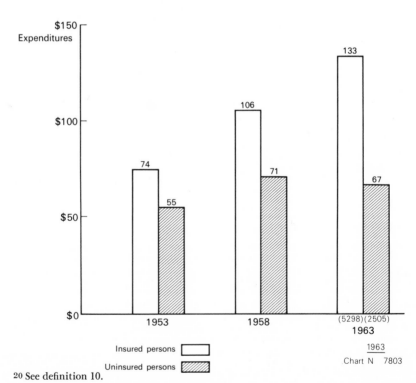

20 See definition 10.

21 "Insured" and "uninsured" refer to hospital insurance status in 1958 and 1963 and any health insurance in 1953.

proportion of mean expenditure per insured person dropped from 74 percent in 1953 to 67 percent in 1958 and 50 percent in 1963. In the latter period the mean for the insured person was $133 compared to $67 for the uninsured person.

Table 73 shows that mean expenditure for insured persons exceeded the mean for uninsured persons for every type of service in 1963. However, the extent of the difference varies. Mean expenditures of the uninsured population for drugs were closest to the mean for the insured group. Mean expenditure for the uninsured was 76 percent of the mean expenditure for the insured. At the other extreme the mean expenditure of the uninsured is only 35 percent of the mean expenditure of the insured for hospital care and 39 percent for dental care.

TABLE 73
Mean health expenditure for insured and uninsured individuals by type of service: 1963

TYPE OF SERVICE	MEAN EXPENDITURES		
	Insured	Uninsured	Uninsured as a percent of insured
Hospital	$ 37	$ 13	35
Physician	41	21	51
Drugs	25	19	76
Dental	18	7	39
"Other"	12	8	67
Total	133	67	50
N	(5298)	(2505)	
			N 7803

Total mean expenditures for the insured are also greater than those for the uninsured for every age and sex group (Table 74). Unlike the differences by type of service, differences of the insured and uninsured are quite similar for each group. Mean expenditures of the uninsured as a proportion of the mean for the insured varies only from 42 percent for persons 55–64 years old to 53 percent for children 0–5 years of age. For both males and females expenditures by the uninsured are about one-half of those for the insured.

These data leave little doubt that insured families spend substantially more for health services than do those without insurance. In 1963 the mean expenditure per insured family ($429) was over twice that for the uninsured family ($201). Differences in income between the insured and uninsured can be only part of the explanation for the patterns found. At every income level insured families spent considerably more. One factor of some importance was free care. The proportion of uninsured families receiving free care was three times that for insured families. Among the major services, expenditures for drugs are most similar for the insured and uninsured, while the biggest differences are found for hospital and dental care. Insured people of all age and sex categories seem to spend roughly twice as much on health services as do their uninsured counterparts.

TABLE 74
Mean health expenditure for insured and uninsured individuals by age and sex: 1963

	MEAN EXPENDITURES		
AGE AND SEX	Insured	Uninsured	Uninsured as a percent of insured
Age			
0-5	$ 55 (663)	$ 29 (306)	53
6-17	67 (1330)	32 (639)	48
18-34	148 (1188)	77 (610)	52
35-54	175 (1272)	87 (464)	50
55-64	198 (434)	83 (172)	42
65 and over	237 (408)	118 (317)	50
Sex			
Male	110 (2557)	55 (1250)	50
Female	155 (2738)	79 (1258)	51
Total	133 (5295)	67 (2508)	50
			N 7803

2. *Expenditures of families with medical debt and free care received*

Of special interest are the expenditure patterns of families that must go into debt[22] to meet their financial obligations for medical care. How do their expenditures and the relation of expenditures to income differ from those for all families in the study? Another important group to consider is composed of families receiving free care. What expenditures in addition to the free care they receive do these families have?

Table 75 compares the level of expenditure of all families in the study with those special groups having debt and receiving substantial free care in 1963. Those receiving substantial free care are divided into families receiving free care primarily because they were unable to pay for it themselves and those who received it for some other reason such as professional courtesy. This division was based upon the family's answer to the question

[22] See definition 27.

"Why was the care received at reduced rates or free of charge?" As might be expected, families reporting a medical debt in 1963 were most likely to report large expenditures. Thus 40 percent of these families reported expenditures exceeding $500 compared to 23 percent of all families in the study. However, families receiving free care primarily for reasons other than inability to pay were also more likely to report large expenditures than would be expected by chance (34 percent).

TABLE 75
Family expenditure for health services by medical debt and free care received: 1963

LEVEL OF EXPENDITURE FOR HEALTH SERVICES	PERCENT FAMILIES WITH MEDICAL DEBT[22]	PERCENT FAMILIES RECEIVING SUBSTANTIAL FREE CARE		PERCENT ALL FAMILIES
		Unable to pay	Other	
$0-49	5	34	6	18
50-199	23	27	33	. 30
200-499	32	25	27	29
500 and over	40	14	34	23
All families	100	100	100	100
N	(463)	(73)	(64)	(2367)

Debt		Unable to pay		Other free	
Table N	463	Table N	73	Table N	64
NA	11	Other free	64	Unable to pay	73
No debt	1893	None free	2230	None free	2230
Sample N	2367	Sample N	2367	Sample N	2367

Thus, of the two types of families reporting substantial care, those unable to pay tend to have low expenditures, as seen by the fact that one-third of these families report expenditures of less than $50, while 18 percent of all families report such low expenditures. In contrast, families receiving substantial free care for other reasons spend considerable sums and thus resemble families in debt rather than the first type receiving free care. The first type generally does not have the resources to buy services. Consequently, their expenditures for health care are low. However, the second type not only receives large quantities of free care but also purchases large quantities. It may be that families in positions to receive such free care (such as doctors' families) simply consume large quantities of services whether they are free or not. Possibly, access to some free care leads to the purchase of additional care.[23]

[23] Another possibility is that free or reduced rate care is partly a function of large prior purchases of care for some families.

Possibly of greater interest than the over-all level of expenditure is the impact of those expenditures on the finances of the family. One method of measuring this impact is to look at family outlay for personal health services as a percentage of total family income. Table 76 shows this impact for families with medical debt and those receiving free care as well as for all families in the study.

Families with medical debt were slightly more likely to spend large proportions of their incomes on medical care than were all families in the study. Thus 25 percent in debt spent 10 percent or more compared to 20

TABLE 76
Family outlay for health as a percent of family income by medical debt and free care received: 1963

OUTLAY AS A PERCENTAGE OF FAMILY INCOME	PERCENT FAMILIES WITH MEDICAL DEBT	PERCENT FAMILIES RECEIVING SUBSTANTIAL FREE CARE		PERCENT ALL FAMILIES
		Unable to pay	Other	
0-4	42	56	45	50
5-9	32	23	33	29
10-19	16	11	16	13
20 or more	9	10	6	7
All families	100	100	100	100
N	(463)	(73)	(64)	(2367)

Debt		Unable to pay		Other free	
Table N	463	Table N	73	Table N	64
NA	11	Other free	64	Unable to pay	73
No debt	1893	None free	2230	None free	2230
Sample N	2367	Sample N	2367	Sample N	2367

percent of all families. However, it is surprising that the differences are not greater. In Chapter IV we saw that families with debts of $40 or more tended to have above average incomes. This would tend to keep outlay as a percentage of income for these families more in line with the measure for the population as a whole. Since there is no great difference in outlay as a percentage of income between families in debt and the total population, it would be interesting to study in detail why these families have debts.

Among families with free care, those receiving it for reasons other than inability to pay spend proportions of their income similar to the proportions spent by all families in the study. These data indicate, as did the data on total expenditures, that substantial free care is only a supplementary source for these families who still spend a relatively large proportion of their incomes for medical care. What is especially interesting is the relatively large proportion of families receiving substantial free care because they are unable to pay who still spent 10 percent or more of their income for medical care (21 percent). While a fairly large proportion of such families (56 percent) spent 4 percent or less of their income for health services, a substantial number in 1963 were still found to use a large proportion of their limited income to pay for health services. While the previous table has shown that their expenditures tended to be small compared to the expenditures for the rest of the population, for many of these families such expenditures still represented a substantial portion of their resources.

VI

SUMMARY AND IMPLICATIONS

This final chapter is an attempt to draw together some of the detailed data presented in the earlier chapters. The first section highlights some basic findings from the text which reveal internal relationships and trends in the health services system. The findings listed are necessarily selective rather than exhaustive. The text should be consulted for more detailed information. The second section contains a discussion of the implications of the findings. These implications relate to the present state of the health care system, future trends, and fruitful areas for future study.

A. SUMMARY HIGHLIGHTS

This summary includes highlights from each of the four data chapters. Findings regarding both the situation in 1963 and trends indicated by combining the data from all three studies are listed. The page numbers after each finding refer to relevant pages covering the subject in the earlier chapters.

1. *Use of services*

People with hospitalized illness episodes and other major non-hospitalized episodes compose a small percentage of the population but consume a majority of all services provided during a survey year. These people differ from the population as a whole with regard to certain basic characteristics, as illustrated by the findings regarding age and race (pp. 10–13).

Forty-one percent of the population in the latest study named a general practitioner as their regular source of medical care while 31 percent mentioned a specialist, 10 percent reported a clinic, and 12 percent claimed no regular source of care. Age, family income, and race were among the variables found to be related to the source reported (pp. 13–18).

Over one-half of the population claimed to have had a physical examination within one year of the interview for the latest study while 10 percent reported never having had an examination. The most prevalent reason given for having examinations was a response to symptoms of illness, but large portions also had "required examination" and "regular routine examinations" (pp. 18–23).

The likelihood that people will see a doctor in response to symptoms of illness is related to the nature of the symptom and the age, sex and family income of the person (pp. 23–26).

About two-thirds of the population had seen a doctor within the year in both 1958 and 1963. Income was directly related to seeing the doctor for young people but showed little relationship for those 55 and over. Site of visit continues to change from home to office and clinic. In almost one-tenth of all visits to a doctor's office the doctor is not seen but treatment is provided by a nurse or technician (pp. 26–31).

The hospitalized surgical procedure rate was 5 per 100 person-years in both 1958 and 1963. More surgery was being performed by surgical specialists in 1963 than in earlier periods (pp. 31–35).

Hospital admission rates increased from 12 to 13 admissions per 100 person-years between 1953 and 1963. The increase was accounted for in large part by higher rates for persons 55 and over (pp. 35–41).

Women who had live births in 1963 sought medical care earlier in the pregnancy and used more physician services but stayed in the hospital fewer days than did women having live births ten years earlier. Differences in use according to income and education were smaller in 1963 than in earlier studies (pp. 41–45).

The proportion of people seeing a dentist within the survey year reached 38 percent in 1963. Income was highly related to use of dental care for persons of all ages (pp. 45–47).

2. *Personal expenditures for health services*

Aggregate personal expenditures more than doubled between 1953 and 1963. However, these data indicate a slower rate of increase in the second half of the decade than was observed in the first half. The components of the consumer dollar changed during this period as the proportion devoted to physician services decreased while that devoted to hospital care increased (pp. 48–52).

Total mean family expenditures for all health services rose from $207 in 1953 to $370 in 1963. Family expenditures were higher in urban areas than in rural areas and rose with family income. However, the lowest income families spent a larger proportion of their income on health services than did higher income families and this difference increased between

1953 and 1963. Eight percent of all families accounted for 36 percent of health expenditures in 1963 (pp. 52–59).

The proportions of all families spending $200 or more for a particular type of service were highest for physician and hospital care, but for every service there were a considerable number of families spending $200 or more in 1963. The proportion of total family expenditure devoted to each type of service varied considerably with level of total family expenditure (pp. 60–61).

Mean expenditure per individual for all personal health services rose from $66 in 1953 to $112 in 1963. Expenditures are higher for females than for males and increase with age (pp. 62–64).

People 65 and over spent more than other age groups on every type of service except dental care in 1963 and females spent more than males for every service. In general, the greatest percentage increases in expenditures for all age and sex groups over the decade were for hospital services and drugs (pp. 64–71).

Mean expenditure for all health services connected with live births rose from $193 in 1953 to $316 in 1963 (pp. 71–74).

3. Methods of paying for personal health services

Almost three-fourths of all American families were covered by some form of health insurance in 1963. The proportion with insurance in 1963 had increased by 11 percentage points since 1953 and 5 percentage points since 1958. The increase in the latter half of the decade was primarily among the categories of families least likely to have had coverage in the past such as those with low incomes, rural-farm residences or aging family heads. Almost one-fourth of all families had major medical coverage in 1963, over 3 times as many as had such coverage five years earlier. Such coverage was primarily restricted to higher income, non-farm families (pp. 76–84).

In 1963 private insurance companies were insuring a somewhat greater proportion of the population against the costs of hospital and surgical services than was Blue Cross-Blue Shield (pp. 84–86).

Over one-half of the population was enrolled in group health insurance while one-fifth was covered by non-group insurance in 1963. Between 1953 and 1963 the proportion of the total population covered by group insurance increased while that covered by non-group remained about the same. Older, low income, and farm people were more likely to have non-group insurance, while younger, higher income, and non-farm persons were more likely to have group coverage. Seventy percent of all insured families were covered through a work group in 1963 and employer contributions to premium costs of such insurance increased between 1953 and 1963 (pp. 86–90).

Health insurance benefits as a proportion of gross expenditure for health services increased from 15 percent to 27 percent for the population as a whole between 1953 and 1963. In each study much larger proportions of the total charges for hospital and surgical than for other services were covered by insurance. Between 1953 and 1963 families with unusually high costs in a given year have benefited most by recent increases in health insurance reimbursements. For families receiving insurance benefits in connection with live births, these benefits as a proportion of expenditures increased from 53 percent in 1953 to 63 percent in 1963 (pp. 90–101).

Blue Cross was somewhat more likely to pay 90 percent or more of the hospital bill for an insured admission than was private insurance in each of the studies (pp. 101–4).

In each period group insurance provided considerably more comprehensive benefits than non-group insurance. These differences appeared to be greater in 1963 than they had been in 1953 (pp. 105–8).

Even though health insurance has grown, use of current income and savings remains an important method of paying for personal health services (pp. 108–12).

Four percent of the families reported receiving funds from non-family members to pay for health services in 1963 and six percent reported providing such funds to non-family members (pp. 112–15).

At the time of the interview for the 1963 study, 20 percent of the families owed something to providers of health services or were still paying on loans they took out to cover medical expenses incurred in 1963 or earlier (pp. 115–17).

Thirty-nine percent of all families reported that one or more family wage earners lost time from work during 1963 because of illness or injury in the family. Fifty-two percent of the workers involved did not lose wages because they were off work. Thirty-seven percent lost wages and did not receive compensation while 11 percent lost wages but were compensated in full or in part (pp. 117–19).

Six percent of the families during 1963 had one or more family members receiving all or most of the care for a hospitalized illness, terminated pregnancy or other major non-hospitalized illness free or at substantially reduced rates (pp. 119–20).

4. *Relationships of use, expenditures, and methods of payment*

Price increases appear to have contributed about twice as much as increases in use to over-all individual health expenditure increases between 1953 and 1963. Most of the expenditure increase for physicians' services seems to be accounted for by price increases while most of the increase for drugs is apparently related to use increases (pp. 122–25).

In 1963 hospitalized surgical procedure rates were 6 per 100 person-years for people with surgical insurance compared to 3 per 100 person-years for those with no insurance. Differences in rates between the insured and uninsured remained when comparisons were made according to age, sex, income, and residence categories (pp. 128–30).

Hospital admission rates per 100 person-years were 15 for people with hospital insurance compared to 9 for those without in 1963. Hospital admission rates for the insured exceeded the rates for the uninsured for every age, sex, income, and residence category in 1963 (pp. 130–34).

Apart from the influence of age and income, a strong relationship remains between having hospital insurance and using dental services. Since insurance is very unlikely to pay for dental services as yet, it appears that there are other characteristics which differentiate insured from uninsured individuals and contribute to the different patterns of use observed in the two groups (p. 135).

In 1963, the mean expenditure for all health services per insured family ($429) was over twice that for the uninsured family ($201). At every income level insured families spent considerably more. Insured people of all age and sex categories spent roughly twice as much on health services as did their uninsured counterparts (pp. 136–40).

Families with medical debt tended to have higher than average expenditures for health. Families receiving free medical care for some reason other than inability to pay also tended to have above average expenditures. Families receiving free care because they were unable to pay had below average expenditures but still spent proportions of their income on health services similar to the proportions spent by the population as a whole (pp. 140–43).

B. IMPLICATIONS

In the United States the mainstream of financing, ownership, and organization of personal health services continues to be the private sector of the economy, aided and abetted at strategic points by various levels of government. The patterns of expenditures and use of personal health services revealed by three nationwide family surveys in 1953, 1958, and 1963 are those which have taken place in this kind of socio-economic and political context.

The American health services system is characterized by a diffuse distribution of decision-making centers and sources of funds. The expenditure and use patterns are, accordingly, the results of a more or less spontaneous play of demand and supply forces during a period of great prosperity, continuing expansion of voluntary health insurance, and over-all improvement in the quality and distribution of facilities.

This continuing expansion and general improvement indicate that the health services system in the United States is a going concern. There are, however, serious deficiencies, some of which will be discussed below. Such deficiencies are not necessarily inherent and can be mitigated or remedied within the going structure.

Approximately three-quarters of the total national expenditure for health services and related items—direct services, research, capital funds, etc.—are from the private sector of the economy. One-quarter is from the public sector—general taxes and compulsory payroll deductions. Fully 80 percent of direct services—hospital, physician, dentists, drugs and medications, and paramedical personnel—are provided and paid for in the private sector.

The term private sector needs some description and explanation in order to place the private health services structure in proper perspective. Personal health services and goods are provided and paid for largely on a nonprofit basis within the private sector in contrast to the profit basis generally characteristic of the private sector for the economy as a whole.

The prevailing social value regards personal health services as "clothed with the public interest." They should not be primarily governed by the usual market place concepts of demand, supply, price, and customers, with the criterion of success being mainly adequate profit margins. Rather than profit, the criterion of success tends to be provision of "adequate" services to the public. Consequently, the personal health services, although largely private, are greatly assisted by public and private charitable sources which provide some of the cost of education, capital funds, and services to low income patients.

Hence, the health services are regarded as a prime example of the "commingling of private, nonprofit, and governmental action" denoted by the term "pluralistic economy."[1] Rather than applying the term "free enterprise" to the American personal health services system, it would be more accurate to apply the term "nonprofit enterprise," including licensure of personnel and regulation-setting standards.

From the data presented in this book, certain pivotal facts appear to be especially important in describing and assessing the personal health service economy in this country over a ten-year period. In the remainder of this chapter these facts will be discussed as they relate to: (1) use of

[1] Eli Ginzberg, Dale L. Hiestand, and Beatrice G. Reubens, *The Pluralistic Economy* (New York: McGraw-Hill Book Co., Inc., 1965), chap. 8, "The Expansion of Nonprofit Enterprise."

health services; (2) personal expenditures for health services; (3) methods of paying for personal health services; and (4) suggested research.

1. Use of health services

A time-honored and repeatedly stated principle in the health field is that those who need care and ask for it should receive it whether or not they can afford to pay for it. There has been little debate over the principle but a great deal of dispute over the methods of implementing this objective. In any case, there are now trends in use of personal health services by family income which show that low income families are similar to higher income families in use of some services but continue to lag behind higher income groups in use of other health services.

Judging by data from the Committee on the Costs of Medical Care (1928–31) and the three surveys presented in this book, it is clear that in general the level of use of personal health services has been rising for low income groups relative to high income groups, although the level of use has increased for high income groups as well. Although there is a decreasing discrepancy between low and high income groups, there are important variations by category of services and goods. It would appear that the services most likely to be related to health crises and illness generally perceived as "serious" by the population show least relationship to family income.

For general hospital care, indeed, the lowest income groups now use more hospital services than the high income groups.[2] For surgery it would seem that the low income groups had fewer operations than middle income groups in 1963 but had rates quite similar to the higher income groups. Insured, low income persons actually have surgical rates slightly higher than the rate for all insured people.

Family income differentials are more pronounced for physician services outside the hospital than for hospital care and surgery. The lower the income, the less likely it is that a physician has been consulted during a twelve-month period. Also, the less likely it is that physicians were consulted for colds and fevers.

However, as age increases, the differential between income groups decreases; 52 percent of the children under age 6 in the income group under $4,000 a year saw a physician at least once during the year, compared with 87 percent among those in income groups of $7,000 or more. Among those

---

[2] This relationship in part reflects the drop in position in the income distribution due to sickness of principal earners that causes shortrun decreases in income. However, apart from this factor, there can be little doubt that hospital usage of high and low income people shows more similarity now than it did at the time of the C.C.M.C. study some 30 years ago.

65 years of age and over approximately two-thirds see a doctor at least once regardless of income group. There is no ready explanation for this intriguing statistic, but it would seem that the older age groups are more likely to be seriously ill than younger age groups. They seek care accordingly, regardless of income. In contrast, a substantial portion of the care provided younger people of the higher income groups is "preventive" or for conditions generally defined as "less serious." Younger people of the lower income groups tend to do without this type of care and are thus less likely to see a doctor in a given year.

When we turn from the services associated with "health crises," we see quite clearly expected differentials by family income: high income groups are more likely to consult specialists; they are more likely to have seen a physician recently; and they are more likely to have seen a physician for physical examinations and checkups. Particularly dramatic is the use of dental services. High income groups are much more likely to seek dental care than low income groups. These data then indicate where effort must be made in terms of types of care and types of people if the goal is to provide more equal distribution of services within the population. However, in addition to these quantitative data, more systematic attempts to measure the distribution of quality and effectiveness of care provided to various sectors of the population are needed to fill out the picture.

Considering the fact that this country does not have a nationwide, uniform, and systematic program of maternal and child health—there are great variations by localities and states—it is of great interest that from 1953 to 1963 there were quite dramatic increases in the proportion of women in low income families who sought prenatal care early in the pregnancy. In 1953, 42 percent of the mothers in the lowest family income group had seen a physician by the end of the first trimester of pregnancy. Ten years later this proportion had increased to 58 percent. The proportion of mothers in the middle income group who saw a physician by the end of the first trimester increased from 66 percent to 86 percent during the period. The upper income group remained quite constant in the range of 86 to 89 percent. Obviously, in general, prenatal care is being spread more evenly, as measured by family income of the mother. However, there are still clusters of populations, concealed by these averages, with a very low volume of prenatal care.

2. Personal expenditures for health services

To learn that the private expenditures for personal health services increased from $10 billion in 1953 to $21 billion in 1963[3] may be startling.

[3] Simultaneously the public sector kept pace and the private and public ratios remained quite constant, indicating great expansive forces in the health economy generally.

These increases in expenditures are frequently regarded with alarm. However, the health services industry is part and parcel of the general economy. This is particularly true where government has as little direct control over health expenditures as in this country.

Indeed, increased use and a constantly improving and inherently expensive medical technology have resulted in expenditures increasing somewhat faster for the health sector than for the rest of the economy. It would seem that the question at issue is the *rate* of increase in expenditures in a dynamic and expanding economy rather than the increase itself. In fact, the question is moot because there are no hard and fast specifications as to the proper rate. There are many general suggestions about rationalizing the organization and distribution of services, but the predicted beneficial results are based on the same degree of faith as the proponents of the status quo display in their opinions.

It has been customary and useful to classify health services and goods by appropriate categories of hospital, physician, dentist, drugs and medications and "other" to reveal the distribution and the relative changes through time in expenditures for these categories. Each category is relatively autonomous in ownership and control. Thus, the varying proportions of expenditures can be said to flow from a more or less spontaneous interplay of decisions regarding various types of services and goods.

The decisions of physicians are related to over 70 percent of all expenditures for personal health services and goods. However, physicians are not directly responsible for the prices of these services and goods, except for their own fees. Prices for other services and goods are established by the relevant provider, institution, manufacturer, or retailer.

The most significant shift in proportion of expenditures has been the increasing proportion flowing to hospitals and the decreasing proportion to physicians. There has also been some increase in the proportion of expenditures for drugs and medications. A component of service which is becoming increasingly visible in the national totals is nursing home care, although it is only a small fraction of the total at present. As Medicare begins to facilitate the use of nursing homes, the allocation of funds to this category is expected to increase markedly.

In terms of price, the hospital continues to remain the most volatile component. During the ten-year period under study, the price of the hospital component increased by 90 percent, followed by the physician component, 37 percent, and the dentist component, 26 percent. While drugs showed only a 9 percent increase in expenditure due to price, apparently large increases in use resulted in total drug expenditures increasing as a proportion of all expenditures for health.

3. Methods of paying for personal health services

Assuming current methods of enrolling people in health insurance—i.e., employer groups and direct selling to individuals who are often self-employed or otherwise not a part of the usual labor market—voluntary health insurance appears to be reaching a point of saturation. Those who are not in employed groups are difficult and expensive to reach. It would seem that direct individual selling can be of value mainly for specialized purposes such as the supplementing of existing coverage. Non-group enrollment as a primary source of coverage appears inefficient since the ratio of benefits to premiums is substantially lower than for group enrollment.

The people not enrolled in voluntary health insurance are largely low income, rural, not employed, and non-white. (The aged are now for all practical purposes covered by Medicare, parts A and B, but there is also a small uncovered residue in this group as well.) Since these people are generally not associated with the labor market and are largely low income, there must be some form of direct subsidy and assistance.

As has already been established, first through federal and state public medical programs and later by Title 19 of the Medicare Act, there is a public policy to allocate more funds for public medical care. There is recognition that voluntary health insurance cannot reasonably be expected to enroll the remaining uninsured elements of the population without some form of public subsidy. Such medical care can be, and is, financed both by paying the premiums of low income persons and by providing services directly.

Over the years there has been a significant shift in the sources of payment for the various categories of services and goods. The primary shift, as indicated above, has been from the patient directly to some type of insurance. Consequently, providers of service have become increasingly involved with large buyers of services and the attendant reimbursement problems and issues related to quality and price.

In 1953 the general hospitals were receiving 50 percent of their non-governmental income from insurance agencies and by 1963, 69 percent. Physicians received 13 percent of their income from insurance in 1953 and 25 percent in 1963. It was primarily surgery, among all physician services, that was affected by the shifting source of payment—in 1953, 38 percent of the charges for surgery were paid by insurance compared with 58 percent in 1963. Insurance payments for obstetrical services increased from 25 to 32 percent of total charges over the 10 years. Other services are so far little affected by insurance, but it seems reasonable to assume that they will also increasingly come within the orbit of insurance payments, although likely not to the same degree as hospital based services.

Not only has there been a shift in source of payment from the patient to an insuring agency, but there has also been a shift of payment of the insurance premium from the employee to the employer. Increasingly, the health insurance premium has become an important item in collective bargaining. Employers have assumed more and more of the premium in lieu of wages and as a business expense which can be deducted for corporate income tax purposes and which is not taxable as employee income. Indirectly, then, some of the cost of personal health services in the private sector is borne by general tax funds of the federal government.

Among all families with some health insurance carried through a work group, 59 percent had some of the premium paid by the employer in 1953. This percentage increased to 79 percent in 1963. The percentage of these families who had *all* the costs of their work group insurance paid by the employer increased from 10 percent in 1953 to 27 percent in 1963.

As their financial involvement increases, it would seem reasonable to assume that employer and labor union interest in expenditures for health services also increases. Such increasing interest provides another important source of surveillance and concern within this pluralistic health care system.

Turning to consideration of payment, there are two schools of thought regarding the role of health insurance. Their positions are frequently unclear and the issues are confused as a result. The benefit levels of voluntary health insurance cannot be evaluated unless these viewpoints are set forth.

One school of thought would have it that practically all of the full range of personal health services should be paid for by insurance before it can be regarded as adequate. Hence, when voluntary health insurance is shown in the 1963 survey to pay for 31 percent of all personal health services for those people having insurance, this percentage represents in effect a gross deficiency of 69 percentage points. It is felt that all health services should be paid by insurance from the first medical contact to the termination of treatment. The rationale usually put forth for this view is that if any payment must be made by the patient at time of service, it will discourage his seeking a physician's care early, during the onset of an illness.

The other school of thought flows directly out of the risk or contingency concept of insurance, which proposes that the purpose of health insurance is to protect families against financial losses. Partial payments in the form of deductibles and coinsurance eliminate small claims, reduce premium charges, and ensure maximum protection against high losses at a reasonable premium. From this viewpoint, it is meaningless to evaluate health insurance primarily in terms of a simple percentage of total expenditures. The valid criterion is the extent to which insurance pays for health service charges above certain magnitudes.

If this criterion is accepted, it is clear that voluntary health insurance has improved considerably from 1953 to 1963. It was seen in Chapter IV that the percentage of total expenditures paid by insurance for families with low levels of expenditure actually fell, while it rose from 23 percent for families with expenditures of $1000 or more in 1953 to 45 percent in 1963. The trend of health insurance benefits is apparently toward the concept of protecting against high cost episodes. The provisions of the Medicare Act, with its rather high deductibles and coinsurance, also illustrate this observation. Obviously, the two schools of thought characterized above are polar types. What has actually taken place and will continue to develop is a combining of these two approaches. There is increasing concern not only with protecting families against financial loss, but also with methods of delivering services and with quality of services. For some time to come there will be a "battle of the gap," i.e., the gap between health insurance benefits and charges.

The data on distribution of family expenditures in this book demonstrate that large health services expenditures can be regarded as a risk in the insurance sense. Consequently, the insurance concept provides a suitable financing method. By all standards, however, voluntary health insurance has hardly begun to approach near-total payment of high magnitude expenditures for the full range of services usually needed for expensive illnesses. Presumably, such coverage will increase if present trends continue.

Recent newspaper and magazine articles, reports of study commissions, and congressional testimonies appear to say that the American health services system is in a serious crisis. But if one reviews the data from these three nationwide surveys and ignores the public clamor, the tremendous dynamism of the system is revealed in increased expenditures and use, gradually rising health insurance benefit levels, and visible improvements in the distribution of services by family income.

It would seem that the atmosphere of crisis is generated in great part by the accelerating expectations of the system. It is expected today to produce results more rapidly, for more people, at more reasonable costs, than at any time in its history. Clearly, the system is under great strain, but it cannot be said to have broken down. It is a viable system by important standards and as measured by past performance. Potential performance is, of course, difficult to predict. However, it is reasonable to assume that the system is not performing at its possible optimum and that improvements can be carried out, building on the present structure.

Passage of the Medicare Act for the aged in 1965, inaugurated July 1,

1966, represents a new stage in public policy regarding the relationship of government to the essentially nongovernmental character of the American health system. It is a new stage because for the first time government becomes involved in providing services to a large segment of the population defined simply by age without regard to income or other special characteristics.

Presumably, this precedent will make it easier to expand government sponsored services to more of the population. That it will be easier is self-evident; that it is inevitable is another matter. Title 18 (Medicare) and Title 19 (medical assistance below certain incomes for anybody) may be the two forces which will sustain the voluntary sector for some time to come.

As indicated earlier, voluntary health insurance under present conditions is approaching the saturation point in enrollment. In addition, health insurance benefits as a proportion of expenditure in the voluntary sector are increasing and will apparently continue to increase. Consequently, government health insurance for the employed segment of the population and their dependents may not become a political issue. This ability to improve benefit levels for the employed segment is strengthened by Title 18 and 19, which eliminate the need for voluntary insurance to attempt coverage for the elderly and for low income persons.

As insurance benefit levels continue to improve gradually, it is likely that high wage levels and increasing employer contributions will absorb, with a minimum of political repercussions, payments for personal health services by insurance and direct payment by patients. Consequently, government and private interests may continue to exist side by side for some time to come. The American health system is a fluid and loose one and seems capable of encompassing considerable differentiation.

4. Suggested research

The foregoing implications flow from an interpretation of data produced by three nationwide family studies. These studies were conducted in order to learn something about consumer health service use, trends in health services expenditures, and the changes in health insurance benefit levels. Such knowledge provides a picture of nationwide patterns suitable for the evaluation of the operation of the total system on a rather broad basis. The usual question after a research project is completed is: Where do we go from here? What further research is indicated and in what directions?

This book provides benchmarks of use and expenditures from three similar surveys conducted at five-year intervals. Such basic benchmarks should be provided on a routine and periodic basis. The health field needs periodic reporting of trends similar to vital statistics and population statistics. It now appears that the National Center for Health Statistics will continue to provide such benchmarks for health service use and expenditure as well as morbidity.

What additional research does this report suggest regarding the operation of the health services system? This research can be of two fundamental types: (1) that which seeks to understand the over-all functioning of the health care system; and (2) that which concentrates on more specific or limited aspects of problems within the system. There is no inherent difference between these two approaches; the distinction is one of emphasis.

The first is oriented toward the interrelationship of the various parts and tends to concentrate on understanding the working of the system as it exists. The second investigates discrete portions without necessarily relating them to the larger structure. In addition, the latter is more often directed toward the definition of problems and issues of policy within the system and means of correcting deficiencies uncovered.

With regard to research, considering the system as a whole, more detailed information than can be provided by a national study is needed. To provide such details regarding the working of the system, we suggest the study of a standard metropolitan statistical area which is relatively self-contained economically and socially. Within this area the flow of patients would be followed through the health services system, using the physicians' offices as the main loci of investigation.

In the American system the facilities, and to a large extent the programs as well, are dependent on the private practice structure for diagnosis and treatment. To date most research on the health services has stopped at the physician's office door, where the great bulk of diagnosis and treatment takes place. All other sites can be considered in a sense "residuals" of the office site. It is proposed to investigate the source of patients, how they flow through physicians' offices, and what their destinations are.

Apart from the total system concept, there are many studies of more specific problems that are necessary and which relate mainly to some of the particulars for efficient implementation of the system. Examples of needed studies are: evaluation of the operation of hospital utilization review committees; methods of quality and cost controls; and problems of queuing at physicians' offices and outpatient departments. Additional examples can be given which are related more directly to data presented in this study. These include more detailed investigations of: (1) relationship of peoples' usual source of medical care to the nature of the health services they receive; (2) the relative contributions of "price," "use," and level of care to increases in health care expenditure; (3) determinants of differences in family use and expenditure patterns; (4) the influence of different types of insurance defined in terms of services covered and the comprehensiveness of that coverage on use patterns; (5) the nature of interfamily transfers to pay for health services; (6) the reasons for family medical debt and the extent of the problem such debt poses; (7) the effects of work loss due to illness and how loss-of-income insurance alters these effects; and (8) the extent of free medical care provided to American families and how it substitutes for or supplements care provided through other means.

In closing, it should be repeated that while more detailed studies are necessary to increase our knowledge, they are not substitutes for periodic "benchmark" information. Basic data such as much of what is presented in this report are needed periodically to provide some measure of changes in the state of the nation's health care system.

Appendixes

I

METHODOLOGY

The specific methodology employed in the 1953 and 1958 studies has been described in previous reports.[1] Considerable attention was devoted to making the 1963 study as comparable as possible to the earlier studies. Modifications were introduced only when resulting gains seemed to more than compensate for loss in comparability. Such modifications are mentioned in the description of the research method that follows. This appendix includes separate sections on sample design, estimating procedures, factors influencing sample estimates, and comparisons of sample data with independent estimates.

A. THE SAMPLE DESIGN[2]

The universe sampled in this study was the total non-institutionalized population of the continental United States. This universe excludes the following individuals: (1) residents in medical, mental, penal, religious, or other institutions who were not residents of a private dwelling at any time during 1963; (2) residents on military reservations (the 1958 and 1963 samples included, however, personnel in the armed forces living off

---

[1] Odin W. Anderson and Jacob J. Feldman, *Family Medical Costs and Voluntary Health Insurance: A Nationwide Survey* (New York: McGraw-Hill Book Co., Inc., 1956), Appendix B; and Odin W. Anderson, Patricia Collette, and Jacob J. Feldman, *Changes in Family Medical Care Expenditures and Voluntary Health Insurance* (Cambridge: Harvard University Press, 1963), Appendix A. Estimates from these earlier studies as well as the latest study reflect the experience of other years to the extent that the three reporting periods were usual or typical. Actually the second study was marked by two unusual events—the Asian influenza epidemic, which affected use of health services, and the 1957–58 business recession, which had some influence on insurance coverage and income. To the best of the authors' knowledge, the 1952–53 and 1963 survey years were not unusual in any way which would affect estimates derived from these studies.

[2] This section is based on an appendix prepared by Seymour Sudman and Jacob J. Feldman in John W. C. Johnstone and Ramon J. Rivera, *Volunteers for Learning* (Chicago: Aldine Publishing Co., 1965), pp. 482–85.

base with their families or in other civilian households); and (3) transient individuals having no usual or permanent residence. The resulting sample included 2,367 families and 7,803 family members. It was a standard multistage area probability sample.

1. *Primary sampling units*

The primary sampling units (PSU's) employed in the 1963 study were derived from NORC's 1953 Master Sample, which produced the samples for the 1953 and 1958 studies. The PSU's in the Master Sample had been selected with probabilities proportionate to their estimated 1953 populations. Population shifts in the past decade have rendered that set of PSU's a less efficient primary stage than one might desire. Nonetheless, since a well-trained and experienced field force was available in that set of PSU's, it was obviously desirable to update the sample by some procedure minimizing the number of sampling units to be changed. A procedure suggested by Nathan Keyfitz was employed.[3] This involved the comparison of the desired 1960 probabilities of selection for PSU's with their original 1950 probabilities. If the originally selected PSU had a lower probability than was warranted by its 1960 population, it was retained in the new sample and assigned the desired probability. If the originally selected PSU had a higher probability than was warranted, it was subjected to the possibility of being dropped. The probability of retention for such a PSU was the ratio of its desired probability to its original probability. Replacements for dropped PSU's were made from among those PSU's which had not fallen into the 1953 sample and for which the 1953 probability was lower than that desired in 1960, the probability of 1960 selection being a function of the amount of growth the unit had undergone.

Basically, this method preserved the stratification based on the 1950 classifications of geographic regions, size of largest town, median family income, economic characteristics, and, in the South, race. Counties which the Census Bureau classified as non-metropolitan in 1950 but as metropolitan in 1960 were, however, shifted to metropolitan strata. The restratification, in all likelihood, served to increase the efficiency of the sample somewhat.

The current set of PSU's is to be used until the 1970 census is available. For this reason, the 1960 census figures were extrapolated to 1967, the midpoint between the availability of the 1960 and 1970 census reports. For each PSU, the extrapolation was based on its population change between 1950 and 1960.

[3] Nathan Keyfitz, "Sampling Probabilities Proportional to Size," *Journal of the American Statistical Association*, 46 (1951): 105–9.

2. Localities

Within each selected PSU, localities were ordered according to cities with block statistics, other urban places, and urbanized and non-urbanized minor civil divisions, with the places ordered by 1960 population within each of these categories. Localities were selected from this list by using a random start and applying a designated interval to the cumulative 1960 population. This provided stratification according to size and urban type of locality and at the same time gave selection with probability proportionate to size.

3. Cluster size

Within each locality, a sample of ultimate clusters, or segments, was selected. From the point of view of minimizing the sampling error of estimates from the survey, the smaller the cluster the better. From the point of view of minimizing the interviewing and other field costs, the larger the cluster the better. After weighing these contradictory injunctions, it was decided that an average of approximately three households per segment would be screened in the family medical care survey. However, in anticipation of interview losses due to vacancies, demolition, refusals, unavailability, language difficulties, etc., an average of four dwelling units per segment was assigned for screening.

The establishment of the desired sampling ratio for the entire United States, the probability of the particular locality, and the desired cluster size predetermined the number of segments to be selected from any given locality. The actual procedure employed in selecting the necessary number of segments from a particular locality depended on whether or not a recent city directory was available. The street address section of a city directory constituted the sampling frame for about 20 percent of the localities. These were generally medium-sized cities.

4. City directory sampling

The first-stage unit of sampling within a directory was usually a column of addresses. Since it was anticipated that each column from the directory would produce on the average about one and one-third discrete geographic clusters for the final sample, the number of columns to be selected for a given locality was set at three-quarters the number of segments required there. The columns were selected systematically with equal probability.

The over-all probability of the column (i.e., the product of the probability of the PSU, the conditional probability of the locality, and the conditional probability of the column) was invariably several times larger than the desired final household probability. Each selected column was therefore divided into several roughly equal-sized groupings of residential directory listings. The number of such groupings in a column was made equal to the integral value nearest to the ratio of the over-all column probability to the desired final household probability. One grouping was then randomly selected from each column.

Since different sample columns in a directory contained widely differing numbers of residential listings, the size of segments in a given locality was rather variable. In addition, geographic homogeneity was one of the criteria of the allocation of directory addresses into groupings. Thus, when a slight variation in grouping size within a column made for greater geographic homogeneity within one or more of the groupings, such variation was permitted. Even so, many of the groupings did contain (as anticipated) two or more discrete geographic clusters.

Directories in which the street address listings for two or more communities were intermixed were sampled in a somewhat modified fashion. A measurement of the amount of space devoted to the sample locality was made for each column in the directory. A sample of columns was then selected with a column's probability being proportionate to the amount of space devoted within it to the sample locality. Once the columns were selected, the procedure followed in the mixed directories was essentially the same as that described above.

In order to correct for the omission of new construction as well as other possible directory errors, a coverage check of the directory listings was conducted for a sample of blocks in one-third of the directory localities. Interviewers canvassed these blocks thoroughly in search of dwelling units omitted from the directory. The sampling ratio employed in selecting blocks and in selecting omitted housing units within blocks was established in such a way that, for any given block, the product of the block's being in the supplementary sample and the sampling ratio employed within the block was exactly equal to the probability which any entry actually appearing in the directory had of falling into the original sample. In other words, housing units appearing in a city directory and those omitted from it were sampled at exactly the same rate.

5. Sampling in other localities

Where city directories were not available, 1960 census data were used. In the larger cities, census tract and block data were used. The tracts were ordered according to median income, and selection was made by using a random start and applying a designated skip interval to the cumulative number of households. Blocks were then selected with probability proportional to the number of dwelling units.

In places without block statistics, enumeration districts were selected with probabilities proportional to the number of households. The selected districts were then divided into segments, and estimates of the number of households within each segment were obtained by field counts. The selection of segments was then made with probability proportionate to the number of households.

In each selected segment or block, a listing of households was carried out by interviewers just prior to the start of the study. Households were selected from these listing sheets with probability determined by the ratio of the final sampling ratio of households to the probability with which the segment had been selected.

6. Families

All families residing in the foregoing primary sample of dwellings were included in the 1963 study in a manner similar to that of the 1953 study. In 1958 the ultimate sampling units were families selected through a double sampling procedure which served to assign higher sampling probabilities to high expenditure families than to low expenditure families.

This procedure was employed in 1958 because a description of high medical expenditure families was a central objective of the survey. In addition double sampling reduced the sampling error of the estimates of some mean and aggregate expenditures.

Several reasons contributed to the decision not to use double sampling in 1963. Screening families to locate those with high expenditures is an expensive interviewing process and the data collected on those not included in the final sample are in part "wasted." While high medical expenditure families were still of interest in 1963, no special analysis of them was planned. Consequently, it was decided to devote all the sampling resources of the study to maintaining as large a sample size as possible without expending a portion of these resources on screening interviews. In addition, the sampling errors of some estimates, while lower when using double sampling, were not considered to be unreasonably high when employing a straight sampling technique. In fact, the sampling errors of some median and percentage estimates were lower using the latter technique. Finally, most tables from the 1958 study were based on the weighted distribution, and subsequently subgroups from the tables could not be combined. Such combining is possible for the 1953 and 1963 studies since all families and individuals are equally weighted.

B. ESTIMATING PROCEDURES

The same general methods of processing the data and deriving estimates for the population were used in 1963 as had been employed in the earlier studies. In 1958 and 1963, however, the use of a twelve-month reporting period for medical utilization and expenditure data in connection with all illnesses eliminated the necessity for several operations in the analytical stage described in the report on the 1953 study.

In cases in which necessary quantitative information was not obtained at all in the interview or in which it was not obtained in sufficiently precise terms, estimates were made in the central office during the processing stage. Estimates made were based on other data from the interview and on information relating to "going rates" in the community from which the sample family came. In the 1953 study some cases were assigned ultimately to an "indeterminate" category. However, in the 1958 and 1963 studies all cases were made "determinate" with respect to charges for major categories of goods and services, utilization in these major categories, and family money income. No estimates were made in any study of the value of free care received.

All the population estimates reported are "ratio" estimates. For example, estimates of total personal consumption expenditures for medical care in 1963 were derived by first determining the fraction of the total civilian non-institutionalized population constituted by the individuals in the sample. This population was estimated as 184,773,000 using data from the Bureau of the Census. Aggregate charges incurred by individuals in the sample were then multiplied by the reciprocal of the fraction.

C. FACTORS INFLUENCING SAMPLE ESTIMATES

Estimates of population characteristics derived from this study may differ from the actual population characteristics because of a number of factors. Some errors in estimates arise from use of samples rather than a complete census. These include sampling variances and problems in executing the sample design. Other errors may result during the reporting, processing, and analyzing of the data. Primary among these are completeness of population coverage and validity of the data. Each of these factors influencing sample estimates is considered below.

1. Sampling variances

The standard error is a measure of sampling variance. It shows the variations that might occur by chance because only a sample of the population is surveyed. It does not include biases resulting from problems in the execution of the sample design or in processing the data. The chances are about 68 out of 100 that an estimate from the sample would differ from a complete census by less than the standard error. The chances are about 95 out of 100 that the difference would be less than twice the standard error and about 99 out of 100 that it would be less than 2½ times as large.

Table A-1 shows in column 3 the standard errors of a number of estimates made in this report.[4] For example, the first error shown tells us that the chances are about 2 out of 3 that the number of hospital admissions in the population per 100 person-years would not differ more than 0.5 admissions from the estimate of 12.9 admissions if there were no non-response or errors of execution.

The computation of standard errors for estimates based on the present sample is complex because the families in this sample were geographically clustered and stratification was used in this selection of the unit. Because of the impossibility of taking into account the full extent of stratification used in our sample design, the method which was used to estimate standard errors tends to lead to conservative results—an overestimate of the magnitude of standard errors. It should be kept in mind that standard errors are themselves subject to estimating errors and should therefore be considered as rough approximations of the limits of likely sampling deviation.

Table A-1 includes standard errors of estimates considered representative of most of the types of estimates presented in this report. Column 4 of the table may be used by the reader to estimate sampling errors for estimates not covered by the table itself. It will usually be satisfactory to estimate the standard error as if one were dealing with a simple random sample and then multiply by the "ratio of error to error for random sample" (column 4) for that characteristic in the table most closely resembling the characteristic for which a standard error is desired.

A major purpose of this report has been to examine changes taking place through the decade. Column 5 of the table shows the magnitude of the difference between the 1953 and 1963 estimates for each characteristic. Column 6 provides the standard error of this difference. For instance, column 5 shows that the estimate of hospital admissions per 100 person-years for the total population increased by 1.3 admissions. Column 6 indicates that if admissions were the same in 1953 and 1963 the chances are about 2 out of 3 that the estimates would vary by no more than 0.6 admissions. Thus, the difference between these estimates is greater than one standard error.

---

[4] A discussion and a parallel table of standard error estimates for the 1953 study are found in Anderson and Feldman, *Family Medical Costs,* pp. 217–23.

TABLE A-1
Sampling errors of selected estimates: 1963

TYPE OF ESTIMATE	SAMPLE SIZE 1963 (1)	ESTIMATE 1963 (2)	STANDARD ERROR OF ESTIMATE (3)	RATIO OF ERROR TO ERROR FOR RANDOM SAMPLE (4)	DIFFERENCE OF 1953 AND 1963 ESTIMATES (5)	STANDARD ERROR OF DIFFERENCE (6)
Estimates of use						
Hospital admissions per 100 person-years						
All persons	7686	12.9	0.5	1.3	1.3	0.6
Persons under 55						
All	6377	11.9	0.5	1.3	0.4	0.7
Insured persons	4374	13.6	0.6	1.2	−0.3	0.9
Uninsured persons	2003	8.3	0.8	1.4	−0.2	1.1
Difference	–	5.3	1.0	1.3	–	–
Persons 55 or over						
All	1309	17.4	1.1	1.4	4.9	1.3
Insured persons	831	19.1	0.6	1.2	2.0	0.9
Uninsured persons	478	14.4	4.4	1.4	4.9	5.0
Difference	–	4.7	4.5	1.4	–	–
Hospital days per 100 person-years						
All persons	7686	95.5	7.5	1.1	9.2	6.2
Persons under 55						
All	6377	72.9	7.1	1.1	0.3	9.7
Insured persons	4374	82.7	8.1	1.0	−2.3	12.8
Uninsured persons	2003	50.9	8.5	1.2	−6.5	11.4
Difference	–	31.8	11.8	1.1	–	–
Persons 55 or over						
All	1309	207.6	27.5	1.1	58.2	33.0
Insured persons	831	199.4	27.8	1.0	6.0	41.9
Uninsured persons	478	221.8	58.2	1.1	101.7	63.3
Difference	–	39.8	64.5	1.1	–	–

TABLE A-1 (Cont.)

TYPE OF ESTIMATE	SAMPLE SIZE 1963 (1)	ESTIMATE 1963 (2)	STANDARD ERROR OF ESTIMATE (3)	RATIO OF ERROR TO ERROR FOR RANDOM SAMPLE (4)	DIFFERENCE OF 1953 AND 1963 ESTIMATES (5)	STANDARD ERROR OF DIFFERENCE (6)
Estimates of use (cont.)						
Hospital days per admission						
All admissions	991	7.4	0.5	1.1	0.0	0.7
Insured admissions						
All	756	7.0	0.6	1.1	0.0	0.9
Persons under 55	595	6.1	0.6	1.0	−0.1	0.9
Persons 55 or over	161	10.4	1.1	1.1	−0.9	1.9
Difference	—	4.3	1.3	1.0	—	—
Uninsured admissions						
All	235	8.8	0.9	1.1	0.5	1.1
Persons under 55	166	6.1	0.7	1.0	−0.5	0.9
Persons 55 or over	69	15.4	2.4	1.0	2.7	2.9
Difference	—	9.3	2.5	1.0	—	—
Expenditure estimates						
Total per person						
All persons	7803	$112.00	$ 4.00	1.2	$ 47.00	$ 4.00
Insured persons	5295	133.00	4.00	1.1	59.00	5.00
Uninsured persons	2508	67.00	5.00	1.4	13.00	6.00
Difference	—	66.00	7.00	1.2	—	—
Physician per person						
All persons	7803	$ 35.00	$ 1.00	1.1	$ 10.00	$ 2.00
Persons under 55	6472	32.00	2.00	1.1	9.00	2.00
Persons 55 or over	1331	48.00	3.00	1.1	13.00	4.00
Difference	—	16.00	4.00	1.1	—	—
Total per family[a]						
All families	2367	$370.00	$12.00	1.1	$164.00	$13.00
Rural families	201	302.00	39.00	1.4	124.00	41.00
Other families	2166	376.00	10.00	0.9	164.00	12.00
Difference	—	74.00	40.00	1.3	—	—

TABLE A-1 (Cont.)

TYPE OF ESTIMATE	SAMPLE SIZE 1963 (1)	ESTIMATE 1963 (2)	STANDARD ERROR OF ESTIMATE (3)	RATIO OF ERROR TO ERROR FOR RANDOM SAMPLE (4)	DIFFERENCE OF 1953 AND 1963 ESTIMATES (5)	STANDARD ERROR OF DIFFERENCE (6)
Expenditure estimates (cont.)						
Hospital per family[a]	2367	$ 97.00	$6.00	1.2	$56.00	$7.00
Physician per family[a]	2367	115.00	4.00	1.1	37.00	4.00
Dental per family[a]	2367	47.00	2.00	1.0	14.00	3.00
Drugs per family[a]	2367	75.00	2.00	1.1	44.00	2.00
Other per family[a]	2367	35.00	2.00	1.1	9.00	3.00
Proportion of total for physician[a]	$875,000	31.0%	0.6%	1.1	-6.6%	1.0%
Percentage estimates						
Percent of persons hospitalized						
All persons	7803	8.2%	0.4%	1.3	0.3%	0.5%
Insured persons	5295	9.9	0.5	1.2	0.1	0.7
Uninsured persons	2508	6.1	0.6	1.3	0.1	0.8
Difference	–	3.2	0.8	1.3	–	–
Percent of families whose total health outlay was less than 5% of their income	2367	50.4%	1.2%	1.2	-8.5%	1.6%
Percent of families with no hospital insurance	2367	26.9%	1.4%	1.6	-9.8%	2.0%

[a]Computed directly from 1963 data. The remaining 1963 standard errors are based on 1953 estimates (Anderson and Feldman, Family Medical Costs, pp. 218-22) adjusted for changes in sample size and magnitude of the estimate. Changes in the standard errors of mean estimates were assumed to be proportional to changes in the mean. This procedure probably led to conservative results in most instances, i.e., an overestimate of error increase. For example, the ratio of the standard deviation to the mean for family total expenditures decreased from 1.5 in 1953 to 1.3 in 1963.

2. *Sampling execution*

Another bias of estimates based on a sample develops because the sampling design is not properly executed. That is, families designated for the sample are not actually interviewed, or families not falling in the sample are interviewed. The inclusion of non-sample families, despite precautionary measures, undoubtedly occurred, but the effect of such mistakes on the accuracy of estimates is considered slight. Non-response error is a more serious concern.

For the 1963 study, 2,852 families were designated in the sample. Interviews were completed for 2,367 families for a completion rate of 83 percent. Table A-2 shows that over three-quarters of the families not inter-

TABLE A-2
Results of interviewing attempts for all sample families: 1963

RESULT	PERCENT OF FAMILIES	
Interviewed	83	
Not interviewed	17	
Refused		12
Broke off		1
Not at home after repeated calls		2
Other (language problem, respondent too ill to be interviewed, etc.)		2
All sample families[a]	100	
N	(2852)	

[a]The initial assignment was 3080 dwelling units. During the course of the field work 355 of these dwellings were found to be razed, vacant, transient or seasonal dwelling units, while 127 additional families were added to the assignment through multiple family dwelling units and multiple dwelling units within the same structure originally listed as single units. The final net assignment after these additions and subtractions was 2852.

viewed either refused to be interviewed, or initially agreed but subsequently broke off the interview, or failed to provide enough information to be included in the analysis. The remainder were families who could not be located at home after repeated visits and families who, while located, were not interviewed for some other reason such as language problems, long-term serious illness of respondent, etc.

The estimates in the report are based on those families which were interviewed. The amount of discrepancy between these estimates and the figures which would have been obtained had interviews been obtained with all families in the sample depends, for any characteristic being estimated, on how different the non-interview families were with respect to this characteristic from those who were interviewed.

Certainly the interviewed families were not identical to those not interviewed, but neither were they completely dissimilar. While we are unable to make any direct comparisons regarding health behavior, Table A-3 shows some basic descriptive characteristics of interviewed and non-interviewed families. In addition we know that interviews were more likely to be completed with farm families and with those living in single unit structures and less likely to be completed with those living in densely populated areas and apartments.

Estimates in this report have not been adjusted for non-response. It would probably be safe to assume in most cases an error due to non-response of not more than $3\frac{1}{2}$ percent. This error would appear if the

TABLE A-3
Comparisons of interviewed and non-interviewed sample families: 1963

CHARACTERISTIC OF POPULATION	FAMILIES	
	Percent interviewed	Percent not interviewed
Location[a]		
Northeast	22	41
North central	29	41
South	32	9
West	17	9
Type of PSU		
10 largest SMSA's	24	41
Other SMSA's	38	25
Counties with largest town of 10,000 or more	16	16
Counties with largest town of less than 10,000	22	18
Interviewer's estimate of level of living[b]		
Above average	17	17
Average	62	57
Below average	21	26
Race[c]		
White	86	90
Non-white	14	10
Total	100	100
N	(2367)	(485)

[a]Same divisions used by the United States Bureau of the Census.

[b]The interviewer was asked to compare the level of living of each family to the average level in the area. They were to take into consideration the family home, its size and its furnishings and the appearance of family members. These percentages exclude 39 interviewed families and 96 non-interviewed families who were not rated. Also excluded are the 62 non-interviewed families who were not at home.

[c]These percentages exclude 29 interviewed and 69 non-interviewed families for whom no race was recorded as well as the 62 non-interviewed families classed as not at home.

interview cases split 50-50 on the item being measured and those not interviewed split 30-70.

In Table A-4 the reasons given by non-respondents for not participating in the study are shown. In many instances the interviewer did not agree that the reason given by the non-respondent was the most important reason for the refusal. Therefore, interviewer explanations for the refusals, when given, are also included. Thus, we see that the reason most often given by both non-respondents and interviewers is a lack of interest on the part of the family. The reason given second most frequently by the non-respondents was that they were too busy and did not have time. However, interviewers did not generally agree with this interpretation.

TABLE A-4

Reasons given by non-respondents and interviewers for refusals, breakoffs, and other losses:[a] 1963

REASON FOR RESPONDENT LOSS	PERCENT OF ALL REASONS GIVEN BY	
	Non-respondents	Interviewers
Not interested enough to be interviewed	40	37
Too busy—doesn't have time	28	3
Information is too personal	15	15
Illness or death in family	11	12
Someone else persuaded main respondent to say "no"	4	7
Language barrier	3	6
Reasons coded for non-respondents only		
We don't like surveys, don't like this particular survey (i.e., will help [hinder] Medicare)	10	—
We aren't "appropriate" for study (i.e., no medical costs)	5	—
No reason given (i.e., slammed door)	17	—
Reasons coded for interviewers only		
Respondent is suspicious of study (i.e., thinks we are selling something)	—	17
Respondent doesn't feel he will know how to answer the questions	—	4
Respondent never really refused—continually broke or postponed appointments	—	9
Total percent	133[b]	110[b]
Total cases	(400)[c]	(224)[d]

[a]Excludes families not at home after repeated calls.

[b]Total exceeds 100 because more than one reason given for some cases.

[c]Excludes 23 cases with "no answer."

[d]Excludes 199 cases where interviewer gave no additional reason for respondent refusal.

The second most frequent reason recorded by interviewers was that the respondent was suspicious of the study or its motives or just didn't like strangers.

3. Completeness of population coverage

In order to derive estimates pertaining to a period as long as a year from a single wave survey, it is necessary to compensate for the absence on the interview date of individuals who had been members of the population at some time during the survey year but had left it. This is of special importance for a study of this type because of the high utilization and expenditures by individuals who die or are institutionalized during the survey year.

An attempt was made to include in the survey at least those decedents and other former members of the population who had, at some time during the survey year, lived with a relative who was still a population member at the end of the survey year. Precautions were taken, however, to make sure that each person who had left the population could be counted as a former member of *only one* end-of-the-year family, thus giving him exactly the same probability of falling in the sample as an individual who was still a member of the population.

By this method it seems that about 70 percent of all survey-year decedents were represented in the sample. However, the coverage rate of decedents who were actually members of the survey universe was somewhat higher because some decedents were residents of institutions during the entire proportion of the survey year through which they had lived and were thus not part of the survey universe.

All individuals who had been living alone or only with individuals who were also to leave the population are excluded. Therefore, the coverage of individuals who left the population is not complete. But, a substantial portion of the greatest utilizers and highest spenders are represented.

4. Validity of the data

The discussion of factors influencing estimates from the study up to this point has dealt with the possibility of real differences between the sample and the universe sampled caused by sampling variance, completion rate, and population coverage. However, estimates may also differ from population characteristics because there are discrepancies between the collected data on utilization and expenditure and the actual experience of the sample. The data are valid to the extent that they accurately reflect the sample's behavior. However, distortions can occur between the time of behavior itself and the description of that behavior in the final report.

Distortions can result from inaccurate respondent reporting, the interviewing process, coding, key punching, data processing, analyzing, and writing of the report.

In this section we will discuss the validity of several types of information given in this report and efforts to improve it. Treated separately will be information provided by respondents and by two separate verification procedures used to increase the validity of health insurance and hospital data. Considering the data checks and verifications reported below and the experience of other studies, we are satisfied that the classifications of individuals and families in terms of their health insurance and their use of, and expenditure for, medical care are fairly accurate. There is little reason to believe that any great number of families were significantly misclassified in relation to charges and care for serious illness, although overstatements and understatements with respect to minor illnesses may be more likely.

a. *Respondent information.* It was anticipated that many families would have little detailed information on their health services use and health insurance readily available. Consequently, letters explaining the studies and the information sought were sent to all sample families in advance of an interviewer's visit. These letters and the interviewers on subsequent visits urged them to consult any documents such as policies, membership cards, medical bills or tax records which could provide reliable information. Approximately one-half of the families consulted documents regarding health behavior.

The interviewer was instructed on first contact to make an appointment for a time when the family members who knew most about family use of health services and health insurance would be available. During the interview, main respondents were urged to consult other family members who might be better informed than they about some questions asked. If important information could not be obtained during the first interview, interviewers were instructed to phone later or make additional personal calls to complete the interview. It was recognized that in instances of change in family composition (other than by birth) during the year, or in families consisting of several related but unmarried adults, it was unlikely that a single family respondent could give accurate information for the entire year about all family members. In such cases interviewers interviewed separately as many family members as necessary.

The interview schedule used in the 1963 study was basically the same as that used in the earlier studies. The complete schedule is found in Appendix III. In each study considerable effort was expended in training the interviewers in the use of the schedule, since the factual and detailed nature of the information requested differed considerably from data usually collected in NORC studies. Much of the 1963 schedule was pre-coded to facilitate data processing. Certain additional questions which had not been asked in 1953 or 1958 were added. The latter included data on the family's regular physician, physical examinations, response to symp-toms, visits to a nurse in a doctor's office, and attitudes toward health. While the length of the interview varied a great deal according to family size and amount of services used, the modal length was about two hours.

Although much of the information provided was based on memory, half of the families referred to documents, and a substantial proportion of the respondent information was verified independently through hospitals and insurance carriers. In classifying the interview data, continual use was made of current directories of physicians, dentists, optometrists, and hos-pitals.

b. *Hospital verification*. In each study an attempt was made to increase the validity of the interview reports of the hospitalization of family mem-bers by checking them against independent data. These data were from the records of institutions—hospitals, sanitaria, etc.—and insurance organi-zations. The hospitalized person or another responsible family member was asked to sign a permission form authorizing the institution to provide us with detailed information on his stay. This information included costs, duration and services received for the stay.

Table A-5 shows the results of the mail questionnaire verification. In

TABLE A-5
Results of hospital admissions verification: 1963

RESULTS OF VERIFICATION	REPORTED PERCENT OF ALL ADMISSIONS	
Source of initial report of admission		
Family	99	
Institution	1	
Type of information received through verification		
Independent information received	88	
Substantiates hospital stay during 1963		78
Fails to substantiate stay during 1963		9
No independent information received	12	
Disposition of admission following verification[a]		
Accepted for analysis[b]	95	
Not accepted for analysis	5	
Total hospital admissions reported	100	
N	(1051)	

[a]Not all stays not verified were rejected. See text.

[b]Twelve of these admissions were in long term stay institutions and were not included in the analysis of short term hospital use.

addition to the stays initially reported by the family, institutional records revealed a few additional stays for patients with multiple admissions. Of all reported admissions, independent information was received for 88 percent. For 9 percent of the total, independent information failed to substantiate a stay reported by the family. These stays were about equally divided between those which the hospital reported occurred totally before or after the survey year 1963 and those for which the hospital had no record of inpatient care for the patient since January 1, 1962, although in the latter instance the patient may have received outpatient care from the hospital.

As a result of the verification, 5 percent of all reported stays were excluded from the final analysis. Not all stays which were not substantiated were rejected, since the proper hospital may not always have been contacted. In addition, while hospital record data were generally given preference, in a few instances data provided by the respondents were accepted because of their apparent validity and documentation.

As in earlier studies, there was no feasible check on the validity of family responses indicating that family members had *not* been hospitalized. A methodological study by the Survey Research Center comparing interviews with hospital records shows respondents underreporting hospital admissions by 10 percent.[5]

The verification data were used to improve the accuracy of the details regarding the admission as well as to determine whether the admission fit into the criteria required by the study. Discrepancies between the family reports of hospitalizations and the official records tended to be minor, although there was an inclination for families to overreport the magnitude of their hospital bills and the length of the hospital stays.

c. *Health insurance verification*.[6] An attempt was made in the 1963 study to validate *all* health insurance coverage reported by the sample. More limited validations were carried out in 1953 and 1958.

In 1963, policies were validated by sending mail questionnaires to insuring organizations for non-group enrollment and to both employers and insurers for group enrollment. Additional information was obtained from the hospital verification since this verification included questions on insurance benefits. From this information, policies could be verified and additional coverage sometimes discovered. It was also possible to find additional coverage through the insurance verification itself. For instance, an

5 "Reporting of Hospitalization in the Health Interview Survey," Public Health Service Publication No. 1000, ser. 2, no. 6 (1965).

6 A more detailed account of the health insurance verification procedure can be found in Ronald Andersen and Donald C. Riedel, "People and Their Hospital Insurance: Comparisons of the Uninsured, Those with One Policy, and Those with Multiple Coverage," Health Information Foundation, Research Series No. 23, 1967.

employer might provide information on previously unrecorded major medical coverage in addition to the basic coverage reported by the employee. Table A-6 shows the results of the health insurance verification.

Seventy-two percent of all policies reported were independently verified as health insurance which was in effect during 1963. For an additional 10 percent an independent source responded but was unable to verify the coverage reported by the respondent. Failure to verify could indicate a number of things including: (1) the respondent did not have the coverage

TABLE A-6
Results of health insurance verification: 1963

VERIFICATION PROCESS	PERCENT OF ALL POLICIES REPORTED	
Source of initial report on policy		
Family	98	
Insurer, employer, or hospital	2	
Type of information received through verification		
Independent information received	82	
Indicates health insurance in effect during 1963		72
Fails to substantiate coverage for 1963		10
No independent information received	17	
Armed Forces Dependents' Medical Care Program (no verification attempted)	1	
Disposition of policy following verification[a]		
Accepted for analysis	96	
Not accepted for analysis	4	
Total health insurance policies reported	100	
N	(2699)	

[a]Not all policies not verified were rejected. See text.

during 1963 or that it was not health insurance as defined in the study; (2) the independent source did not have enough information or erred when attempting to match records with interview data; or (3) the proper independent source was not contacted. For 17 percent of all policies reported, no verification was attempted because we did not have sufficient information regarding an independent source or the policy was not followed up as a result of a processing error.

Data from the family interview were compared with those obtained from the verification. The number of policies accepted for the final analysis was 2,598. Further comparisons were made to provide the most accurate information regarding type of carrier, enrollment, services covered, and premium cost. As in the previous studies, all classificatory decisions concerning the nature of an individual's health insurance status, regardless of the source of data, were made in the central office and none were made in the field. Much time and effort were spent in making each classification as accurate as possible, and many reference sources—government publications, Blue Cross and Blue Shield guides, publications of private insurance organizations, pamphlets, brochures, and sample policies furnished by employers—were used.

Some health insurance was most likely not reported by the respondent and not discovered by the verification. Based on a methodological check of group enrollment, it was concluded in the 1953 report that the underestimate of the population with hospital insurance due to underreporting was probably less than two percent.[7] There is little reason to believe that the underestimate should differ significantly in the 1963 study.

D. COMPARABILITY OF SAMPLE ESTIMATES WITH INDEPENDENT ESTIMATES

This section provides some idea of how sample estimates compare to estimates from other sources. Included are comparisons of demographic characteristics as reported by the Bureau of the Census. A second series of comparisons involves characteristics of actual health behavior such as use of and expenditures for health care and health insurance coverage as reported by the National Center for Health Statistics, the American Hospital Association, the Social Security Administration, and the Health Insurance Council.

1. Demographic characteristics

The comparison of the sample distributions of demographic variables with independently derived distributions shown in Table A-7 provides little evidence of severe bias. These comparisons were not "forced" to come out the way they did by the imposition of external quota controls in the selection of our sample. Since the sample was a strictly random one, the correspondence between estimates derived from it and estimates from independent sources cannot be an artificial consequence of the sampling procedures employed.

The demographic representativeness of the sample does not in any way *prove* that the sample is representative with regard to medical and insurance variables. Nevertheless, had the sample appeared to be badly biased with regard to demographic variables, there would have been considerable cause for concern over other possible biases. The apparent absence of severe demographic biases in this sample and the samples of earlier studies increases our confidence in the estimates made in this report.

[7] Anderson and Feldman, *Family Medical Costs*, pp. 234–35.

TABLE A-7

Comparison of demographic characteristics of NORC sample, February, 1964, with census estimates of the U.S. population

CHARACTERISTIC OF POPULATION	PERCENT	
	NORC	Census[8]
Sex		
Male	49	49[9] (March, 1964)
Female	51	51
Age		
0-4	10	11[10] (July, 1963)
5-14	21	21
15-19	9	8
20-24	6	6
25-34	12	12
35-44	13	13
45-54	11	11
55-64	8	9
65-74	6	6
75 and over	3	3
NA	1	—
Region		
Northeast	20	25[11] (March, 1964)
North central	29	28
South	33	30
West	18	16
Residence		
Urban	67	71[12] (April, 1963)
Rural non-farm	23	22
Rural farm	10	7
Color		
White	85	88[13] (March, 1964)
Non-white	15	12
Marital status (14 years and over)		
Single	23	23[14] (March, 1964)
Married	65	64
Widowed, divorced, separated	12	12
School years completed (25 years and over)		
0-4	5	7[15] (March, 1964)
5-8	27	27
9-11	19	18
12	30	30
13-15	10	9
16 and over	9	9
Labor force participation (14 years and over)		
Yes	52	54[16] (March, 1964)
No	48	46

TABLE A-7 (Cont.)

CHARACTERISTIC OF POPULATION	PERCENT	
	NORC	Census[8]
Major occupation group (14 years and over)		
Professional	12	13[17] (March, 1964)
Manager, official	11	11
Clerical	15	16
Sales	6	7
Craftsmen	15	12
Operatives	16	19
Service	12	13
Non-farm laborer	8	5
Farmers and managers	3	3
Farm workers and foremen	2	2
Family income before taxes		
Under $1,000	4	8[18] (1963)
1,000-1,999	9	10
2,000-3,499	14	13
3,500-4,999	13	13
5,000-7,499	25	23
7,500-9,999	15	15
10,000-12,499	10	8
12,500 and over	10	9
Number of persons in family		
1	16	16[19] (March, 1964)
2	26	27
3	18	17
4	17	17
5	11	11
6	6	6
7 and over	6	6
Live births per 1000 persons	20.6	21.9[20] (1963)
Deaths per 1000 persons	7.0	9.6[20] (1963)

8 Unless otherwise indicated these estimates exclude (or have been adjusted to exclude): (1) the institutionalized population as defined in *U.S. Census of Population: 1960, Inmates of Institutions,* Final Report PC(2)-8A; (2) members of the armed forces except those living off post or on post with their families.

9 *Current Population Reports,* P-20, no. 142, derived from Table B.

10 *Ibid.,* P-25, no. 276. This estimate excludes all members of the armed forces.

11 *Ibid.,* P-20, no. 142, derived from Table A.

12 *Current Population Reports,* P-27, no. 34, and *U.S. Census of Population: 1960,* vol. I.

13 *Current Population Reports,* P-20, no. 142.

14 *Ibid.,* P-20, no. 135.

15 *Ibid.,* P-20, no. 138.

16 *Ibid.,* P-20, no. 141, derived from Table 8.

17 *Ibid.,* P-20, no. 141, derived from Table 9.

18 *Ibid.,* P-60, no. 43, Table 1. Based on income distribution for families and unrelated individuals.

19 *Ibid.,* P-20, no. 139. Based on household size distribution including heads and all related persons.

20 *Ibid.,* P-25, no. 331, Table A.

2. Health behavior

Comparisons of estimates of actual health use, expenditures, and insurance coverage using the 1963 study's data and independent sources provide a more direct means for assessing the validity of the estimates made. For these comparisons data from the National Health Survey based on nationwide household interview surveys are used along with data collected from providers of care and insuring agencies.

Table A-8 compares estimates of use from the NORC sample with those

TABLE A-8
Comparison of estimates of health service use from the NORC sample with independent estimates: 1963

HEALTH SERVICE USE	NORC	NHS[21]	AHA[22]
Short term hospital			
Admissions per 100 persons per year	13	13[a]	14[b]
Mean length of stay	7.4	8.4	7.7
Total hospital days per 100 persons per year	96	111	104
Physician			
Percent seeing a physician within a year	65	66	—
Number of visits per person per year	4.6	4.5	—
Dentist			
Percent seeing a dentist within a year	38	42	—

[a]Hospital discharges.

[b]Base for rates is total civilian resident population while NORC and NHS rates are based on the civilian non-institutionalized population.

from the National Health Survey (NHS) and the American Hospital Association (AHA). Admission rates to short-term hospitals are similar for each source. Length of stay and total hospital day figures are somewhat higher for NHS than for the others, with the AHA figures exceeding NORC.

Differences between the NHS and NORC surveys may relate to the

21 National Health Survey data on use were taken from the following reports: (1) Hospital use: "Hospital Discharges and Length of Stay: Short Stay Hospitals, United States—July 1963–June 1964," PHS Publication No. 1000, ser. 10, no. 30 (June, 1966). (2) Physician use: "Volume of Physician Visits by Place of Visit and Type of Service, United States—July 1963–June 1964," PHS Publication No. 1000, ser. 10, no. 18 (June, 1965); and "Physician Visits, Interval of Visits and Children's Routine Checkup, United State—July 1963–June 1964," PHS Publication No. 1000, ser. 10, no. 19 (June, 1965). (3) Dental use: "Dental Visits, Time Interval since Last Visit, United States—July 1963–June 1964," PHS Publication No. 1000, ser. 10, no. 29 (April, 1966).

22 *Guide Issue, Journal of the American Hospital Association*, 39, pt. 2 (August 1, 1965): 438; and 40, pt. 2 (August 1, 1966): 432.

variance between the estimates: (a) the NHS study, while based on an average twelve-month period, includes data for some families from 1962 and others from 1964 as well as 1963 information. All NORC data is from 1963. (b) The NHS report is based on hospital discharges reported to have occurred within six months of the week of the interview while NORC estimates are based on reports for the full twelve months of 1963. Methodological studies have shown some increase in underreporting of hospitalizations with increase in time interval between the discharge and the interview.[23] (c) NHS data have been adjusted to include the hospital experience during the reference period of persons who died during that period prior to the time of interview. While the NORC interviewing technique picked up the hospital experiences of some of these decedents, the NHS adjustment overall probably shows more decedent use, especially for persons living alone prior to hospitalization. (d) The verification process for the NORC study eliminated much of the "overreporting" of hospitalization and in addition provided independent information on the length of hospital stays. Since people have a tendency to overreport length of stay, both of these factors would tend to make the NORC estimates lower than those of NHS, which were not verified through an independent source.[24]

The AHA data is based on mail questionnaire data provided by hospitals, generally covering a period from October 1, 1962, to September 30, 1963. Considering the divergent source of data for the NORC and AHA estimates it is surprising they are as close as they are. What seems even more surprising is that NORC's estimates of hospital use are closer to those of AHA than to those of NHS.

The physician use rates shown by NORC and NHS appear quite similar. However, a physician visit according to the NHS definition includes phone calls while such calls are excluded by NORC. Excluding such calls from the NHS estimate reduces the mean number of physician visits per year to 4.1. Another difference between the NORC and NHS estimates of mean visits per year is that the NHS estimate is based on a two-week recall period while the NORC estimate is based on a year recall period. This difference in recall period is also true with regard to the estimate of mean number of dental visits. As for hospital care, the data on which the physician and dental use estimates by NHS are based span a period from mid-1962 to mid-1964.

Table A-9 provides some comparisons of estimates of individual expenditure for personal health services provided by NHS and the Social Security Administration (SSA) with those made from the NORC sample.

---

[23] "Reporting of Hospitalization in the Health Interview Survey," PHS Publication No. 1000, ser. 2, no. 6 (July, 1965).

[24] *Ibid.*

The NHS estimate of total expenditure is highest, followed by SSA and NORC. Looking at expenditure by type of service we find the SSA estimate considerably higher than the others for hospital care while NHS shows the highest estimate for physician expenditures.

The NHS estimates are based on material collected by self-enumeration from July to December, 1962. Thus the method of collection and the period covered differ somewhat from the NORC study. The definitions of health expenditures for the two studies seem to correspond fairly closely, with one exception. Emergency or outpatient treatment in a hospital is classified as hospital expense in the NORC study and as "other expense" in the NHS study.

TABLE A-9

Comparison of estimates of private expenditures for personal health services from NORC sample with independent estimates: 1963

MEAN EXPENDITURE PER PERSON PER YEAR	NORC	NHS[25]	SSA[26]
Total	$112	$129	$118
Hospital	29	30	37
Physician	35	43	34
Drugs	23	26	22
Dental	15	19	12
Nursing home	a	a	3
Other	10	11	10

[a] Included but probably underestimated in the hospital component.

While we cannot say specifically why the NHS estimate is higher, we can mention some factors which may be important. Reported hospitalizations were verified with the hospitals in the NORC study but not in the NHS study. Since some hospitalizations and their corresponding costs were eliminated by this process and since people seem to have a tendency to overreport expenditures, this verification process probably had an over-all effect of reducing expenditure estimates based on the NORC sample. In addition, the self-enumeration method used by NHS apparently produces estimates of expenditures somewhat higher than the interview technique used by NORC.[27] This difference has been reported to be greatest for

[25] "Medical Care, Health Status, and Family Income, United States," PHS Publication No. 1000, ser. 10, no. 9 (May, 1964), p. 44.

[26] Louis S. Reed and Ruth S. Hanft, "National Health Expenditures, 1950–1964," *Social Security Bulletin*, 29 (January, 1966): 15.

[27] "Measurement of Personal Health Expenditures," PHS Publication No. 1000, ser. 2, no. 2 (June, 1963).

physician expenditures and in fact the NHS estimate for physician expenditure is $8 more per person than that made by NORC.

The SSA estimate of expenditures has been reduced by the cost of insurance, since this cost is not included in the NORC estimate. The nursing care components in the NORC and NHS estimates are included in the hospital component, though, because of the nature of survey collection, private expenditures for nursing home care are probably underestimated in the latter estimates.

Excluding the nursing home component, the NORC and SSA estimates are very close. They would be even closer if family expenditures for nonfamily members, which are excluded in the NORC estimates, were included, as they apparently are in the SSA estimates.

TABLE A-10

Comparison of estimates of voluntary health insurance coverage from NORC sample with independent estimates: 1963

HEALTH INSURANCE COVERAGE	NORC	NHS[29]	HIC [30]
Percent of total population with:			
Any health insurance coverage	69	—	77
Hospital insurance	68	70	77
Surgical insurance	65	65	71
Percent of those with hospital coverage insured by:			
Blue Cross	46[a]	45[a]	42[a]
Private insurance	53	54	61
Independent	7		5
Unknown	1	7	—

[a]Percentages exceed 100 as a result of multiple coverage.

It should be remembered that the estimates from SSA and NORC are based on entirely different types of surveys. While the NORC estimates are derived from charges reported by consumers, SSA estimates are based on producer income data. Responses to either or both surveys may have been subject to bias of over- or underreporting of a fairly substantial nature.[28]

Table A-10 provides comparison estimates of voluntary health insurance coverage as provided by NORC, NHS and the Health Insurance Council

28 Many of the differences between these types of data are discussed in Anderson, Collette, and Feldman, *Changes in Medical Care Expenditures*, Appendix D, pp. 207–13.

29 "Health Insurance Coverage, United States—July 1962–June 1963," PHS Publication No. 1000, ser. 10, no. 11 (August, 1964); and "Health Insurance—Type of Insuring Organization and Multiple Coverage, United States, July 1962–June 1963," PHS Publication No. 1000, ser. 10, no. 16 (April, 1965).

30 "Source Book of Health Insurance Data, 1964," Health Insurance Institute.

(HIC). Estimates by NORC and NHS are fairly close, while estimates by HIC, based on surveys of insuring agencies, show a higher proportion of the population with some insurance, and among those with insurance a higher proportion insured by private insurance companies. These differences between household surveys and surveys of insuring agencies have been found consistently since 1953, though the magnitudes of the differences found here are among the largest reported.[31]

[31] A discussion of these differences is found in Anderson, Collette, and Feldman, *Changes in Medical Care Expenditures*, pp. 122–24.

II

DEFINITION OF TERMS

1. *Basic health insurance:* Hospital and/or surgical-medical insurance.

2. *Benefits from health insurance:* Includes only payments by insurance designed specifically to cover medical expenses incurred in connection with illness, such as hospital expense, surgical, and major medical expense insurance. Excluded are benefits from straight accident insurance, disability or loss-of-income insurance with no separable payment for hospital expenses, and life insurance. A benefit designated as covering medical care expenses under the accident clause of a policy designed to cover expenses connected with illness was, however, classed as a health insurance benefit.

3. *Dental care:* Positive response to question, "Did you (PERSON) have any dental care such as teeth cleaned, X-rayed, filled or pulled, or any bridgework done last year?"

4. *Enrollment:* Method by which families and individuals subscribe to health insurance. Two categories were used in this study:

(a) *Group:* Enrollment through membership in an organization covered by one general health insurance policy. Method generally used by employees and their dependents.

(b) *Non-group:* Single policy purchased or maintained by an individual providing health insurance protection for himself and/or his dependents.

5. *Expenditures for personal health services:* Estimated charges incurred by families for medical and dental services. Includes health insurance benefits but excludes health insurance premiums. Includes charges incurred by family during survey year which had not been paid at time of interview. Definitions and estimated expenditures in 1963 for the components of the total are given in Table M.

6. *Eye care:* Positive response to question "Did you (PERSON) have glasses made or replaced or have an eye examination within the year?"

7. *Family:* One person or a group of persons, living together and related to each other by blood, marriage or adoption. However, when there were

TABLE M

SERVICE OR GOODS	AMOUNT (Billions of dollars)	
All physicians	$ 6.4	
Surgery in hospital[a]		1.3
Surgery out of hospital[a]		0.2
Obstetrics[b]		.6
Oculist, ophthalmologist[c]		.1
Other physician in hospital[d]		.7
Other physician, house call[d]		.3
Other physician, office[d]		3.2
Hospital	5.4	
Hospital inpatient charges[e]		5.1
Hospital outpatient charges[f]		0.3
Prescriptions and other medicines	4.2	
Prescribed drugs[g]		2.8
Non-prescribed medicines and drugs[h]		1.4
Other medical goods and services	1.9	
Non-medical practitioners[i]		0.6
Other medical care[j]		1.3
Dentist[k]	2.7	
Total	20.7[l]	

[a]Surgery: Physicians' charges for all cutting procedures except caesarian delivery, circumcision of the newborn, and the suturing of wounds, but including the setting of dislocations and fractures. In general, they consist of the charge for the operation only, but in a few instances include also charges for pre-operative and post-operative care when these could not be distinguished from the charge for the operation itself. They include charges for physicians assisting at the operation but exclude charges by the anesthesiologist and charges for oral surgery when performed by a dentist.

[b]Obstetrics: Physicians' charges in connection with prenatal care and delivery regardless of when in the survey year the child was born. Included are charges for a caesarian delivery, for circumcision when performed right after birth, for a D & C in connection with the delivery, and for the anesthesiologist.

[c]Oculist, ophthalmologist: Physicians' charges for refraction, diagnosis, and treatment of the eye. Excludes charges for surgery of the eye, which are included under "surgery," and for optical appliances, included under "other medical care."

[d]Other physician: Charges for care other than surgery, obstetrics, or by an oculist or ophthalmologist. Includes charges for care by the practitioner himself and for special tests and X-rays, treatments drugs, and medications when the physician himself bills the patient for such services without necessarily performing them himself.

[e]Hospital inpatient: Charges incurred in connection with an inpatient admission. They include room-and-board charges, laboratory fees, drugs, X-rays, operating and delivery room fees, and the usual "extras." They include charges for pathologist, radiologist, and anesthesiologist only when these are included in the hospital bill, but always exclude charges for special-duty nursing in the hospital.

[f]Hospital outpatient: Charges for services given in a hospital outpatient clinic or emergency room by a salaried physician or technician in the employ of a hospital. Includes charges by a hospital laboratory or outpatient department for tests, X-rays, treatments, etc. Covers charges for outpatient care only, and excludes charges for tests, treatments, etc., of hospital inpatients, as described in note e above. Excludes charges for service in the outpatient department or emergency room by a private physician.

[g]Prescribed drugs: Charges for drugs and medicines prescribed at some time by the physician, other medical practitioner, or dentist, and purchased by the consumer directly from the pharmacy or elsewhere. It excludes medicines administered by the doctor or dentist and charged on his bill as well as medicines received in a hospital and included in the hospital bill.

hNon-prescribed medicines and drugs: Charges for all other medicines, tonics, vitamins, drops, etc., not included in note g above.

iNon-medical practitioners: Includes the following—charges for special-duty nursing in hospital in addition to that provided by the hospital as part of its regular service and included in the regular hospital bill; service by an optometrist, optician, or optical company excluding charges for eye glasses (the latter are included in "other medical care"); practitioners other than physicians or dentists, such as physical therapists, practical nurses, midwives, the registered nurse in the home, chiropodists, Christian Science practitioners, and chiropractors.

jOther medical care: Charges for appliances and prostheses such as eyeglasses, hearing aids, crutches, wheelchairs, braces, orthopedic shoes, elastic stockings, and vaporizers. Also includes ambulance fees, charge for oxygen if not billed by a hospital or doctor directly, dressings and bandages purchased for the use of a patient at home, charges for diagnostic tests and X-rays given by a non-hospital laboratory and for which the patient was billed directly, and so on. Excludes charges for dental appliances.

kDentist: Charges by the dentist for his service and that of his auxiliary personnel, and for dental appliances. Includes also expenditures to cover charges made to him by dental laboratories and dental manufacturers for work done at his request.

lComponents do not equal total because of rounding.

two related married couples living in a single dwelling unit, each married couple and its unmarried children are a separate family. Any person who is unrelated to anyone else in the dwelling unit is a separate family.

8. *Family income:* Total family money income before taxes for the survey year. Income from wages, salaries, own business or farm, professional work or trade, pensions, rents, welfare agencies, unemployment compensation, alimony, regular contributions from friends or relatives, dividends, interest, and similar sources are included. Income in kind—the value of free rent or non-cash benefits—is excluded. In the 1958 and 1963 studies, data on income were obtained through a series of questions covering the earned income of each worker in the family and unearned and other income for the family as a whole. Total family income is the sum of these components.

9. *Family income level:* Division of families according to family income into roughly the upper third, middle third, and lower third. The actual incomes represented by each group changed through each time interval in accordance with the over-all rising level of income. The incomes represented by each category in each year are given in Table N.

TABLE N

	INCOMES REPRESENTED BY EACH FAMILY INCOME LEVEL		
YEAR	Lower	Middle	Upper
1953	Under $3,000	$3,000-4,999	$5,000 and over
1958	Under 3,500	3,500-5,999	6,000 and over
1963	Under 4,000	4,000-6,999	7,000 and over

10. *Free medical care:* Medical goods and services provided to the family at no direct cost or at substantially reduced rates and without benefits being provided by any type of health insurance plan. Some sources of

such care include the Veterans Administration; Armed Services for service personnel; other federal facilities (U.S. Public Health Service hospitals and Maritime hospitals); state or local government hospitals, clinics, and other facilities; private charitable organizations; workmen's compensation and employers' liability insurance; health care facilities of educational or industrial organizations; professional courtesy by doctors for friends, relatives, or colleagues or because of the patient's economic circumstances; medical facilities doing research; services paid by some non-family member directly or through the insurance this person holds (e.g., liability insurance). For a family to be defined as receiving free care in this study such care must have been provided for one or more members having a hospitalized illness, a non-hospitalized illness episode or a terminated pregnancy. In addition, all or most of the care for the condition must have been provided free.

11. *Head of family:* Self-defined by family respondents, with one exception—the male member of a married couple was always coded head. If respondent was unable to decide who was family head, the person owning the dwelling unit, the one who signed the mortgage or lease, or the one mainly responsible for rent was coded head.

12. *Health insurance:* Any plan specifically designed to pay all or part of the health expenses, as outlined in Definition 5, of the insured individual. Included are plans limited to the "dread diseases" and individuals covered under the Uniformed Services Dependents Medical Care Program (in 1958 and 1963). The latter were included since coverage under this plan largely removed them from the health insurance market and because the program provides fairly generous coverage for use of civilian medical facilities. Under this definition present coverage under Title 18 would be defined as health insurance, but services provided under Title 19 would be classified as free care. See Definition 10. Excluded are: (a) free care such as public assistance, care for veterans, care given under the Crippled Children Program or similar programs, and care for persons admitted for research purposes; (b) insurance which pays bills only for accidents or work-related diseases; (c) insurance which pays only for loss of income resulting from illness or injury.

13. *Hospital admission:* Overnight stay in and/or surgery performed in hospitals classified as general or special short term by the American Hospital Association and in hospitals not listed by the AHA but not clearly long term. Excluded are admissions to hospitals classified as general or special long term, mental and allied, and tuberculosis hospitals. Only admissions beginning during the survey year are included. The delivery admission for an obstetrical case is counted as one admission for the mother and none for the infant. However, if the infant stays in the hos-

pital after the mother goes home or if the infant is readmitted after being discharged, a separate admission is counted for the infant.

14. *Hospital days:* Days spent in general or special short-term hospitals during the survey year.

15. *Hospital insurance:* Health insurance designed to pay all or part of the hospital bill for the insured person. Hospital bill includes only the bill submitted by the hospital itself, not the doctor's bill or the bill for special nurses. Insurance which pays a flat amount when the person is ill or injured is classified as hospital insurance only when the patient receives a larger amount when he is hospitalized than when he is not hospitalized.

16. *Hospitalized illness episode:* All medical care received during 1963 for an illness or condition for which an individual spent one night or more in a hospital, sanitarium, convalescent or rest home, and/or for which any form of surgery was performed at a hospital during the survey year. Multiple admissions for the same condition are treated as part of the same hospitalized illness episode. Pregnancies and associated hopitalizations are not included as hospitalized illness episodes. The National Health Survey concept of "hospital episode" differs in that it is synonymous with hospital admission. ("Persons hospitalized by number of hospital episodes and days in a year." National Center for Health Statistics, ser. 10, no. 20, June, 1965.)

17. *Industry of main earner:* Coded according to U.S. Bureau of the Census, *Classified Index of Occupations and Industries,* 1950.

18. *Insured family:* Family in which one or more members were covered by some type of health insurance (unless a particular type is indicated in the text) on the last day of the survey year.

19. *Insured hospital admission:* Patient had some hospital insurance in effect at time of admission regardless of whether insurance actually provided any benefits to cover costs of the admission.

20. *Insured hospitalized surgical procedure:* Hospital patient had some surgical-medical insurance in effect at the time surgical procedure was done regardless of whether insurance actually provided any benefits to cover costs of the procedure.

21. *Insured person:* Individual covered by any type of health insurance (unless a particular type is indicated in the text) on the last day of the survey year or on the last day individual was in the population for sample individuals leaving population during the survey year (e.g., those dying or becoming institutionalized). In calculating percentages of persons insured for various types of services, NA's (people for whom information on coverage was not provided in the interview and could not be determined by our verification procedures) were included in base (treated as not insured). This practice differed from the usual procedure of excluding NA's

from the base. However, extensive efforts were made to locate and code the presence of, and the type of, all insurance in the family. Consequently, there was no evidence indicating insurance for the remaining NA's and they were included in the uninsured categories. Table O shows the number of such individuals and families for each type of insurance and how the exclusion of them from the base would have affected the resulting estimates of coverage in 1963. In no instance is the difference in estimates more than one percentage point.

TABLE O

	PERCENT INSURED					
	Individuals			Families		
TYPE OF INSURANCE	Including NA	Excluding NA	NA	Including NA	Excluding NA	NA
Any health insurance	69	69	(13)	74	74	(4)
Hospital	68	68	(51)	73	74	(16)
Surgical-medical	66	67	(77)	71	72	(26)
Major-medical	22	23	(162)	24	24	(59)

22. *Insurer:* Organization providing protection against the costs of hospital and medical care arising from illness or injury. Four types of insurers were analyzed in this study:

(a) *Private insurance:* a private corporation engaged in the business of furnishing health insurance protection to the public.

(b) *Blue Cross-Blue Shield:* independent nonprofit membership corporations providing protection against the costs of hospital care, surgery and other items of medical care.

(c) *Independent plans:* Organizations which are *not* Blue Cross or Blue Shield or private insurance companies, and which directly provide or pay for health services on a group prepayment, risk-spreading basis. Some of these plans serve the general population of an area while the majority are organizations (usually of employed persons) restricting service to the members of the organization and usually their dependents.

(d) *Armed Forces Dependents' Medical Care Program:* Federal government financed plan to pay for hospital and medical services used by dependents of armed forces personnel.

23. *Loss-of-income benefits:* Based on response of family reporting a loss of income due to illness or accidents to following question, "Did (family member losing wages) receive any workmen's compensation, or any cash benefits from an insurance company, union, fraternal order, or any other source to help cover the loss of income?"

24. *Main earner in family:* Every family was defined as having a main earner who must have been a family member on the last day of the survey year. The main earner was determined as follows:

(a) *One person family:* Individual automatically coded main earner.

(b) *Family includes two adults (14 or over) who are a married couple.*

(1) Male coded main earner unless not in labor force (retired, disabled, unable to work). Even if male head was currently unemployed, or only part-time worker, he was coded main earner.

(2) If male head not in labor force but wife was in labor force, wife was coded main earner.

(3) If neither male nor female was in labor force, male was coded main earner.

(c) *Family includes 3 or more adults including a married couple.*

(1) With adult children, none of whom was in the labor force, coded as in *b* above.

(2) With adult children or other adult relatives in labor force, husband, if working full time, coded main earner.

(3) In all other *c* situations, the family member earning the most money coded as main earner.

(d) *Family includes two or more adults none of whom is married.*

(1) If only one adult in labor force, he was coded main earner.

(2) If two or more adults in labor force, the one earning the most money was coded main earner.

(3) If no adults in labor force, that person judged to have the greatest potential earning power, or having largest past earnings, was coded main earner.

25. *Major medical insurance:* Health insurance especially designed to help offset the heavy medical expenses resulting from catastrophic or prolonged illness or injury. Such insurance typically includes a cash deductible ($25 or more), coinsurance (75–80 percent), a maximum payment ($5,000–10,000), and coverage of most non-hospital as well as hospital expenses associated with illness.

26. *Mean length of hospital stay:* Sum of short-term hospital days falling within the twelve-month survey year, divided by admissions included in the definition "hospital admission." The sum of days includes those associated with admissions beginning before the survey year. The latter admissions are not included in the denominator, which includes only admissions beginning during the survey year.

27. *Medical debt:* The definition from the 1953 study differs from the definition of medical indebtedness used in the 1963 study. The 1953 definition *excluded* debts to financial institutions and individuals which were incurred to pay for personal health services or goods, but they are in-

cluded in 1963. The 1953 definition included debts owed to hospitals, physicians, dentists and other suppliers of medical goods and services at the end of the survey year *less* any amount which the family planned to pay on such bills during the month following the interview. The last stipulation was not included in the 1963 definition since the interviewing started in February of 1964 and covered the calendar year 1963. Since the definitions are not the same, no direct comparisons should be made regarding medical debt between the 1953 and 1963 studies. However, a very general type of comparison can be made with the 20 percent figure arrived at in 1963 by adding the families with outstanding medical indebtedness (15 percent of the 1953 sample) and those borrowing during the survey year to pay for personal health services (4 percent of the 1953 sample). The resulting 19 percent proportion with some financial obligation for health services is similar to the 20 percent figure arrived at in 1963. Evidently the picture, at least in terms of the proportions of families involved, changed little during the decade.

28. *Non-hospitalized illness episode:* Condition not resulting in a hospitalization but requiring one or more of the following during 1963: (a) five or more physician visits; (b) fifty dollars or more for medical expenses; (c) regular care or treatment because of a long-standing medical condition.

29. *Outlay for personal health services:* Computed as follows: total charges for health services received during the survey year; *plus* prepayment and insurance premiums for insurance designed specifically to cover charges for personal health services (including family but excluding employer contributions); *plus* payments by the family for personal health services received by persons not family members; *minus* health insurance benefits covering personal health services received during the survey year; *minus* amounts still owed for personal health services; *minus* accident or liability insurance benefits covering personal health services received during the survey year; *minus* payments from friends and relatives outside the family toward charges for personal health services incurred by family members during the survey year.

30. *Person-years:* Base for some of the rates presented in text. Calculated by summing the total months spent by sample members in the population universe during the survey year and dividing this sum by 12. The purpose of this base is to adjust for infants and other sample members who were not in the population the entire survey year, such as those who died or became institutionalized during the year. Hence, the terms hospital admissions per 100 "person-years" and hospital days per 100 "person-years."

31. *Physical examination:* Positive response by family to question, "How long ago did you (PERSON) last have a physical examination or checkup?" Examinations were classified according to a checklist of reasons as follows:

Classification	*Checklist reason*
Symptom	"Wasn't feeling good, was bothered by some symptom or condition."
Required	"Examination was *required* for a job, school, insurance, armed forces, summer camp, or something like that."
Preventive	"There was nothing particularly wrong and the examination wasn't required—it was just time for a checkup or physical examination."

32. *Physician visit:* Seeing either a doctor or osteopath or his nurse or technician at the following sites: (a) visits at the *office* of a physician in private practice; (b) visits at a hospital outpatient, industrial, school, "well baby," or public health department *clinic;* (c) visits made by a physician to the patient's own *home;* and (d) visits made to a *hospital* inpatient by patient's own physician or hospital staff physician.

33. *Race:* Each family member was coded according to the race of the household head if known, or the race of the main respondent as observed by the interviewer. People of Mexican or Spanish descent were coded as "white." American Indians and Orientals were coded as "non-white."

34. *Regular source of medical care:* Coded for each sample member as follows—

"General Practitioner"—Individual listed in *AMA Directory 1963* with primary specialty as "general practitioner," "unspecified" or "specialty not recognized"; or individual not found in AMA or AOA directories but family classifies him as "regular family doctor."

"Specialist"—Individual listed in *AMA Directory* with primary specialty as some recognized specialty; or individual not found in AMA or AOA Directory but family classifies him as "some type of specialist."

"Clinic"—No individual is mentioned but the name of a clinic or outpatient service is given by the family as a regular source of care.

"Osteopath"—Individual listed in the *1964 Yearbook and Directory of Osteopathic Physicians;* individual not found in the AMA or AOA directories but family classifies him as "osteopath."

"Other care"—Family classifies regular source of care as chiropractor or other practitioner such as a visiting nurse, Christian Science practitioner, homeopath, podiatrist, naturopath or anyone else without a formal medical degree who gives health care.

"Indeterminate"—No regular source is specified or family does not know type of regular source.

"No regular source of care"—Family indicates that there is no "particular" medical person or clinic that individual usually goes to when sick or for advice about health.

35. *Residence:* Classification of each household according to urban-rural and farm-non-farm dwelling. The definition of "urban" for the 1953 and 1958 studies is that used in the 1950 Census of Population. The definition of "urban" used in the 1963 study is that used in the 1960 Census of Population. While there were some changes between the 1950 and 1960 designations of urban towns and townships in New Jersey and Pennsylvania, the definitions as they apply to the country as a whole remained substantially the same.

"Large urban metropolitan area" referred to the urban parts of Standard Metropolitan Areas of 1 million or more according to the 1950 census for the 1953 and 1958 studies. The same term was used to designate urban residences of the 10 largest SMSA's according to the 1960 census in the 1963 study. For all three studies "other urban" includes all people living in urban areas not defined in that study as "large urban area."

In each study the rural population was divided into farm and non-farm according to the interviewer's designation whether the family was living on a farm or in a non-farm residence.

36. *Savings:* Based on interview question to family as follows, "We're interested in current savings such as in banks, savings and loan associations, or government bonds that the family might use to meet heavy medical costs in an emergency. . . ."

37. *Surgical-medical insurance:* Health insurance which pays in whole or part the bill of the physician for surgery, whether performed in a hospital or the doctor's office, and/or insurance which pays the doctor's bill for non-surgical care such as home and office calls for special diagnostic examinations.

38. *Surgical procedure:* Any cutting procedure (including caesarean deliveries, but not normal deliveries) or setting of a dislocation or fracture. Endoscopic procedures, suturing of wounds, and circumcision of newborn infants, often classified as surgical procedures, are not so classified in this study.

39. *Terminated pregnancy:* All medical care received in connection with a pregnancy that ended in 1963 through a live birth, still birth or miscarriage.

III

QUESTIONNAIRE

NOTE: The questionnaire shown in this report has been altered from the form actually used in the field to the extent that answer space for more than one family member, wage earner, and insurance policy included in the original form does not appear in this edited version. In each case the deleted material exactly replicates that shown here.

NORC SRS-180
January, 1964

| TIME INTERVIEW BEGAN: |
| AM |
| PM |

SURVEY RESEARCH SERVICE
National Opinion Research Center
University of Chicago

1-4

HOUSEHOLD ENUMERATION FOLDER

Begin Deck 01

FAMILY NAME _____

ADDRESS _____

_____

Segment No. [ ][ ][ ][ ][ ]   17-22

Household No. [ ][ ]   23-24

Family Unit [ ]   25

Circle one:

Located on farm 1   26/0

Non-farm: single family house 2

Non-farm: duplex or two-family
    structure 3

Non-farm: multi-unit structure
    (e.g., apartment) 4

Circle one:

Inside largest city in the primary unit 6   27/5

In a suburb of the largest city in primary
  sampling unit 7

In the outskirts (including nearby small
  towns of the primary sampling units) .. 8

In open country 9

RECORD OF CALLS FOR HOUSEHOLD

Call	Date	Time	Results
1			
2			
3			
4			
5			
6			
Notes:			

INTRODUCTION:

Hello: I'm _____ from the National Opinion Research Center. We're conducting a nation-wide study of family health practices and the costs of medical care. You should have received letters explaining this study.

To start, I'd like to know who lives here.

1. Who is the head of your household? **Enter name on the first line in the table below.**

2. Who else lives in your household? **List relationship of each before going on to the next. List names in the following order: Head's spouse; unmarried children; married children, spouses and offspring; other relatives; persons unrelated to anyone in the family.**

   Have we missed anyone? Children or babies? Someone away for a short time, at school or college, on business? A lodger or roomer?

3. **Enter "1" under "Family Unit" (Item 3) for head, head's spouse, unmarried children, married children and other relatives** *not now living with their spouses.*

   Enter "2," "3," etc. for additional married couples with *both partners now living in household* **and for their unmarried children; also for persons** *unrelated* **to anyone in the household. Transfer** *unrelated persons* **to another folder and conduct** *separate* **interview beginning with Q. 4.**

PEOPLE IN HOUSEHOLD NOW OR ONLY TEMPORARILY AWAY			
1-2. First Last		Relation to HEAD	3. Family Unit
		HEAD	

Ask 4A and 4B for every household.

    4A. Did any relative live with you during 1963 who has since died or who isn't living with you now? **Check one.**

        Yes _____ **Enter each name in separate column on page 3.**

        No _____

    4B. Did any member of this family live with some other *relative* in the past year? **Check one.**

        Yes _____ **Enter name(s) of relative(s) on page 3.**

        No _____

If "yes" to "4A" *or* **"4B" ask "5" for each name.**

If "no" to *both* **"4A" and "4B" skip to the directions at the bottom of page 3.**

PEOPLE NOT IN HOUSEHOLD NOW			
4A or B. Name:	**4A or B.** Name:	**4A or B.** Name:	**4A or B.** Name:
5. Relation to Head: No Relat. ____ : **Stop**	**5.** Relation to Head: No Relat. ____ : **Stop**	**5.** Relation to Head: No Relat. ____ : **Stop**	**5.** Relation to Head: No Relat. ____ : **Stop**
6. In Other Household ____ : **Stop** Dead . . . . ____ Institution ⎫ Armed Forces ⎪ Outside U.S. ⎬ ____ Other, D.K. ⎭	**6.** In Other Household ____ : **Stop** Dead . . . . ____ Institution ⎫ Armed Forces ⎪ Outside U.S. ⎬ ____ Other, D.K. ⎭	**6.** In Other Household ____ : **Stop** Dead . . . . ____ Institution ⎫ Armed Forces ⎪ Outside U.S. ⎬ ____ Other, D.K. ⎭	**6.** In Other Household ____ : **Stop** Dead . . . . ____ Institution ⎫ Armed Forces ⎪ Outside U.S. ⎬ ____ Other, D.K. ⎭
7. Yes ____ No ____ : **Stop**	**7.** Yes ____ No ____ : **Stop**	**7.** Yes ____ No ____ : **Stop**	**7.** Yes ____ No ____ : **Stop**
8. No. Months . . . ____	**8.** No. Months . . . ____	**8.** No. Months . . . ____	**8.** No. Months . . . ____
9. Family Unit . . ____	**9.** Family Unit . . ____	**9.** Family Unit . . ____	**9.** Family Unit . . ____

5. How is (PERSON) related to present household head? **If no relation to anyone in family, draw a line thru name — go no further with person. If related, ask 6.**

6. Where is this person now? **If "in other household," draw a line thru name — go no further with person. Otherwise ask 7.**

7. Just before (PERSON) (died, was institutionalized, entered the armed forces, left the U.S.) was he living with any of you who are now in this family? **If "no," draw a line thru name—go no further with person. If "yes," ask 8.**

8. How many months during 1963 was (PERSON) in the same household as any family member(s)? **Enter No. of months.**

9. **Enter "1," "2" etc., giving this person the same family unit number as those he lived with or those who lived with him.**

Now transfer *all* members of additional family units ("2" family, "3" family, etc.) as recorded in items 3 and 9 to separate enumeration folders — conduct separate interviews with each additional family unit beginning with Q. 10. Ask 10 (back of folder) for first Family Unit.

10. Now I need some general information about each of the family members. **List separately below names of family unit members assigned the same number in Q's 3 *and* 9. Record the following information:**

Begin Deck 02

FOR EACH FAMILY MEMBER				14 YEARS OR OLDER ONLY					
	5-6	7-8	9	10-11	12		13	14	15-16
Name	Person Number	AGE	Sex	No. Years School	Marital Status		Member of Labor Union Now	Service in Regular Armed Forces	
			M F		S M W D-S		Yes No	Yes No	
	0 1		1 2		3 4 5 6		7 8	0 1	
	0 2		1 2		3 4 5 6		7 8	0 1	
	0 3		1 2		3 4 5 6		7 8	0 1	
	0 4		1 2		3 4 5 6		7 8	0 1	
	0 5		1 2		3 4 5 6		7 8	0 1	
	0 6		1 2		3 4 5 6		7 8	0 1	
	0 7		1 2		3 4 5 6		7 8	0 1	
	0 8		1 2		3 4 5 6		7 8	0 1	
	0 9		1 2		3 4 5 6		7 8	0 1	
	1 0		1 2		3 4 5 6		7 8	0 1	
	1 1		1 2		3 4 5 6		7 8	0 1	
	1 2		1 2		3 4 5 6		7 8	0 1	

Deck 01

11. Record family's total size   Size .... ⬜⬜   28-29

12. What is (HEAD's) religious preference?

    Specify if "Protestant" or Other:

Protestant 0   30-31
Catholic 1   y
Jewish 2
Other 3
None 4

13. Where did (HEAD) live when he (she) was about 16 years old? (What state, territory, or foreign country?) **If D.K. skip to 15**   32-33

    14. Was this in a large city (100,000+) a town or suburban area, or in open country (on a farm)?

City 6   34
Town 7   5
Open Country 8
D.K. 9

15. Were either of (HEAD's) parents born outside the U.S.? **If "Yes," specify place:**

Yes 1   35
No 2   0
D.K. 3

16. Was any language other than English spoken in (HEAD's) childhood home? **Specify language:**

Yes 5   36
No 6   4
D.K. 7

17. What kind of work did (HEAD's) father do when (HEAD) was about 16 years old?

                                        37-38
                                Occupation   y

                                        39-40
                                Industry   y

SURVEY RESEARCH SERVICE

National Opinion Research Center

University of Chicago

1-4

MAIN QUESTIONNAIRE

Family Name: _____

Hsld. No.

Fam. Unit

Begin Deck 11

Now we're ready to talk about the different kinds of medical care each person in the family may have had in 1963. I want to find out about the care and expenses [Name(s) of person(s) in the unit at the end of 1963] had for the WHOLE YEAR, 1963.

If someone left the family unit during the year: I need to know about the medical care and expenses (Name(s) of person(s) *leaving* the Family Unit during the year) had WHILE LIVING WITH YOU during 1963.

1. I'd like to talk with whomever knows the most about the health and costs of medical care during 1963 for your family. **Enter name and person Number (Q. 10, Folder).**

Main respondent(s): _____   7-8

_____   9-10

---

2. **Review listing (Folder Q. 10). If you note a baby born during 1963 code "Yes" (circle 1), otherwise code "No" (circle 2).**   Yes: **Fill out a Terminated Pregnancy Supplement (yellow)** 1   11 / 0

No: **Ask 3 if applicable** 2

---

3. **If there is a married woman under 45 in the family:** Were there any (other) pregnancies in the family during 1963? I'm interested in all pregnancies including current ones and even those that ended in miscarriages.   Yes: **Ask 4** 4   12 / 3

No: **Turn to page 2** 5

No woman Under 45: **Turn to page 2** 6

---

4. Was (MOTHER) still pregnant at the end of last year, that is on December 31, 1963?   Yes: **Fill out a Current Pregnancy Supplement (yellow)** 8   13 / 7

No: **Fill out a Terminated Pregnancy Supplement (yellow)** 9

202

Enter in separate columns name and person number of each family member listed in Q. 10 of enumeration folder *except* baby under one year old. Record information separately for each member.

Name: _____

Per. No.

[|] 5-6

	Begin Deck 21

5. Were you (PERSON) a patient in a hospital, sanatorium, convalescent or nursing home (apart from having a baby) last year, that is from January 1, through December 31, 1963? **Fill out Hospital Supplement (pink) for each member checked "yes."**

Yes: Fill out
   Hosp. Supp. ...... 1 $\frac{7}{0}$
No 2

6. During 1963 did you (PERSON) have any (other) illness, accident, or condition for which doctors or osteopaths were seen *five* or more times?

Yes .... 4 $\frac{8}{3}$
No 5

7. Did you (PERSON) have any (other) illness, condition or accident for which the charges were as much as *$50 altogether* for doctor's care, medicine, treatments, and so on from January through December of 1963?

Yes .... 7 $\frac{9}{6}$
No 8

8. Did any family member have any (other) one long standing medical condition for which they've needed *regular care or medicines* during 1963 (things like high blood pressure, heart condition, arthritis, sinus trouble, or diabetes)? **Check each member's column.**

Yes .... 1 $\frac{10}{0}$
No 2

9. **Fill out a Major Illness Supplement (blue) for each member with a "yes" checked in Q's. 6, 7, or 8. Record in each column whether or not at least one Major Illness Supplement was filled out for that person.**

Maj. Ill. Supp.
   Filled Out .... 4 $\frac{11}{3}$
No Maj. Ill. Supp. 5

MINOR TREATMENT

Up to now we've been talking about illnesses or conditions that may have involved quite a bit of expense during the past twelve months. Now I'd like to find out about more routine, minor medical care which we haven't talked about.

10. Did you (PERSON) see a doctor or osteopath at your home for any illness or condition (other than what we've talked about already) during 1963? If "No" for entire family skip to Q. 13.

Yes: Ask 11-12 ...... 0 $\frac{12}{y}$
No: Ret. to 10 NM ... X

  11. How many times did you (PERSON) see the doctor in your home?

Times: ...... [|] $\frac{13-14}{y}$

  12. How much was the bill for home visits including *both* what you paid and anything insurance paid?

$ ...... [|] $\frac{15-17}{y}$

13. Did you (PERSON) visit a private doctor's office during 1963 (besides what we've already covered)? How about for routine checkups, shots or vaccinations, or any other test or treatment? If "No" for entire family, skip to Q. 17.

Yes: Ask 14-16 ...... 0 $\frac{18}{y}$
No: Ret. to 13 NM ... X

  14. How many times did (PATIENT) visit a doctor's office when you didn't see the doctor but were taken care of by a nurse or technician? (Got shots, tests, X-rays or something like that.)

Times: ...... [|] $\frac{19-20}{y}$

  15. How many times did (PATIENT) see a doctor or osteopath at his office?

Times: ...... [|] $\frac{21-22}{y}$

  16. How much did the doctor charge for *all* the care (PATIENT) got at the *office*? Let's include bills for examinations, shots, tests, X-rays and so on, given by the doctor or his nurse, counting anything insurance may have paid.

$ ...... [|] $\frac{23-25}{y}$

203

Enter in separate columns name and person number of each family member listed in Q. 10 of enumeration folder *except* baby under one year old. Record information separately for each member.

---

17. For each member with doctor visits (Qs. 10 and 13): What kind of illness(es) or condition(s) did (PATIENT) see the doctor for?

Illness:

26

27

---

18. Apart from anything mentioned so far, did anyone in the family go to a hospital outpatient service or emergency room, an industrial or school clinic, or a company or insurance doctor for any tests, shots, or vaccinations or treatments of any kind? **Mark each member's column. If "No" for entire family, skip to Q. 22.**

Yes: Ask 19-21 ...... 0 28

No: .... X y

---

19. How many times did you (PERSON) visit there when you were seen by a nurse, technician or someone else other than a doctor? **If none record "0."**

Times ...... 29-30 y

---

20. How many times did you (PERSON) visit a doctor there? **If none record "0."**

Times ...... 31-32 y

---

21. What was the total cost of all of these visits, including anything that insurance paid?

$ ...... 33-35 y

---

22. Did any family member (you) have *any other care* during 1963 from a person who is not a regular doctor, such as a physical therapist, chiropractor, chiropodist, or visiting nurse? **Mark each member's column. If "No" for entire family, skip to Q. 30.**

Yes: Ask-23-26 ...... 0 36

No: .... X y

---

23. What kind of practitioner was this person?

Practitioner:

37

24. How many times did you (PERSON) see the (PRACTITIONER)?

38-39 y

25. How much did the (PRACTITIONER) charge altogether for this?

$ ...... 40-42 y

26. Did you (PERSON) have any *other* care from someone who is not a regular doctor?

Yes: Ask 27-29 ...... 0 43 y

No: X

---

27. What kind of practitioner was this person?

Practitioner:

44

28. How many times did you (PERSON) see this (PRACTITIONER)?

45-46 y

29. What were the charges altogether for this?

$ ...... 47-49 y

---

30. *Besides what we have already talked about,* did anyone get any: *medical tests* (X-rays, blood tests, electrocardiograms, or urine analysis)—*special treatments* (heat treatments, massages, allergy shots, X-ray treatments)—*medical appliances* (hearing aids, crutches, braces, wheel chair)? **Mark each member's column. If "No" for entire family, skip to Q. 32.**

Yes: Ask 31 .... 0 50 y

No: X

---

31. How much was the cost altogether, including what you paid and anything insurance paid?

$ ...... 51-53 y

---

32. During 1963 how much did the family spend on medicines *prescribed* by a doctor for (PERSON)—other than any we've counted already. Include any insurance payments *for medicine.*

$ ...... 54-56 y

---

33. And how much did you spend on medicines for (PERSON) which were *not* prescribed by a doctor—I mean medicines like vitamins, tonics, cold pills, nose drops, cough medicines and so on?

$ ...... 57-59 y

Enter in separate columns name and person number of each family member listed in Q. 10 of enumeration folder *except* baby under one year old. Record information separately for each member.

Name:		Per. No.
		5-6

---

34. If any minor medical expenses reported: Has anyone in the family received any medical insurance benefits in connection with any of these minor medical expenses—that is, insurance benefits (that we haven't talked about before) for home or office physician visits, drugs, or anything else? **Mark each member's column. If "No" for entire family, skip to 38.**

Yes: Ask 35-37 0   60   y

No: X

---

35. Which of these expenses we've talked about did insurance cover?

Expenses covered: 61   62

36. What was the name of the insurance or plan that paid the benefits?

Name of insurance: 63   64

37. About how much did the insurance pay on these expenses for (PERSON)?

$ ..   65-68   y

DENTAL AND OPTICAL EXPENSES
                Begin Deck 22

Now that we've covered medical care, I'd like to ask about other kinds of health expenses your family had in 1963.

---

38. Did you (PERSON) have any dental care such as teeth cleaned, X-rayed, filled or pulled, or any bridge work done last year?

Yes: Ask 39 0   7   y

No: Ret. to 38 NM ... X

---

39. About how much were you (was PERSON) charged for dental services in 1963?

8-11   y

---

40. Did you (PERSON) have glasses made or replaced or have an eye examination within the year 1963 (other than what we've talked about)?

Yes: Ask 41-45 0   12   y

No: Ret. to 40 NM ... X

---

41. What is the name of the individual you or clinic (PERSON) saw?

First: 13

Last: 14

42. What is his address?

Street:

City:

43. About how much was the charge for eye examination and treatment in 1963?

$ ..   15-18   y

44. And how much for glasses?

$ ...   19-22   y

45. If only total bill for *both* received—enter amount:

$ ...   23-26   y

FREE CARE

46. (Besides what we've talked about) During 1963, did anyone in the family receive any medical care or tests at reduced rates or free of charge because of government help, professional courtesy, participation in medical research or for any other reason? **Mark each member's column. If "No" for entire family, skip to Q. 49.**

Yes: Ask 47-48 0   27   y

No: X

---

47. What kind of care or medicine was it?

28

29

48. Why was the care received at reduced rates or free of charge?

30

31

205

Enter in separate columns name and person number of each family member listed in Q. 10 of enumeration folder *except* baby under one year old. Record information separately for each member.

Name:	Per. No.		5-6

PRACTITIONERS AND EXAMINATIONS

49. Is there a particular medical person or clinic you (PERSON) usually go(es) to when sick or for advice about health?

Yes: **Ask 50-52** ...... 0 $\frac{32}{y}$
No or DK: **Ret. to**
49 NM X

50. Do you (Does PERSON) go to a clinic, a regular family doctor, some type of specialist, osteopath, chiropractor, or what? **(Circle one)**

Clin. 1   Chiro. ... 5 $\frac{33}{0}$
Fam. Dr. . 2   Other ... 6
Spec. 3   DK 7
Osteo. ... 4

51. What is the name of (PERSON) (CLINIC)?

First: 34

Last: 35

52. What is the address?

Street:

City:

53. How long ago did you (PERSON) last have a physical examination or check up? **Specify in wks., mos., yrs. or record "never" and ask 53 NM.**

			36-38
			y

Last exam.:

54. Which of the reasons on Card A best describes why you (PERSON) had the examination?

Not feeling good: $\frac{39}{0}$
   Ask 55 1
Required: **Ask 55** 2
Time for exam.:
   Ret. to 53 NM X

55. How long ago did you (PERSON) last have a physical examination or check up *even though* you (he, she) *felt all right* and the examination *wasn't required?* **Specify in wks., mos., etc. or record "never."**

			40-42
			y

Exam.:

56. Have you (has PERSON) ever had any shots or oral vaccine for polio?

Yes .... 1 $\frac{43}{0}$
No 2
DK 3

57. Have you (has PERSON) ever had any flu shots or innoculations?

Yes .... 5 $\frac{44}{4}$
No 6
DK 7

58. Have you (has PERSON) ever had a chest X-ray for TB (Tubeculosis)?

Yes .... 1 $\frac{45}{0}$
No 2
DK 3

FAMILY HEALTH

59. As a result of illness and injury approximately how many days during 1963 were you (was PERSON) kept in bed, indoors, or away from usual activities?

			46-48
			y

60. Would you say your (PERSON's) health, in general, is excellent, good, fair or poor?

Ex. .... 5 $\frac{49}{4}$
Gd. 6
Fr. 7
Pr. 8

206

Enter in separate columns name and person number of each family member listed in Q. 10 of enumeration folder *except* baby under one year old. Record information separately for each member.

61. Please turn to Card B. Let's go over these conditions together. Ask: (1) Did anyone have (SYMPTOM) during 1963? (2) If "Yes" to "1": Did (PERSON) see a doctor about it during 1963 or since the first of the year? (3) If "No" to "2": Has (PERSON) *ever* seen a doctor about this condition or one like it?

Circle: "N" if NO ONE IN FAMILY had symptom.
     0 or 6   if person had symptom and saw doctor IN 1963 OR SINCE.
     1 or 7   if person had symptom and saw doctor BEFORE 1963.
     2 or 8   if person had symptom and NEVER saw doctor.
     3 or 9   if person had symptom but it ISN'T KNOWN if he ever saw a doctor about it.

Column headers (diagonal): Doctor 1963 or since / Doctor before 1963 / No doctor / Doctor DK / No An / No Sy

			Doctor 1963 or since	Doctor before 1963	No doctor	Doctor DK		No An	No Sy
a.	Cough any time during the day or night which lasted for three weeks?	N	0	1	2	3	(50)	Y	X
b.	Sudden feelings of weakness or faintness?	N	6	7	8	9	(51)	4	5
c.	Getting up some mornings tired and exhausted even with a usual amount of rest?	N	0	1	2	3	(52)	Y	X
d.	Feeling tired for weeks at a time for no special reason?	N	6	7	8	9	(53)	4	5
e.	Frequent headaches?	N	0	1	2	3	(54)	Y	X
f.	Skin rash or breaking out on any part of the body?	N	6	7	8	9	(55)	4	5
g.	Diarrhea (loose bowel movements) for four or five days?	N	0	1	2	3	(56)	Y	X
h.	Shortness of breath even after light work?	N	6	7	8	9	(57)	4	5
i.	Waking up with stiff or aching joints or muscles?	N	0	1	2	3	(58)	Y	X
j.	Pains or swelling in any joint during the day?	N	6	7	8	9	(59)	4	5
k.	Frequent backaches?	N	0	1	2	3	(60)	Y	X
l.	Unexplained loss of over ten pounds in weight?	N	6	7	8	9	(61)	4	5
m.	Repeated pains in or near the heart?	N	0	1	2	3	(62)	Y	X
n.	Repeated indigestion or upset stomach?	N	6	7	8	9	(63)	4	5
o.	Repeated vomiting for a day or more?	N	0	1	2	3	(64)	Y	X
p.	Sore throat or running nose with a fever as high as 100°F. for at least two days?	N	6	7	8	9	(65)	4	5
q.	Nose stopped up, or sneezing, for two weeks or more?	N	0	1	2	3	(66)	Y	X
r.	Unexpected bleeding from any part of the body not caused by accident or injury?	N	6	7	8	9	(67)	4	5
s.	Abdominal pains (pains in the belly or gut) for at least a couple of days?	N	0	1	2	3	(68)	Y	X
t.	Any infections, irritations, or pains in the eyes or ears?	N	6	7	8	9	(69)	4	5

62. Besides any of the expenses we've already talked about did your family have to pay any of the expenses for anyone staying in a nursing home, convalescent home, old peoples home, sanatorium or other place like that during 1963?

Yes: **Ask 63-66** 0   14
No: **Skip to 67** X   y

Relationship:

63. How is (PERSON) related to the family? **If not related, record family friend, etc.**

15

---

64. What kind of place was this? **If "other" specify below:**

Nursing home . 1   Old people's   16
                       home ... 4   0
Convalescent
   home 2   Other 5
Sanatorium .. 3

Name:

65. Can you give me the name and address of (PLACE)?

17

18
Street   City

---

66. About how much did it cost your family for the care (PERSON) received in (PLACE) in 1963?

$ ..... 19-23 / y

---

67. Apart from any of the costs we've considered so far, did you pay any other hospital, medical or dental bills in 1963, for anyone, either related to you or not?

Yes: **Ask 68-69** 0   24
No: **Skip to 70** X   y

Relationship:

68. Who is this person? (What relationship to family?)

25

---

69. How much did you pay for the medical bills of (PERSON) in 1963?

$ ..... 26-30 / y

---

70. During 1963 did anyone, either a friend or a relative, not in the family now, pay anything toward the medical expenses of anyone in the family now?

Yes: **Ask 71** 0   31
No: **Skip to 72** X   y

---

71. How much did they pay toward the family's medical expenses?

$ ..... 32-36 / y

---

72. Do you owe anything for medical care received in 1963 or before? I mean bills from hospitals, doctors, dentists and so forth as well as loans still to be paid that you took out to meet medical expenses.

Yes: **Ask 73** 0   37
No: **Skip to 74** X   y

---

73. How much do you owe?

$ ..... 38-42 / y

---

74. Were your medical and dental expenses this past year *higher*, *about the same*, or *lower* than your medical and dental expenses the past two or three years?

Higher 1   43
Same 2   0
Lower 3

75. If hospital or medical insurance was mentioned earlier: I'd like to get some more information about your health insurance. Circle "X" and fill out Insurance Supplement.

Medical insurance mentioned:
Fill out Insurance Supp. .... X 44
                                  y
No medical insurance
mentioned: Ask 76 0

76. If hospital or medical insurance has not been mentioned: Do you (or does anyone here) have any kind of medical, surgical, or hospital insurance or plan that meets any part of a doctor's bill or hospital expenses, or did any of you have any insurance like this at any time during 1963?

Yes: Fill out Insurance
    Supplement .... X 45
                                  y
No: Ask 77 0

77. Do (any of) you belong to any organization such as a union or lodge, having a medical plan which provides for any sort of hospital care for its members—or did any of you belong to such an organization at any time in 1963?

Yes: Fill out Insurance
    Supplement 1 46
                                  0
No: Ask 78 2

WORK LOSS FROM ILLNESS   *Begin Deck 12*

78. Did anyone in the family lose any time from work in 1963 because of illness or accident, either his own or someone elses?

Yes: Ask 79 0   8
                                                 y
No: Skip to 87 X

79. Who lost the time? Anyone else? Enter names and person nos. Ask 80, etc. for each name.

| Name: | | 9-10 | Name: | | 28-29 |

80. Who's illness was it?

Person's own illness . 1	11	Person's own illness . 1	30
	0		0
Someone's else's illness 2		Someone's else's illness 2	

81. About how much time did (he, she) lose from work because of illness? Specify days, weeks, etc.

| Time: | | 12-13 | Time: | | 31-32 |
| | | y | | | y |

82. Did (he, she) lose any wages or salary because of this absence?

| Yes: Ask 83-84 ..... 0 | 14 | Yes: Ask 83-84 ..... 0 | 33 |
| No .... X | y | No .... X | y |

83. About how much did (he, she) lose?

| $ | | 15-19 | $ | | 34-38 |
| | | y | | | y |

84. Did (he, she) receive any workmen's compensation or any cash benefits from an insurance company, union, fraternal order, or any other source to help cover the loss of income?

| Yes: Ask 85-86 ..... 0 | 20 | Yes: Ask 85-86 ..... 0 | 39 |
| No .... X | y | No .... X | y |

85. Where did these benefits come from?

| 21 | 40 |
| 22 | 41 |

86. About how much were the benefits for 1963?

| $ | | 23-27 | $ | | 42-46 |
| | | y | | | y |

SAVINGS FOR MEDICAL BILLS

87. We're interested in current savings, such as in banks, savings and loan associations, or government bonds that the family might use to meet heavy medical costs in an emergency. Which number on Card C describes such savings in your family?

Less than $200 .... 1 47
200-499 .... 2 y
500-999 3
1000-2999 4
3000-4999 5
5000+ 6

Enter in separate columns names and person No. of family members 14 years of age and older. (If member has died or left household ask questions in terms of the period in which he or she was actually in household.)

Name: 5-6

88. Which number on Card D best describes person's current situation?

Work full time: **Skip to 91** ... 1   7
Work part time: **Skip to 91** .. 2   0
Laid-off—unemployed: **Ask 89** 3
Retired: **Ask 89** 4
Housewife: **Skip to 90** 5
Student: **Skip to 90** 6
Unable to work: **Ask 89** 7
Other: **Ask 89** 8

89. In what year did (PERSON) last have a regular job or do regular work in his (her) own trade, profession or business?

Year given: **Skip to 91** X   8
Never: **Ask 90** 0   y

90. Did (PERSON) earn $100 or more from working during 1963?

Yes: **Ask 91** 8   9
No: **Return to 88 NM** 9   7

91. What kind of work does (did) (PERSON) do?

Occupation: 10-11
y

92. What kind of business or industry does (did) (PERSON) work in?

Industry: 12-13
y

93. Is (was) this job supposed to be a permanent job or is (was) it temporary or seasonal?

Permanent 8   14
Temporary or Seasonal 9   7

94. Does (did) (PERSON) work for a private employer or company, a government agency, or for himself?

Own business: **Skip to 96** X   15
Private employer: **Ask 95** 0   y
Government: **Ask 95** 1
Other: **Ask 95** 2

95. Where does (did) (PERSON) work? **Record name and address of company or place of employment.**

Name: 16

Street   *City*   17

96. Which category on Card E includes the number of people that usually work for (PERSON) (COMPANY)?

1- 2 1   21- 50 ... 5   18
3- 4 2   51-100 ... 6   0
5- 9 3   101-499 ... 7
10-20 4   500+ 8
                   DK 9

97. How many weeks did (PERSON) work last year including paid vacation time? **If "O," return to 88 for next member.**

Weeks: 19-20
| | | y

98. How much was (PERSON's) income from working in 1963 after business expenses were subtracted but before taxes were deducted? **Return to 88 NM.**

$ .. | | | | | | 21-26
y

99. Did anyone in the family receive any income during the past year other than what you've told me about—such as money from interests, dividends, rents, pensions, Social Security, friends and relatives, alimony, allotments from the armed forces, unemployment insurance, (or relief payments)?

Deck 12

Yes: **Ask 100** 0   48
No: **Skip to 101** X   y

100. How much was the total income from these sources?

$ .. | | | | | | 49-54
y

101. Which of the categories on Card F tells how your 1963 family income compares with the average income your household has had over the past two or three years? **Ask 102 on opposite page.**

Very much higher:
    Ask 102-103 1   55
Some higher: **Ask 102-103** ... 2   0
About same: **Skip to 104** 3
Some lower: **Ask 102-103** 4
Very much lower:
    Ask 102-103 5
DK: **Skip to 104** 6

102. Was your income (higher) (lower) because of unusual circumstances or for reasons likely to continue?	Unusual circumstances ...... 8 Likely to continue 9	56 7
103. What were they? (reasons or circumstances for income change.)		57 58
104. How do you expect your 1963 family income to compare with your average family income over the next two or three years? Use a category on Card G.	Very much higher .... 1 Some higher .... 2 About same .... 3 Some lower .... 4 Very much lower .... 5 Too uncertain to guess 6	59 y

Give one Health Opinions Questionnaire to each household head and spouse. Up to this point we've been talking about *facts*. To finish the interview I'd like to ask your *opinion* about some matters related to health. Please mark your answers on this form. **Be sure to leave a form for each absent head and spouse.**

HOSPITAL PERMISSION FORM

Begin Deck 13

Number of hospitalizations (including hospitalized pregnancies) in this interview unit during the past twelve months .... ☐☐ 7-8

You are to get a permission form signed for EACH person hospitalized. A separate form must be filled out for each hospital in which a person was hospitalized.

Ask for AUTHORIZATION: To complete the picture of the health care American people are getting, we would like to get some further information from hospitals regarding their charges for room and board, for laboratory services, medications and the like. We'd appreciate it very much if you would sign this form which authorizes the hospital to give us the information we need.

For each hospitalization fill in the following information:

Name of person hospitalized	Check one			If refused: Reason offered
	Form signed	Will mail	Refused	

INTERVIEWER'S SUMMARY

Date interview completed: _____

Total time of interview: _____

Signature of interviewer:

_____

Health Opin. Quest. left for: .... Male head ...... 1 Female head .... 2 Spouse 3   9/0

1. What was the race of the main respondent(s)?

White 5
Negro 6
Other: **Specify** _____ 7   10/4

2. In general how accurate would you say the cost data are?

Inaccurate 1
Fairly accurate 2
Very accurate 3   11/0

3. Which bills or records did the respondent(s) check to give you the cost information?   12

4. Which, if any, of the cost data do you think is inaccurate and why?   13

5. Apart from the cost data, is there any other information in this interview that you are doubtful about?

Yes: **Answer 6** 0
No: **Skip to 7** X   14/y

6. Which information are you doubtful about and why?   15

7. How would you rate the overall cooperation received from the family during the interview?

Excellent 5   Fair 7
Good 6   Poor 8   16/4

8. How would you compare the level of living of this family to the average level in this area?

Very high 1   Low 4
High 2   Very low 5
Average 3   17/0

9. If you were not able to secure all information on the family's income for 1963, estimate it here.

$ .... ☐☐☐☐☐   18-23/y

10. Fill in the number of each type of completed supplements accompanying the main questionnaire.

Term. Preg. ..... ☐24☐25
Cur. Preg. ..... ☐26☐27
Hospital .... ☐28☐29
Maj. Ill. .... ☐30☐31

Insurance .... ☐32☐33
Health Op. ... ☐34☐35
Hosp. Per. Forms ..... ☐36☐37

212

PART I — TERMINATED PREGNANCY SUPPLEMENT

(If pregnancy ended by December 31, 1963)

[ ][ ][ ] 1-4

Family Name_____

Respondent's Name_____

Hsld. No. [ ]

Family Unit

Mother's Name_____ and Per. No. [ ] 5-6

Term. Pregnancy [ ][ ] of [ ] 7-10

Begin Deck 31

Baby's Name or "Stillbirth" or "Miscarriage" _____ [ ][ ] 15-16 y

1. Did (MOTHER) spend one night or more in a hospital in connection with this pregnancy?

Yes: **Ask 2** 0 17
No: **Skip to 14** .... X y

2. How many times was (MOTHER) in the hospital during this pregnancy? **Use another Pregnancy Supplement to record third, etc., hospitalizations.**

Times .... [ ][ ] 18-19 y

Begin Deck 36

	First Hospital Stay	Second Hospital Stay
Ask Qs. 3-13 *separately for each hospital stay.*	Stay [ ] of [ ] 11-14	Stay [ ] of [ ] 11-14
3. What hospital was (MOTHER) in?	Name _____ 15 / 16	Name _____ 15 / 16
	Street City 17	Street City 17
4. How many days was (MOTHER) in the hospital?	Days .... [ ][ ] 18-20 y	Days .... [ ][ ] 18-20 y
5. What were the approximate dates? If dates not known, record time of month (Beginning, Middle, End).	From _____ Mo. Day Year / To _____ Mo. Day Year	From _____ Mo. Day Year / To _____ Mo. Day Year
6. Were there one, two, or three or more hospital beds in (MOTHER'S) room? **Record accommodation with fewest beds.**	One .... 1 21 0 / Two .... 2 / Three or more 3	One .... 1 21 0 / Two .... 2 / Three or more 3
7. How much was the *hospital* bill *counting* anything insurance may have paid, but *not counting* what the doctor charged for delivering the baby?	$ .... [ ][ ][ ][ ][ ] 22-26 y	$ .... [ ][ ][ ][ ][ ] 22-26 y
8. Did any kind of hospital plan or insurance cover any part of the cost of hospitalization—or will any plan, even though it hasn't paid yet?	Yes: **Ask 9-13** .... 5 27 4 / No 6	Yes: **Ask 9-13** .... 5 27 4 / No 6
9. If **insurance**: What plans or insurance covered the hospitalization costs? **More than one may be recorded.**	Plan (1): _____ 28 / 29 / Plan (2): _____ 30 / 31	Plan (1): _____ 28 / 29 / Plan (2): _____ 30 / 31
10. Has the insurance [Plan (1), Plan (2)] paid yet? **Circle one for each plan.**	Plan (1): Yes No / Plan (2): Yes No	Plan (1): Yes No / Plan (2): Yes No

11. How much did (the first, second) insurance pay on the hospitalization?

(1) $ [ ][ ][ ][ ] <u>32-36</u>/y   (1) $.. [ ][ ][ ][ ] <u>32-36</u>/y

(2) $ [ ][ ][ ][ ] <u>37-41</u>/y   (2) $.. [ ][ ][ ][ ] <u>37-41</u>/y

12. And how much did you yourself (the family) have to pay?

$ .... [ ][ ][ ][ ] <u>42-46</u>/y $ ..... [ ][ ][ ][ ] <u>42-46</u>/y

13. **Add amounts in 11 and 12. If total differs from amount in 7, probe for correction.**

Total: $ ....   Total: $ ....

Deck 31

14. Who was (MOTHER's) doctor during the pregnancy? **If treated at clinic, give name and address of clinic. If "don't know" or no doctor, explain.**

First   *Last*   20 / 21

Street   *City*   22 / 23

15. **Unless miscarriage:** Who *delivered* baby? **List name and address** *only if* **different from Q. 14.**

First   *Last*   24 / 25

Street   *City*   26 / 27

16. **Unless miscarriage:** Was this a Caesarean delivery?

Yes 1 28
No 2 0

17. **If miscarriage:** Did mother have a dilation and curettage (D & C) (Scraping) at the time of the miscarriage?

Yes: **Ask 18** .... 5 <u>29</u>/y
No: **Skip to 19** .... 6 y

    18. Who performed the dilation and curettage?

First   *Last*   30 / 31

Street   *City*   32 / 33

19. How many weeks had (MOTHER) been pregnant before seeing a doctor (going to a clinic) in connection with this pregnancy?

No. weeks .... [ ][ ] <u>34-35</u>/y

20. Did (MOTHER) ever go to a doctor's office for prenatal care *when she didn't see the doctor at all* but received tests, shots, or other care from a nurse or technician?

Yes: **Ask 21** .... 0 <u>36</u>/y
No: **Skip to 22** .... X y

    21. How many times?

Nurse visits .... [ ][ ][ ] <u>37-39</u>/y

22. How many times did (MOTHER) see a doctor at his *office* about the pregnancy?

Office visits .... [ ][ ][ ] <u>40-42</u>/y

23. How many times did a doctor come to the *home?*

Home visits .... [ ][ ][ ] <u>43-45</u>/y

24. (Besides these visits) did (MOTHER) go to a maternity clinic for any care or tests in connection with this pregnancy?

Yes: **Ask 25** .... 0 <u>46</u>/y
No: **Skip to 26** .... X y

    25. How many times?

Clinic visits .... [ ][ ][ ] <u>47-49</u>/y

26. How much did (MAIN DOCTOR, Q. 14) charge for the pregnancy and delivery (or miscarriage) *including* anything insurance may have paid?

$ ..... [ ][ ][ ][ ][ ] <u>50-54</u>/y

27. Did any kind of medical plan or insurance cover any part of this cost or will it, even though it hasn't paid yet?

Yes: **Ask 28-32** .... 0 <u>55</u>/y
No: **Skip to 33** .... X y

    28. What insurance or plans paid on the doctor's bills? Did any other insurance pay part of his bill? **More than one plan may be listed.**

Plan (1):   56 / 57

Plan (2):   58 / 59

    29. Has the insurance paid yet? **If more than one plan, ask for each separately.**

(1)   Yes ____   No ____

(2)   Yes ____   No ____

30. How much did the insurance pay toward the doctor's bill?

(1) $ .. [| | | |] 60-64 y

(2) $ .. [| | | |] 65-69 y

31. And how much did you yourself (the family) have to pay? $ .. [| | | |] 70-74 y

32. Add amounts in Qs. 30 and 31. If the total differs from amount in Q. 26, probe for correction. Total: $ . . . .

33. A. Ask everybody: Did (MOTHER) have any *other* medical care connected with the pregnancy that was not included in the hospital or doctor's bills we just talked about — for things like — (Read through list, circling *yes* or *no* for each one): *Begin Deck 32*

Item	A Yes No	B Total	C Insurance Paid	D Name of Insurance	E "Net"	
Prescriptions?	0 X 15 y	16 17 18 19	20 21 22 23	24 25	26 27 28 29	
Non-prescribed medicines?	0 X 30 y	31 32 33 34	35 36 37 38	39 40	41 42 43 44	
Visits to some other doctor or clinic?	0 X 45 y	46 47 48 49	50 51 52 53	54 55	56 57 58 59	
Blood tests or other laboratory work?	0 X 60 y	61 62 63 64	65 66 67 68	69 70	71 72 73 74	*Begin Deck 33*
An anesthetist's fee?	0 X 15 y	16 17 18 19	20 21 22 23	24 25	26 27 28 29	
A practical nurse at home?	0 X 30 y	31 32 33 34	35 36 37 38	39 40	41 42 43 44	
Anything else? If "yes," list below:						
(1)	0 X 45 y	46 47 48 49	50 51 52 53	54 55	56 57 58 59	
(2)	0 X 60 y	61 62 63 64	65 66 67 68	69 70	71 72 73 74	

Ask B-E about first item circled *yes*. Then go on to next *yes* item.

B. What were (your, her) *total* expenses for (ITEM) in connection with the pregnancy—including anything that insurance may have paid? **(Enter under "B" above.)**

C. And how much of that was paid by insurance? **(Enter amount under "C" above. If *none*, enter "0" and skip to next *yes* item.)**

D. What insurance paid that? **[Enter name(s) of insurance under "D" above.]**

E. Then that left **(amount in "B" minus amount in "C") that you had to pay. Is that right? (If *yes*, enter amount in "E" above. If *no*, make necessary correction.)**

34. Did (MOTHER) *or* (BABY) get any medical care or tests, or medicines in connection with the pregnancy at reduced rates or free of charge because of "professional courtesy" or because they were taking part in medical research (or because they were receiving public aid) or for any other reason?   *Begin Deck 34*

Yes: **Ask 35-36** 0 15
No: **Skip to 37** . . . . X y

35. What care was this?   Kind of care   16 17

36. If care free or at reduced rate: Why was (MOTHER or BABY) able to get this care at reduced rate or free of charge?   Reason   18 19

37. This Supplement is being used in connection with: A live birth: **Ask 38, etc.** .. 0   20 / y

A still birth or miscarriage:
Ret. to Main Quest. Q. 3. X

---

38. Now a few questions about the baby: Where was (he, she) born—in a hospital, at home, or somewhere else?

Home 1 21
Hospital 2 0
Other: **specify**
                 3

---

39. Did the baby stay in the hospital one or more nights after (MOTHER) returned home during 1963?

Yes: **Fill out Hosp. Supp.** 5 22
No 6 4

---

40. Has the baby had any illness or condition for which (he, she) had to return one or more nights after being home last year?

Yes: **Fill out Hosp. Supp.** 8 23
No 9 7

---

41. Did the doctor visit the baby at home last year?

Yes: **Ask 42-43** 0 24
No: **Skip to 44** .... X y

> **42.** How many times?   *Home visits* .... [ ][ ][ ]   25-27 / y
>
> **43.** How much were you charged for these visits? $ .... [ ][ ][ ][ ]   28-31 / y

---

44. Did you take the baby to a doctor's office or clinic in 1963?

Yes: **Ask 45-46** 0 32
No: **Skip to 47** .... X y

> **45.** How many times?   *Off.-Clin. visits* ..... [ ][ ][ ]   33-35 / y
>
> **46.** What was the charge for these visits? $ .... [ ][ ][ ][ ]   36-39 / y

---

47. **If baby has seen doctor:** Why did (BABY) see the doctor?   40 / 41

---

48. **If baby has seen doctor:** Was any part of the cost of these visits paid for by any kind of medical plan or insurance?

Yes: **Ask 49-50** 0 42
No: **Skip to 51** .... X y

> **49.** What plan or insurance is that?   43 / 44
>
> **50.** How much did insurance pay for (BABY's) doctor visits? $ ...... [ ][ ][ ][ ]   45-48 / y

---

51. How much did you have to spend for medicines the doctor *prescribed* for the baby? $ ...... [ ][ ][ ][ ]   49-52 / y

---

52. And about how much did you have to spend for other non-prescribed medicines? $ ...... [ ][ ][ ][ ]   53-56 / y

---

53. Did you have any *other expenses* for the baby during 1963 for X-rays, or laboratory tests of any kind (**if male baby:** a separate charge for a circumcision), or for appliances or equipment like braces, vaporizer, or special shoes or anything like that?

Yes: **Ask 54 A-B** 0 57
No: **Skip to 55** .... X y

A   B

> **54. A.** What were the expenses for? **List under "A."**
> 1. _____ 58   [ ][ ][ ] 59-61
> 2. _____ 62   [ ][ ][ ] 63-65
>   **B.** What was the cost for (EXPENSE)? **Record under "B."**
> 3. _____ 66   [ ][ ][ ] 67-69

---

55. **If medicine or "other" expenses:** Did insurance pay any of the expenses for medicines or (**read items listed in 54A**)?

Yes: **Ask 56-57** 0 70
No: **Skip to 58** .... X y

Begin Deck 35

> **56.** What insurance was that?   15 / 16
>
> **57.** How much did (or will) it pay toward (medicine, "other expenses")?   *Medicine* $ [ ][ ][ ][ ] 17-20   *"Other Care"* $ [ ][ ][ ][ ] 21-24

---

58. Who is the baby's doctor (or, what doctor do you think you will probably take the baby to)? **If clinic, enter its name and address.**

First   *Last*   25 / 26
Street   *City*   27 / 28

Return to Main Questionnaire Q. 3.

216

PART II — CURRENT PREGNANCY SUPPLEMENT
(As of December 31, 1963)

Family Name _____

Respondent's Name _____

Hsld. No. [ ][ ]

Family Unit [ ]

Mother's Name _____ and Per. No.

1-4 [ ][ ][ ][ ]

5-6 [ ][ ]

Begin Deck 37

---

0. Did (MOTHER) spend one or more nights in the hospital *during 1963* in connection with this pregnancy?

Yes: **Fill out a Term. Preg. Supp.** .... Y
No: Ask 1 .... N

1. Did (you, she) see a doctor or go to a clinic in connection with this pregnancy?

Yes: Ask 2-5 .... 0 15
No: Skip to 6 .... X y

   2. How many times did (MOTHER) see a doctor at his office in connection with this pregnancy?

Office visits .... [ ][ ][ ] 16-18 / y

   3. And how many times did a doctor come to the home to see (MOTHER) in connection with this pregnancy in 1963?

Home visits .... [ ][ ][ ] 19-21 / y

   4. (Besides this) did (MOTHER) go to a maternity clinic or any other kind of clinic last year?

Yes: Ask 5 .... 0 22
No: Skip to 6 .... X y

   5. How many times?

Clinic visits .... [ ][ ][ ] 23-25 / y

6. Who is (MOTHER's) doctor for this pregnancy [or what doctor will (MOTHER) probably go to for care during this pregnancy]? **(If clinic, give name and address of clinic.)**

First _____ *Last* _____ 26 / 27
Street _____ *City* _____ 28 / 29

7. **If mother has been to a doctor or clinic in connection with this pregnancy in 1963, ask:** Did you pay out anything for doctor care in connection with this pregnancy during 1963?

Yes: Ask 8 .... 0 30
No: Skip to 11 .... X y

   8. Was this (were these) amount(s) an advance payment on the doctor's final bill, or was the doctor billing you as you went along?

Adv. Payment: **Skip to 11** 0 31
Billing along: **Ask 9-10** .... X y

   9. How much did you pay out for visits to the doctor at his *office* or *clinic* in 1963?

$ .... [ ][ ][ ] 32-35 / y

   10. And how much have you paid out for times the doctor saw (MOTHER) at *home* during 1963?

$ .... [ ][ ][ ] 36-39 / y

11. How much did you spend in 1963 for medicines the doctor *prescribed* for (MOTHER) in connection with this pregnancy?

$ .... [ ][ ][ ] 40-43 / y

12. How much for non-prescribed medicines for (MOTHER) for the pregnancy last year?

$ .... [ ][ ][ ] 44-47 / y

13. Did you spend anything for blood tests or other laboratory tests in 1963 for the pregnancy—for X-rays, or a practical nurse at home, or special medical appliances or anything like that last year?

Yes: Ask 14 A-B 0 48
No: Skip to 15 .... X y

   14. A. What were these expenses for? **List under "A."**

     B. How much did (ITEM) cost? **Record under "B."**

	A What expense was for:	B Cost	
1. _____	49	[ ][ ][ ]	50-53
2. _____	54	[ ][ ][ ]	55-58
3. _____	59	[ ][ ][ ]	60-63

15. Did (MOTHER) get any of this medical care or tests or medicines in connection with the pregnancy in 1963 at reduced rates or free of charge because of "professional courtesy" or because she was taking part in medical research, (or because she was receiving public aid) or for any other reason?

Yes: Ask 16-17 .... 0 64
No .... X y

   16. What kind of care was this?

65 / 66

   17. **If care free or at reduced rate:** Why was (MOTHER) able to get this care at reduced or free of charge?

67 / 68

Return to Main Questionnaire, Q. 3.

HOSPITAL SUPPLEMENT

Family
Name _____   Hsld. No. [ ][ ]   [ ][ ][ ][ ] 1-4

Respondent's
Name _____   Family Unit [ ][ ]   Patient's
                                                    Name _____ [ ][ ] 5-6
                                                    and Per. No.

                                         Hospitalized Illness [ ][ ] of [ ][ ] 7-10

                                                                    Begin Deck 41

---

1. What was the *main* reason (PATIENT) had to go to the hospital?   15
   Enter kind of illness, accident or condition.   16
                                                                            17

---

2. Did you receive any benefits from a major medical or catastrophe   Yes: **Ask 3-4** 0 18
   insurance plan in connection with this illness for care received in
   1963?   No or DK: **Skip to 5** X

   ---

   3. What is the name of this insurance?   19
                                                                            20

   ---

   4. *Altogether,* how much did you receive from this insurance to
      cover the costs of care connected with this illness in 1963? $ .... [ ][ ][ ][ ][ ] 21-25
                                                                                            y

---

5. How many times was (PATIENT) in the hospital for this condi-
   tion during 1963? **Use another Hospital Supplement for third,**   Times .... [ ][ ] 26-27
   fourth, etc. hospitalizations.   y

                                                                    Begin Deck 48

Ask Qs. 6-11 *separately* for each hospital stay.	Stay [ ][ ] of [ ][ ] 11-14	Stay [ ][ ] of [ ][ ] 11-14
	First Hospital Stay	**Second Hospital Stay**
6. What hospital was (PA-TIENT) in?	*Name:* 15 16	*Name:* 15 16
	Street *City* 17	*Street* *City* 17
7. How many days was (PA-TIENT) in the hospital?	Days .... [ ][ ][ ] 18-20 y	Days .... [ ][ ][ ] 18-20 y
8. What were the approximate dates? **If dates not known, record time of month (Beginning, Middle, End).**	From: _____ Mo. Day Year To: _____ Mo. Day Year	From: _____ Mo. Day Year To: _____ Mo. Day Year
9. Were there one, two or three or more hospital beds in (PATIENT's) room? **Record accommodation with fewest beds.**	One .... 1 $\frac{21}{0}$ Two .... 2 Three or more 3	One .... 1 $\frac{21}{0}$ Two .... 2 Three or more 3
10. How much was the *hospital* bill *counting* anything insurance may have paid, but *not counting* doctor's bills or any surgeon's fees?	$ .... [ ][ ][ ][ ][ ] 22-26 y	$ .... [ ][ ][ ][ ][ ] 22-26 y

	First Hospital Stay	**Second Hospital Stay**

11. (Apart from major medical coverage) did any kind of hospital plan or insurance cover any part of the cost of hospitalization — or will any plan even though it hasn't paid yet?

First Hospital Stay

Yes: **Ask 12-16** .... 5 $\frac{27}{4}$

No 6

Second Hospital Stay

Yes: **Ask 12-16** .... 5 $\frac{27}{4}$

No 6

12. What insurance or plans covered the hospitalization costs? **More than one may be recorded.**

Plan (1):   28 / 29

Plan (2):   30 / 31

Plan (1):   28 / 29

Plan (2):   30 / 31

13. Has the insurance [Plan (1), Plan (2)] paid yet?

Plan (1)   Yes   No

Plan (2)   Yes   No

Plan (1)   Yes   No

Plan (2)   Yes   No

14. How much did (the first, second) insurance pay on the hospitalization?

(1) $.   32-36 / y

(2) $.   37-41 / y

(1) $.   32-36 / y

(2) $.   37-41 / y

15. And how much did you (your family) have to pay for the hospital bill that was not covered by any insurance (except major medical)?

$ .....   42-46 / y

$ .....   42-46 / y

16. **Add amounts in Qs. 14 and 15. If total differs from amount in Q. 10, probe for correction.**

Total: $ _____

Total: $ _____

Deck 41

17. Did (PATIENT) have any kind of operation or have any broken or dislocated bones set while in the hospital that time (either time)?

Yes: **Ask 18** 1   28
No: **Skip to 29** 2   0

18. How many times was (PATIENT) *on the operating table* for (CONDITION) during 1963. **If more than two operations use another supplement for third, etc. operation.**

Operations .....   29-30 / y

Begin Deck 49

Ask Qs. 19-23 separately for each operation.

19. **If more than one hospitalization (Q. 5):** During which *hospital stay* was the operation performed? **Record number of hospitalization.**

Operation [ ] of [ ] 11-14
First Operation

Hospital stay .... [ ] 15-16 / y

Operation [ ] of [ ] 11-14
Second Operation

Hospital stay .... [ ] 15-16 / y

219

20. What *kind* of operation or bone setting was it?

First Operation — Operation: 17 / 18 / 19

Second Operation — Operation: 17 / 18 / 19

---

21. Who was the doctor who performed the operation (or set the broken bones)? what is his address?

First Operation — Name: 20 / 21 / 22   Street   City

Second Operation — Name: 20 / 21 / 22   Street   City

---

22. How much was the *surgeon's total* bill for the operation — including anything that insurance paid as well as what you paid?

First Operation — $ .... ☐☐☐☐☐ 23-27

Second Operation — $ ... ☐☐☐☐☐ 23-27

---

23. Did any kind of surgical plan or insurance (other than the major medical we've already talked about) cover any part of the cost of the operation—or will any plan, even though it hasn't paid yet?

First Operation — Yes: **Ask 24-28** 0   28 / No X   y

Second Operation — Yes: **Ask 24-28** 0   28 / No X   y

---

24. **If insurance:** What insurance or plans covered the operation? **More than one may be recorded.**

First Operation — First Plan: 29 / 30   Second Plan: 31 / 32

Second Operation — First Plan: 29 / 30   Second Plan: 31 / 32

---

25. Has the insurance [Plan (1), Plan (2)] paid yet?

First Operation — Plan (1)   Yes   No   Plan (2)   Yes   No

Second Operation — Plan (1)   Yes   No   Plan (2)   Yes   No

---

26. How much (did) (will) the insurance [Plan (1), Plan (2)] pay on the (NAME OF OPERATION in Q. 20)?

First Operation — (1) $. ☐☐☐☐ 33-37 / (2) $. ☐☐☐☐ 38-42

Second Operation — (1) $. ☐☐☐☐ 33-37 / (2) $. ☐☐☐☐ 38-42

---

27. How much of the charge for (NAME OF OPERATION) did you have that was *not* covered by insurance (other than major medical)?

First Operation — $ ... ☐☐☐☐☐ 43-47

Second Operation — $ .... ☐☐☐☐☐ 43-47

---

28. **Add amounts in Qs. 26 and 27. If total differs from amount in Q. 22, probe for correction.**

First Operation — Total: $ _____

Second Operation — Total: $ _____

29. A. Did (PATIENT) have any other expenses in the hospital that were *not covered* on the hospital bill, for which (he, she) was billed *separately* — expenses for things like — (**Read through list checking *yes* or *no* for each item**): *Deck 41*

Expense	A Yes No	B Total	C Ins. Paid	D Name of Ins.	E "Net"
An anesthe-tist's fee that was *not charged on* hospital bill?	0 X $\frac{31}{y}$	32 33 34 35	36 37 38 39	40 41	42 43 44 45
A pathologist's *separate* charge for laboratory tests?	0 X $\frac{46}{y}$	47 48 49 50	51 52 53 54	55 56	57 58 59 60
A radiologist's *separate* charge for X-ray tests or treatments?	0 X $\frac{61}{y}$	62 63 64 65	66 67 68 69	70 71	72 73 74 75
Special hospital nursing?	0 X $\frac{15}{y}$	16 17 18 19	20 21 22 23	24 25	26 27 28 29
Oxygen?	0 X $\frac{30}{y}$	31 32 33 34	35 36 37 38	39 40	41 42 43 44
Ambulance?	0 X $\frac{45}{y}$	46 47 48 49	50 51 52 53	54 55	56 57 58 59
Anything else? (If yes, specify)	0 X $\frac{60}{y}$	61 62 63 64	65 66 67 68	69 70	71 72 73 74

Begin Deck 42

Ask B-E about first item checked "yes." Then go on to next "yes" item.

B. What were the (PATIENT's) total expenses for (ITEM)—including anything insurance paid as well as what you paid? (**Enter amount under "B" above.**)

C. And was anything paid on (ITEM) by the insurance (besides major medical)? (**Enter amount under "C".**) **If nothing enter "0" under "C" and skip to next "yes" item.**

D. What insurance plan paid this amount? [**Enter name(s) of insurance under "D" above.**]

E. Then that left (**amount in "B" minus amount in "C"**) that you had to pay (except for major medical insurance) . . . is that right?

If Yes: enter amount under "E" above. If No: make necessary corrections.

221

30. How many times did a doctor or osteopath visit (PATIENT while (he, she) was actually in the hospital? **If none, record "0."**   *Hosp. visits* ......   `[  |  |  ]` 15-17 / y

31. **If hospital visit:** What were the total charges for these hospital visits? **If total included in surgeon's bill, record "0."** $ ......   `[  |  |  ]` 18-21 / y

32. In 1963, how many times did any doctor or osteopath come to the home to see (PATIENT) about this condition? **If none, record "0."**   *Home visits* ......   `[  |  |  ]` 22-24 / y

33. What were the total expenses for these home visits? $ ......   `[  |  |  ]` 25-28 / y

34. Did (PATIENT) go to a doctor's office when (he, she) *didn't see the doctor at all,* but got shots, X-ray, or some other test or treatment from a nurse, technician or another assistant?   Yes: **Ask 35** 0   29 / y
   No: **Skip to 36** X

35. How many times did this happen?   *Nurse visits* ......   `[  |  |  ]` 30-32 / y

36. During 1963, how many times did (PATIENT) see a doctor or osteopath about this condition at the doctor's office? **If none, record "0."**   *Office visits* ......   `[  |  |  ]` 33-35 / y

37. **If any office care (Qs. 34 and 36):** How much did the doctors charge for all the care (PATIENT) got at the office from both doctors and nurses? $ ......   `[  |  |  ]` 36-39 / y

38. Did (PATIENT) go to an out-patient clinic, or service or emergency room at a hospital, or to an industrial clinic or to any other place where they got care from a doctor or nurse in connection with this condition this past year?   Yes: **Ask 39-40** 0   40 / y
   No: **Skip to 41** X

39. How many times?   Clinic visits   `[  |  |  ]` 41-43 / y

40. What was the total charge for these visits? $ ......   `[  |  |  ]` 44-47 / y

41. Do you have any *medical insurance* (other than major medical) that helped you (will help you) pay any of these *doctor bills?*   Yes: **Ask 42-43** 0   48 / y
   No: **Skip to 44** X

42. What insurance or plan helped? **More than one may be recorded.**   *Plan (1):*   49 / 50
   Plan (2):   51 / 52

43. How much did (will) insurance pay on? **Read each that applies. Make sure amounts are not already recorded in insurance for surgeon's fee. If insurance paid nothing, record "0" in appropriate boxes.**
   Hospital visits $. `[  |  |  ]` 53-56 / y
   Home visits $... `[  |  |  ]` 57-60 / y
   All office care $.. `[  |  |  ]` 61-64 / y
   Clinic visits $... `[  |  |  ]` 65-68 / y

44. A. During the last twelve months did (PATIENT) have any *other* expenses for this condition — that is, *not counting* what you've already told me about? Expenses for things like — (**Read through list, checking *Yes* or *No* for each item**):

Begin Deck 44

Expenses	Yes	A No		B Total				C Ins. Paid				D "Net"			
Medicines the doctor or hospital prescribed for this condition?	0	X	15/y	16	17	18	19	20	21	22	23	24	25	26	27
Other *non-prescribed* medicines for this condition?	0	X	28/y	29	30	31	32	33	34	35	36	37	38	39	40
X-ray tests?	0	X	41/y	42	43	44	45	46	47	48	49	50	51	52	53
Other special tests like blood tests, electro-cardiograms, urine analyses, and so on?	0	X	54/y	55	56	57	58	59	60	61	62	63	64	65	66
Special treatments like X-ray treatments, heat or diathermy treatments, massages, and so on?	0	X	15/y	16	17	18	19	20	21	22	23	24	25	26	27
Home nursing care (for which you were charged)?	0	X	28/y	29	30	31	32	33	34	35	36	37	38	39	40
Any medical equipment or appliances like braces, crutches, wheel chair, vaporizer, or anything like that?	0	X	41/y	42	43	44	45	46	47	48	49	50	51	52	53
Anything else? If "Yes," list:	0	X	54/y	55	56	57	58	59	60	61	62	63	64	65	66

Begin Deck 45 (row: Other special tests)

Ask B-E about first item checked "Yes." Then go on to next "Yes" item.

B. What were (PATIENT's) total expenses for (ITEM) — including anything insurance paid as well as what you paid? (**Enter amount under "B" above.**)

C. And was anything paid on (ITEM) by insurance (besides major medical)? **Enter amount under "C" above. If none, enter "0" under "C" and skip to next "Yes" item.**

D. Then that left (**amount in "B" minus amount in "C"**) that you had to pay (not counting major medical). Is that right? **If yes: enter amount under "D" above. If No: make necessary corrections.**

---

45. **If insurance paid part of expenses in Q. 44:** What insurance plan paid on the expenses?   67   68

---

46. Did (PATIENT) get any medical care, or tests, or medicine for this condition last year at reduced rates or free of charge because of professional courtesy, participation in medical research, (public relief), or for any other reason?

Yes: **Ask 47-48** 0 69/y

No: **Skip to 49** X

47. What kind of care was this?   70   71

48. **If free or reduced rate care:** Why was (PATIENT) able to get this care at a reduced rate or free of charge?   72   73

---

49. Now, was (PATIENT) in a hospital for one night or more for any *other* illness, accident or condition during 1963.

Yes: **Fill out another Hospital Supplement** ... 1 ⁷⁴/₀

No: **Return to Main Questionnaire Q. 6, or Preg. Supp. Qs. 39 or 40.** 2

NORC SRS-180
January, 1964

MAJOR ILLNESS SUPPLEMENT

| | | | | 1-4 |

Family name _____

Respondent's name _____

Hsld. No.

Family Unit No.

Name and Per. No. of member _____

Illness [ ] of [ ]   5-6

7-10

1. What was the condition (injury, illness) (PATIENT) had?

Begin Deck 51
11
12
13

2. During 1963, how many times did a doctor or osteopath come to the *home* to see (PATIENT) about this condition? If **"none," record "0."**

Home visits   14-16
y

If "0" skip to 4.

   3. If **home visits**: How much were your total charges for these home visits, including anything that insurance may have paid?

$ 17-20
y

4. Did (PATIENT) get shots, X-rays, or some other kind of test or treatment for this condition from a nurse, technician or other assistant in a doctor's office *without actually seeing the doctor?*

Yes: Ask 5 0   21
No: Skip to 6 X   y

   5. How many times did this happen?

Nurse visits   22-24
y

6. During 1963, how many times did (PATIENT) see a doctor or osteopath about this condition at the doctor's office?

Office visits   25-27
y

7. **If any nurse or office visits (Qs. 5 and 6)**: How much did the doctor charge for *all* the care (PATIENT) got at the *office?* Let's also include bills for examinations, shots, tests, X-rays and so on given by the doctor *or* his nurse, and also include anything insurance may have paid.

$ 28-31
y

8. Did (PATIENT) go to an out-patient clinic, service, or emergency room at a hospital, or to an industrial clinic, or any other clinic for examinations, tests, or care *in connection with this condition last year?*

Yes: Ask 9-10 0   32
No: Skip to 11 X   y

   9. How many times?

Clinic visits   33-35
y

   10. And how much were the total charges for these clinic visits including anything insurance may have paid?

$ 36-39
y

224

11. A. Did (PATIENT) have any *other* expenses for *this* condition in the past year—for things like (**Read through list, coding "Yes" or "No" for each item.**)

	A Yes No			B Expense			
Medicines the doctors *prescribed* for this condition?	0 X	40 y		41	42	43	44
Other *non-prescribed* medicines?	0 X	45 y		46	47	48	49
X-ray tests?	0 X	50 y		51	52	53	54
Other special tests like blood tests, electrocardiograms, urine analyses, and so on?	0 X	55 y		56	57	58	59
Special treatments like X-ray treatments, massages, heat or diathermy treatments or any other kind of treatment?	0 X	60 y		61	62	63	64
Home nursing care (for which you were charged)?	0 X	65 y		66	67	68	69
Any medical equipment or appliances like braces, crutches, wheelchair, a vaporizer or anything like that?	0 X	11 y		12	13	14	15
Anything else? **If "Yes" specify:**	0 X	16 y		17	18	19	20

Begin Deck 52

11. B. **Ask about each item checked "Yes":** What were (PATIENT's) *total* expenses for (ITEM)— including anything that insurance may have paid? **Enter amounts under "B" above.**

12. Did you receive any benefits from a *major* medical or a catastrophe insurance plan in connection with this illness for care received in 1963?

Yes: **Ask 13-14** 0   21
No or DK: **Skip to 15** X   y

   13. What is the name of this insurance?

22
23

   ·**14.** *Altogether,* how much did you receive to cover costs for medical care for this condition in 1963? $ . . .

24-28
y

15. Did any kind of insurance or *medical care* plan (other than major medical) cover any part of these costs—or will it even though it hasn't paid.yet?

Yes: **Ask 16-17** 0   29
No: **Skip to 18** X   y

16. What is the name of the insurance?
More than one may be listed.

Plan (1):   30
Plan (2):   31
                32
                33

   17. How much did insurance pay on? **Read each that applies:**

		34	35	36	37
Doctor visits to your home:	$				
Visits to doctor's office or clinic:	$	38	39	40	41
Drugs and medicines:	$	42	43	44	45
Other medical expenses (tests, treatments, nursing care, medical appliances) :	$	46	47	48	49

18. Did (PATIENT) get any medical care or tests or medicines for (CONDITION) last year at reduced rates or free of charge, because of professional courtesy, participation in medical research, public relief, or any other reason?

Yes: **Ask 19-20** 0   50
No: **Skip to 21** X   y

   19. What kind of care or medicine was it?

51
52

   20. Why was (PATIENT) able to get this care at a reduced rate or free of charge?

53
54

21. Has (this patient) had any other illness, accident, or condition for which expenses in 1963 amounted to $50 or more, or for which doctor or osteopath was seen 5 or more times, or for which regular care or treatment was required?

Yes: **Fill out another**
     Major Illness Supp. 1   55
No: **Return to**
     Q. 9 Main Questionnaire . . . 2   0

| | | | 1-4 |

Family name _____

Respondent's name _____

Hsld. No. ☐☐

Family
Unit No. ☐

Begin Deck 91

Plan ☐☐ of ☐☐ 7-10

1. Enter name of each policy in separate column. If more than four, use another supplement. As well as you remember, what is the full name of each of your health insurance policies or plans? Do you or (NAMES OF OTHER FAMILY MEMBERS) have *any* other hospital or medical insurance or plans, or did any of you have one during 1963—even though you don't have it now?	*Name of Plan or Insurance:* 11 12
2. Are any of these *"Major Medical"* or *Catastrophic* type plans? Have any of you had any such plans in the past year that we haven't yet listed? **Enter any new plans mentioned in the answer spaces for Q. 1. Circle each plan "Yes," "No," or "DK" in Q. 2.**	Yes .... 1 No .... 2 13 DK 3 0

3. Mark each plan coded "Yes" in Q. 2 as "Major Medical." Classify *each* of the remaining plans as *either* **"Blue Plan" or "other."**	Major Medical:
	   Skip to 7 .... 5 14
	 "Blue Plan": 4
	   Skip to 8 6
	 Other: **Ask Q. 4** 7

4. If "other": Does (NAME OF PLAN) cover expenses in the case of *accident only* or does it cover expenses of medical care *for illness too?* **If "accident only," draw "X" through name of policy. Ask no more questions about it.**	Accident only: **Stop** . X 15 Illness too: **Ask 5** ... 0 y
5. If "other": Does this plan just pay a *flat amount* of weekly benefit whenever you are ill and can't work, even if you have to go to the hospital, or does it pay according to the amount of your expenses for medical care? **If "flat amount," draw "X" through policy name. Ask no more questions about it.**	Flat amount: **Stop** .. X 16 Pay according to expenses: **Ask 6** .. 0 y
6. If "other": Does this policy pay only on expenses connected with polio or some other *serious* or *rare* diseases or does it pay on other illnesses too?	Dread diseases ..... 1 17 Other too 2 0
7. If Major Medical in Q. 3: Is this insurance *only* Major Medical or is it part of a basic plan that also gives you regular hospital and/or surgical coverage?	Only Major Medical . 4 *Also* hospitalization . 5 18 *Also* surgical .... 6 3 *Both* hosp. & surg. ... 7
8. If "Blue Plan" in Q. 3: Do you have *both* "Blue Cross" and "Blue Shield?"	Yes, both: .... 1 Blue Cross: .... 2 19 Blue Shield: 3 0
Ask Qs. 9-14 for each policy *except* **Major Medical (Q. 3) and dread disease (Q. 6).**	
9. Would this plan cover any part of the *hospital* charges if someone had to go to the hospital?	Yes .... 5 20 No 6 4
10. Would (NAME OF PLAN) cover any part of the *surgical* expenses if someone had to have an operation?	Yes .... 8 21 No 9 7
11. Would this plan cover any doctor bills in the hospital *other than for surgery?*	Yes .... 1 22 No 2 0
12. Would it pay any part of bills for visits to a doctor at a *doctor's office* or provide free office visits to certain doctors?	Yes .... 4 23 No 5 3
13. Would it pay any part of the doctor's charges for *house calls?*	Yes .... 7 24 No 8 6
14. Would it cover any charges for *prescribed medicines* taken outside the hospital?	Yes .... 1 25 No 2 0

Enter names of plans and policies in same order as listed on Side 1. If a plan has been scratched out leave that column blank.	*Name:*
15. Do you happen to have a copy of the (NAME) policy or a membership card from it?	Yes: **Ask 16** .... 1 26 No: **Skip to 17** 2 0
16. A. Fill in as much of the following information about each policy as is readily accessible. Full name of Insurance Company or Underwriter:	*Name:*
B. Policy or Certificate Number:	*Policy No.:*
C. Type of policy or certificate:	*Type Policy:*
17. How many months during 1963 was this plan in effect? If "all year," code 12.	27-28 Months .... y **If less than 12, ask 18.**
18. Was this plan in effect December 31, 1963?	Yes .... 1 29 No, dropped 2 0

19. Enter on separate lines names of all family members. Include babies, members now deceased, in institutions, etc. Be sure Person No. corresponds to name as given in Q. 10 of the Folder. Ask for each person about each policy. A. How many months during 1963 was (PERSON) covered by (NAME OF PLAN)? B. **Ask unless dropped policy (Q. 18):** Was (PERSON) covered by this plan on December 31?	NAME OF PERSON	PER. NO.	A. MOS. COVERED	B. COVERED DEC. 31
	Name:	0 1	Mos.. 30 31	Yes . 1 32 No .. 2 0
	Name:	0 2	Mos.. 33 34	Yes . 4 35 No .. 5 3
	Name:	0 3	Mos.. 36 37	Yes . 7 38 No .. 8 6
	Name:	0 4	Mos., 39 40	Yes . 1 41 No .. 2 0
	Name:	0 5	Mos.. 42 43	Yes . 4 44 No .. 5 3
	Name:	0 6	Mos.. 45 46	Yes . 7 47 No .. 8 6
	Name:	0 7	Mos.. 48 49	Yes . 1 50 No .. 2 0
	Name:	0 8	Mos.. 51 52	Yes . 4 53 No .. 5 3
	Name:	0 9	Mos.. 54 55	Yes . 7 56, No .. 8 6
	Name:	1 0	Mos.. 57 58	Yes . 1 59 No .. 2 0

Ask Qs. 20-21 for each policy.	Name: Pers. No.
20. In whose name is (was) this policy or plan membership—that is, which person is (was) the main subscriber?	60-61 0
21. How did (SUBSCRIBER) first happen to get this insurance — through work, through some other group, or directly with the insurance company or what?	Work Group or Union .... 1 62 Other Group .... 2 0 Directly .... 3 Other 4

Ask Q. 22 for each policy in effect (Q. 18).	Work Group or
	  Union: **Ask 23** 6 63
	                     5

22. How does (SUBSCRIBER) carry this insurance *now*—through work or a union, through membership in some other kind of group (Grange, Farm Bureau, Medical Society, etc.) or directly through the insurance company or what?	Other Group: **Skip to 25** .... 7 Directly: **Skip to 25** . 8 Other: **Skip to 25** ... 9
23. Ask Qs. 23-25 as applicable for policies in effect *and* dropped. Does the employer pay *all* of the cost of this insurance, a *part* of the cost or *none* of the cost?	All: **Ret. to 22,** **next policy** .... 1 64 Part: **Ask 24-25** .... 2 0 None: **Ask 24-25** 3
24. Is the amount that (SUBSCRIBER) pays (paid) for this insurance deducted from his salary or pay check by the employer?	Yes .... 5 65 No .... 6 4 DK 7
25. (Outside of what the employer pays) How much, does (did) this insurance cost the family itself *per year?*	$ .. 66-69 y

When *all* questions have been asked for *all* policies return to Q. 78 Main Questionnaire.

NORC SRS-180
January, 1964

NATIONAL OPINION RESEARCH CENTER
University of Chicago

HEALTH OPINIONS QUESTIONNAIRE

| | | | | 1-4 |

Person No. .... | | | 5-6

SEGMENT NO.						
HOUSEHOLD NO.		
FAMILY UNIT	

Begin Deck 92

FILLED IN BY: *(circle one)*	$\frac{7}{0}$
Male head with spouse in household 1	
Male head without spouse in household 2	
Female head without spouse in household 3	
Wife of head 4	
Other: specify _____ 5	

(circle one)	$\frac{8}{6}$
Filled out in presence of interviewer 7	
Filled out alone 8	

228

1. Here are some things people sometimes say about health care, doctors, and hospitals. Do you "strongly agree," "tend to agree," "tend to disagree," or "strongly disagree" with each statement? **Please circle the number under the phrase which best describes your own feeling toward each one. Circle only one number for each statement.**

	Strongly Agree	Tend to Agree	Tend to Disagree	Strongly Disagree	
Even if a person is feeling good, he should get a general physical examination every year.	1	2	3	4	$\frac{9}{0}$
If you wait long enough, you can get over most any disease without getting medical aid.	6	7	8	9	$\frac{10}{5}$
Good personal health depends more on an individual's strong will power than on vaccinations, shots, and vitamins.	1	2	3	4	$\frac{11}{0}$
Some home remedies are still better than prescribed drugs for curing illness.	6	7	8	9	$\frac{12}{5}$
No matter how well a person follows his doctor's orders, he has to expect a good deal of illness in his lifetime.	1	2	3	4	$\frac{13}{0}$
A person understands his own health better than most doctors do.	6	7	8	9	$\frac{14}{5}$
Modern medicine can cure most any illness.	1	2	3	4	$\frac{15}{0}$
I'll avoid seeing a doctor whenever possible.	6	7	8	9	$\frac{16}{5}$
I wouldn't go to a hospital unless there was just no other way to take care of me.	1	2	3	4	$\frac{17}{0}$
The medical profession is about the highest calling a man can have in this country.	6	7	8	9	$\frac{18}{5}$
Most doctors are more interested in their incomes than in making sure everyone receives adequate medical care.	1	2	3	4	$\frac{19}{0}$
If a doctor told me I needed a major operation, I would have it done immediately.	6	7	8	9	$\frac{20}{5}$
Choosing your own doctor is about the most important thing in getting good medical care.	1	2	3	4	$\frac{21}{0}$
The care I have generally received from doctors in the last few years was excellent.	6	7	8	9	$\frac{22}{5}$
I do the best I can to take care of my own health.	1	2	3	4	$\frac{23}{0}$
Thinking back to my own childhood, say up to the time I was 16, I remember a great deal of illness and death in my family.	6	7	8	9	$\frac{24}{5}$
The costs of medical care, in general, are much too high.	1	2	3	4	$\frac{25}{0}$
Some kind of health insurance which covers all the medical expenses I (and my family) might have, is a good idea.	6	7	8	9	$\frac{26}{5}$
Health insurance which covers all medical costs, but is good *only* with hospitals and doctors who sign up with it is a good idea.	1	2	3	4	$\frac{27}{0}$

2. Some people think you should go to a doctor at the first signs of trouble. Others believe that most symptoms usually go away and you should wait until you are sure there is something wrong. Do you agree or disagree that *you should see a doctor right away* for each of the following symptoms? **Circle only one number for each symptom.**

	Strongly Agree	Tend to Agree	Tend to Disagree	Strongly Disagree	
Sore throat or running nose for a couple of days, but no fever.	6	7	8	9	28/5
Sore throat or running nose with a fever as high as 100°F for two days or more.	1	2	3	4	29/0
Diarrhea (loose bowel movements) for about a week.	6	7	8	9	30/5
Feeling tired for several weeks for no special reason.	1	2	3	4	31/0
Unexplained loss of over 10 pounds in weight.	6	7	8	9	32/5
Severe shortness of breath after light work.	1	2	3	4	33/0

3. Which of the following reasons have ever *kept you from seeing a doctor?* **Circle the number under the "yes" if the reason kept you from seeing a doctor, or the number under the "no" if the reason did not keep you from seeing a doctor.**

	Yes	No	
I didn't want to spend the money on a doctor unless I had to.	6	7	34/5
I was too busy to see a doctor; I just didn't have time.	1	2	35/0
I don't like to bother the doctor unless it's necessary.	6	7	36/5
The doctor might find something really wrong with me.	1	2	37/0

4. It is sometimes necessary to make sacrifices to safeguard or improve one's health. How likely would you be to make each of the following changes if doctors said that it was necessary to protect your health? **Circle only one number for each change.**

	Very Likely	Likely	Unlikely	Very Unlikely	
Get more rest and sleep.	6	7	8	9	38/5
Get more exercise.	1	2	3	4	39/0
Stop eating some favorite foods.	6	7	8	9	40/5
Cut down on the amount of work you do.	1	2	3	4	41/0
Spend less time doing things with family and friends.	6	7	8	9	42/5
Spend several weeks in a convalescent hospital.	1	2	3	4	43/0
Move to a different part of the country.	6	7	8	9	44/5

5. Read each statement below about what symptoms may be early signs of various common diseases. Circle the number under "agree," "disagree," or "undecided" depending on your opinion about each statement. Circle only one number for each statement.

	Agree	Disagree	Undecided	
Shortness of breath after light exercise may be a sign of *cancer*.	1	2	3	$\frac{45}{0}$
Shortness of breath after light exercise may be a sign of *heart disease*.	6	7	8	$\frac{46}{5}$
Coughing or spitting up of blood may be a sign of *tuberculosis*.	1	2	3	$\frac{47}{0}$
Coughing or spitting up of blood may be a sign of *diabetes*.	6	7	8	$\frac{48}{5}$
Open sores or ulcers that do not heal may be a sign of *cancer*.	1	2	3	$\frac{49}{0}$
Open sores or ulcers that do not heal may be a sign of *heart disease*.	6	7	8	$\frac{50}{5}$
Unexplained loss of weight may be a sign of *tuberculosis*.	1	2	3	$\frac{51}{0}$
Unexplained loss of weight may be a sign of *diabetes*.	6	7	8	$\frac{52}{5}$
Pains in the chest may be a sign of *heart disease*.	1	2	3	$\frac{53}{0}$
Pains in the chest may be a sign of *tuberculosis*.	6	7	8	$\frac{54}{5}$

PERMISSION FORM

Household No._____ Family Name_____ Pers. No. [|]

This information is to be filled in by the participating hospital

Item	Total Hospital Charges for Item *If "None" so indicate*	Amount Paid to Hospital by Plan or Insurance to Cover Specific Items *If "None" so indicate*	Remarks
a) Room and board .... No. of days _____ Daily room and board rate $_____	$	$	
b) Laboratory	$	$	
c) Drugs	$	$	
d) Operating room	$	$	
e) Anesthesia	$	$	
f) X-ray	$	$	
g) Other (*specify*)	$	$	
	$	$	
	$	$	
	$	$	
Total	$	$	

Total paid by patient (exclusive of direct payments by the insurance to the hospital). $_____

Full name of hospital plan or insurance: _____

I hereby authorize the _____ Hospital of _____
                        (enter name of hospital)   (enter city and state)
to furnish NATIONAL OPINION RESEARCH CENTER of the University of Chicago with the above information regarding the hospitalization of:

_____
(enter full name of person hospitalized)

It is understood that this information is entirely confidential and will be used for statistical purposes only, in connection with a Health Study NORC is conducting for the HEALTH INFORMATION FOUNDATION.

Signed:_____ Date:_____

NORC SRS-180
January, 1964

Name of Person Hospitalized_____ Address of Person Hospitalized_____

Pers. No. ☐☐ _____   _____

1. Number of times person was in hospital from January 1, 1963, through December 31, 1963: _____
   (If "0," skip to Item 3 at bottom of page.)

2. The charges below cover the following period of hospitalization (occurring between January 1, 1963, and December 31, 1963). Please use separate form for each hospitalization. In the event that the stay for a hospitalization partly preceeded or extended beyond the 1963 period, include only those charges incurred in 1963.

   Date of Admission: _____ Date of Discharge: _____

   (Month, Day, Year)   *(Month, Day, Year)*

Item	Total Hospital Charges for Item *(If "None" so indicate)*	Amount Paid to Hospital by Plan or Insurance to Cover Specific Items *(If "None" so Indicate)*	Remarks
a) Room and board .... No. of days _____ Daily room and board rate $_____	$	$	
b) Laboratory	$	$	
c) Drugs	$	$	
d) Operating room	$	$	
e) Anesthesia	$	$	
f) X-ray	$	$	
g) Other (specify)	$	$	
	$	$	
	$	$	
Total	$	$	

Total paid by patient (exclusive of direct payments by the insurance to the hospital) : .... $_____   *(Amt. here plus amts. paid by insurance should equal total. If not, please explain.)*

Full name of hospital plan or insurance : _____

Was there any special billing by: Anesthetist? ☐ Yes ☐ No   Radiologist? ☐ Yes ☐ No
                                  Pathologist? ☐ Yes ☐ No   Special nurse? ☐ Yes ☐ No

Name of doctor mainly in charge of patient's care
   while patient was in hospital: _____
                                        (First)   *(Last)*

Name of surgeon (if surgical case) : _____
                                        (First)   *(Last)*

Name of surgical procedure (if surgical case) : _____

3. If there is NO record of a hospitalization for this person during the period January 1, 1963 through December 31, 1963, please indicate whether or not there is a record of hospitalization for this person during the year 1962, or since January 1, 1964.

   ☐ This person was hospitalized during the period January 1, 1962 through December 31, 1962.
   ☐ This person has been hospitalized at some time since January 1, 1964.
   ☐ We have *no* record of any hospitalizations for this person since January 1, 1962.

   Name of person preparing this report : _____ Position : _____
   Name and address of hospital : _____

Case		1-4
Person		5-6
Plan		7-8

HEALTH INSURANCE VERIFICATION FORM

National Opinion Research Center
University of Chicago

| Employee or Member's name: | Type Policy: |
| Street: City-State | Identification: |

1. Was the person listed above covered by health or sickness insurance through your company or plan during <u>any part</u> of the calendar year 1963? (Circle one number)

BEGIN DECK 1

Yes 1

No . . . . . 2 ⟶ SKIP TO Q, 16, P. 4 10/

2. A. What types of coverage were in effect during 1963? (Circle a letter under "Yes" or "No" for each type of coverage in Column A)

FOR EACH TYPE OF COVERAGE IN EFFECT DURING 1963, ANSWER B.

B. Under what type of contract was this coverage provided? (Circle one for eacn coverage in effect in Column B. If "Other" specify here: _____)

	A Covered During 1963		B Type of Contract				
	Yes	No	One Person	Two Person	Family	Other	
Hospitalization	0	X	4	5	6	7	11-12
Surgical-Medical	0	X	4	5	6	7	13-14
Major Medical	0	X	4	5	6	7	15-16
Other (Specify: _____)	0	X	4	5	6	7	17-18

3. How much did the employee and employer each pay <u>per year</u> on hospital, surgical-medical and major medical insurance? Do not include group life insurance or annuity, or accident or cash sickness insurance.

(Record employ<u>ee</u> [member] yearly contribution to nearest dollar)→ [   ] 19-21

(Record employ<u>er</u> [organization] yearly contribution to nearest dollar ⟶ [   ] 22-24

PLEASE ANSWER ALL OF THE FOLLOWING QUESTIONS WHICH ARE RELEVANT:

IF COVERAGE INCLUDED

(1) Hospitalization — Q's. 4- 5, P. 2
(2) Surgical-Medical — Q's. 6- 9, P. 2
(3) Hospitalization, Surgical-Medical or Major Medical — Q. 10, P. 3
(4) Major medical — Q's. 11-12, P. 3
(5) <u>Any</u> health insurance — Q's. 13-15, Pgs. 3-4

234

IF 1963 COVERAGE INCLUDED HOSPITALIZATION BENEFITS, ANSWER Q's. 4-5:

4. A. What was the maximum allowance per day for hospital room and board?

    (Enter number of dollars per day)────────> [|] 25-26

    B. What was the maximum number of hospital days covered?

    (Enter number of days) ────────> [| | |] 27-30

---

5. What was the maximum payment for hospital charges other than room and board such as X-rays and laboratory tests?

    (Enter maximum number of dollars)────> [| | |] 31-34

===

IF 1963 COVERAGE INCLUDED SURGICAL-MEDICAL BENEFITS, ANSWER Q's. 6-9:

6. What was the maximum payment for a surgical procedure?
    (Enter maximum number of dollars) ────> [| | |] 35-38

---

7. What was the maximum payment for the following procedures?

    Appendectomy────────> [| | |] 39-42

    Inquinal herniorrhaphy ────> [| | |] 43-46

8. A. Were the following types of physician visits covered? (Circle a letter under "Yes" or "No" for each type of visit in Column A)

    FOR EACH TYPE OF VISIT COVERED, ANSWER B AND C:

    B. What was the maximum payment per visit? (Record the maximum number of dollars in Column B)

    C. What was the maximum number of visits covered? (Record number in Column C)

	A Covered in 1963		B Payment Per Visit	C Number of Visits	
	Yes	No			
Visits in a hospital	O	X	[	]	[		]	47-52
Visits in a doctor's private office	O	X	[	]	[		]	53-58
House calls	O	X	[	]	[		]	59-64

9. A. Were charges for electrocardiograms given in physicians' private offices covered? (Circle one number)
    ──────── Yes . . 1 (Answer 9 B)   6 5/0
             No . . 2

    B. What is the maximum payment per EKG? (Record)────> [| |] 66-68

235

IF 1963 COVERAGE INCLUDED HOSPITALIZATION, SURGICAL-MEDICAL, OR MAJOR MEDICAL BENEFITS, ANSWER Q. 10 FOR EACH TYPE COVERAGE IN EFFECT.

10 A. Did this coverage have a deductible? (Circle a letter in Column A)

FOR EACH COVERAGE WITH A DEDUCTIBLE, ANSWER B, C, AND D.

B. Was the deductible an initial cash deductible, a corridor cash deductible, or a care deductible which eliminates the costs of the first one or two days of care or of visits? (Circle a number in Column B)

C. How much was the deductible? (Record in Column C the number of dollars for a cash deductible or the type and amount of care for a care deductible)

D. What was the coinsurance? (Record the per cent or dollar amount in Column D. If there was no coinsurance for the coverage, record "0")

BEGIN DECK 2

	A Deductible		B Type Deductible			C Amount of Deductible	D Coinsurance % or $	
	Yes	No	Initial Cash	Corridor Cash	Care			
Hospitalization	0	X	3	4	5			10-17
Surgical-Medical	0	X	3	4	5			18-25
Major-Medical	0	X	3	4	5			26-33

IF 1963 COVERAGE INCLUDED MAJOR MEDICAL BENEFITS, ANSWER Q's. 11-12.

11. How much is the maximum benefit payment? (Record in dollars) ⟶ ☐☐☐☐☐ 34-38

12. Was Major Medical coverage optional for this individual? (Circle one number)

Yes 1 39/

No 2

IF ANY HEALTH INSURANCE COVERAGE IN 1963, ANSWER Q's. 13-15:

13 A. Did this insurance provide benefits for the services listed below? (Circle a letter under "Yes" or "No" in Column A for each service listed)

FOR EACH TYPE OF BENEFIT PROVIDED, ANSWER B AND C.

B. Was this benefit provided under basic or Major Medical coverage? (Circle one number for each benefit provided in Column B. If "Other" specify here:

_____)

C. What was the maximum payment? (Record the maximum number of dollars for each benefit in Column C)

	A Service		B Type Coverage			C Maximum Payment	
	Yes	No	Basic	Major Medical	Other		
Treatment in Outpatient Department of Hospital	0	X	3	4	5		40-46
Home Care Services	0	X	3	4	5		47-53
Nursing Home Care	0	X	3	4	5		54-60
Tests and Treatments (e.g., X-rays) in Doctor's office	0	X	3	4	5		61-67 BEGIN DECK 3
Out of Hospital Medication	0	X	3	4	5		10-16
Hospitalized Mental Illness	0	X	3	4	5		17-23
Non-hospitalized Mental Illness	0	X	3	4	5		24-30

236

14. A. Did this insurance cover any dependent children of the policyholder or main subscriber? (Circle one number)

————————————————————Yes 1   31/0

No . . . . 2—> SKIP TO Q. 15

B. Up to what age were dependent children covered? (Record)—> ☐☐   32-33

---

15. Please list identifying numbers, letters, and names of health insurance policies, riders, and endorsements in the space below:

—> SKIP TO BOX FOR COMMENTS

IF NO RECORD OF HEALTH INSURANCE FOR THIS PERSON DURING 1963:

16. Was this person covered during 1962 or since January 1, 1964? (Circle one)

Covered during 1962 1   **34/0**

<————————————Covered since January 1, 1964 2

No record of coverage during either period . 3

PLEASE USE THIS BOX FOR ANY COMMENTS WHICH MIGHT CLARIFY INFORMATION IN THIS FORM:

Name of Organization (employer, union): _____

Street: _____ City & State: _____

Name of Plan or Insurance Company: _____

Name of person completing form: _____ Position: _____

Case ▭▭▭▭ 1-4

HEALTH INSURANCE VERIFICATION FORM

Person ▭▭ 5-6

National Opinion Research Center
University of Chicago

Form ▭ 9/

Plan ▭▭ 7-8

3,5

Policy Holder or Subscriber's Name:	Type Policy:
Street:	
City & State:	Identification:

1. Was the person listed above covered by health or sickness insurance through your company or plan during **any part** of the calendar year 1963? (Circle one number)   BEGIN DECK 1

   Yes 1   10/0

   No . . . . 2 ——> SKIP TO Q. 15, P. 4

2. A. What types of coverage were in effect during 1963? (Circle a letter under "Yes" or "No" for each type of coverage in Column A)

   FOR EACH TYPE OF COVERAGE IN EFFECT DURING 1963, ANSWER B AND C.

   B. Under what type of contract was this coverage provided? (Circle one for each coverage in effect in Column B. If "Other" specify here: _____)

   C. How much was the annual premium for this coverage? (Record the premium for each coverage in Column C. If a single premium is for more than one type of coverage, record the total annual premium in the boxes below the chart)

	A Covered During 1963		B Type of Contract				C Annual Premium	
	Yes	No	One-Person	Two-Person	Family	Other	(Round to Nearest Dollar)	
Hospitalization	O	X	4	5	6	7	▭▭▭	11-15
Surgical-Medical	O	X	4	5	6	7	▭▭▭	16-20
Major Medical	O	X	4	5	6	7	▭▭▭	21-25
Other (Specify: _____)	O	X	4	5	6	7	▭▭▭	26-30
TOTAL ANNUAL PREMIUM							▭▭▭	31-33

238

IF 1963 COVERAGE INCLUDED HOSPITALIZATION, SURGICAL-MEDICAL, OR MAJOR MEDICAL BENEFITS, ANSWER Q. 9 FOR EACH TYPE COVERAGE IN EFFECT.

9. A. Did this coverage have a deductible? (Circle a letter in Column A)

   FOR EACH COVERAGE WITH A DEDUCTIBLE, ANSWER B, C, AND D.

   B. Was the deductible an initial cash deductible, a corridor cash deductible, or a care deductible which eliminates the costs of the first one or two days of care or visits? (Circle a number in Column B)

   C. How much was the deductible? (Record in Column C the number of dollars for a cash deductible or the type and amount of care for a care deductible)

   D. What was the coinsurance? (Record the per cent or dollar amount in Column D. If there was no coinsurance for the coverage, record "0.")

BEGIN DECK 2

	A Deductible		B Type Deductible			C Amount of Deductible	D Co-insurance % or $	
	Yes	No	Initial Cash	Corridor Cash	Care			
Hospitalization	O	X	3	4	5			10-17
Surgical-Medical	O	X	3	4	5			18-25
Major Medical	O	X	3	4	5			26-33

IF 1963 COVERAGE INCLUDED MAJOR MEDICAL BENEFITS, ANSWER Q. 10.

10. How much is the maximum benefit payment?
    (Record in dollars)→$ [   ]   34-38

IF ANY HEALTH INSURANCE COVERAGE IN 1963, ANSWER Q's 11-14.

11. A. Did this insurance provide benefits for the services listed below? (Circle a letter under "Yes" or "No" in Column A for each service listed)

    FOR EACH TYPE OF BENEFIT PROVIDED, ANSWER B AND C.

    B. Was this benefit provided under basic or major medical coverage? (Circle one number for each benefit provided in Column B. If "Other," specify here: _____)

    C. What was the maximum payment? (Record the maximum number of dollars for each benefit in Column C)

	A Service		B Type Coverage			C Maximum Payment	
	Yes	No	Basic	Major Medical	Other		
Treatment in Out-patient Dept. of Hospital	O	X	3	4	5		39-45
Home Care Services	O	X	3	4	5		46-52
Nursing Home Care	O	X	3	4	5		53-59
Tests and Treatments (e.g., X-rays) in Doctor's Office	O	X	3	4	5		60-66 BEGIN DECK 3
Out of Hospital Medication	O	X	3	4	5		10-16
Hospitalized Mental Illness	O	X	3	4	5		17-23
Non-Hospitalized Mental Illness	O	X	3	4	5		24-30

239

12. What type of policy was in effect during 1963? (Circle one number)

Individual 1   31/0
Conversion 2
"Senior Citizen" 3
Other (Circle and specify:_____) 4

13. A. Did this insurance cover any dependent children of the policyholder or main subscriber? (Circle one number)

Yes 1   32/0
No . . . . . 2→ SKIP TO Q. 14

B. Up to what age were dependent children covered? (Record)____→ [ ] 33-34

14. Please list identifying numbers, letters, and names of health insurance policies, riders, and endorsements in the space below.

→ SKIP TO BOX FOR COMMENTS

IF NO RECORD OF HEALTH INSURANCE FOR THIS PERSON DURING 1963:

15. Was this person covered during 1962 or since January 1, 1964? (Circle one number)

Covered during 1962 1   35/0
Covered since January 1, 1964 2
No record of coverage during either period 3

PLEASE USE THIS BOX FOR ANY COMMENTS WHICH MIGHT CLARIFY INFORMATION IN THIS FORM:

Name of Carrier or Plan: _____

Street: _____ City & State: _____

Name of person preparing form: _____ Position: _____

INDEX

241